WITHDRAWN

LITTLE AMERICA

AERIAL EXPLORATION IN THE ANTARCTIC
THE FLIGHT TO THE SOUTH POLE

RICHARD EVELYN BYRD.
Rear Admiral, U. S. N., Ret.

LITTLE AMERICA

AERIAL EXPLORATION IN THE ANTARCTIC
THE FLIGHT TO THE SOUTH POLE

By

RICHARD EVELYN BYRD

Rear Admiral, U.S.N., Ret.

WITH 74 ILLUSTRATIONS AND MAPS

G. P. PUTNAM'S SONS
NEW YORK   LONDON
1930

LITTLE AMERICA

Copyright, 1930
by
Richard E. Byrd

First Impression, November, 1930
Second Impression, November, 1930
Third Impression, December, 1930
Fourth Impression, December, 1930
Fifth Impression, December, 1930

SET AND PRINTED BY
THE KNICKERBOCKER PRESS
MADE IN THE U. S. A.

TO MY MOTHER

ELEANOR BOLLING BYRD

FOREWORD

THE efficiency of a polar expedition varies on the whole according to the adequacy of its preparations, the worth of its equipment and scientific gear, the services of its personnel and staff of scientists and the length of its stay in the field. These things require a great deal of money nowadays, and no explorer could possibly foot the bill on the strength of his own pocketbook. He is dependent upon the generosity of friends and the public. This has been true in my case especially, for the problem of financing two of my last three expeditions has fallen first upon me and then upon friends. This last expedition to the Antarctic was, for reasons explained in subsequent pages, a costly one. Preparations for it were extensive, its equipment and scientific gear was new, modern and, in many cases, especially designed for the problem; its scientific staff was more than competent and the expedition itself was away from the United States for nearly two years. This was according to the original plan, the realization of which was possible only through the support of friends, who out of their keen interest in scientific research provided the sinews of exploration.

To them, therefore, I must acknowledge my debt first of all. In a sense this is the debt of the nation, for the expedition, which had for its immediate objectives the investigation of the south polar regions, had also as its purpose the extension of national efforts in a field which had been sadly neglected, the Antarctic continent.

So many names come into mind at once that it is difficult to know where to begin.

There are, for example, Mr. John D. Rockefeller, Jr., and Mr. Edsel Ford. They were not only principal backers of this last expedition, but also of the North Polar expedition. What they gave me in friendship, sympathy and aid when things were darkest are beyond price.

There are men and organizations that stand with them—

Mr. Charles Evans Hughes, the Fisher brothers, Mr. Vincent Astor, Dr. John H. Finley, Dr. Isaiah Bowman and the American Geographical Society, Mr. K. H. Fulton, Mr. George Coe Graves, Mr. George A. Thorne, Jr., Mr. R. W. Bingham, Mr. Paul Block, Mr. Charles V. Bob, Mr. Robert W. Daniel, Mr. Charles F. de Ganahl, Mr. F. Fuller, the Daniel Guggenheim Fund for the Promotion of Aeronautics, Mr. August Heckscher, Mr. George L. Johnson, Mr. Sam Katz, Paramount News, Mr. F. H. Rawson, Estate of Henry W. Oliver, Mr. Julius Rosenwald, the late Thomas Fortune Ryan, The Tidewater Oil Company, Mr. William H. Todd, Mr. Harold S. Vanderbilt, Mr. Donald Woodward and Mr. Robert S. Breyer.

To the National Geographic Society and its officers, Dr. Gilbert Grosvenor and Dr. John Oliver La Gorce, I owe much. They assisted in the financing of the first expedition I accompanied to the Arctic, and to this last expedition to the south polar regions they made a large contribution, in addition to supplying the services of one of our scientists. They stood squarely behind the expedition, ready and eager to help in every way.

So, too, in the case of my dear friend, Mr. Raymond B. Fosdick. Time and time again, when the going was discouragingly hard he came to the fore and smoothed the way.

To Mr. Adolph Ochs, publisher of the New York *Times,* Mr. Arthur Sulzberger and Mr. Frederick T. Birchall, both of the *Times;* Mr. Joseph Pulitzer, publisher of the St. Louis *Post-Dispatch;* Mr. David Lawrence, of the Consolidated Press, and the editors and publishers of the associated newspapers which published the reports on our expedition, I have a large obligation. They understood what we were up against and were always thoughtful and cooperative.

There are as well the hundreds of American firms which most generously donated valuable supplies. And there were also hundreds of persons who helped the expedition in many ways—giving money, services and cooperation. Among these I include the hundreds of persons who made small contributions to the expedition.

There are many more, all equally deserving of mention, and it is a pity that they cannot all be mentioned. Merely to list the names would fill many pages; and my publishers are already in despair at the number that have thus far appeared.

Yet I do not feel that the story of the expedition is too fully told. There are many things which, I have been informed, are not interesting to the general public but belong rather to the four fat volumes dealing with the scientific results of the expedition on which the scientific staff is now working. So, presto, out they go.

Then, too, there are incidents which, because of their distance from the main scene of operations, could not be incorporated except as a very incongruous tail on a story the body of which is perhaps much too large. I have in mind such an incident as that which took place on the arrival of the *Eleanor Bolling* at Panama, in May, 1930, on the return home. It was the first time these men had set foot on American soil in nearly two years. They eagerly looked forward to their first holiday in two months after a blistering voyage across the Pacific. Yet when told, on landing, that the *City,* which was 500 miles out, was shy of coal, beset by head winds, and far behind her schedule, they instantly volunteered to cut the holiday short and go out to her assistance. It made no difference that they were short-handed themselves. Captain Brown and his crew put out to sea without hesitation; and Chief Engineer McPherson went into the fireroom and handled a shovel himself.

This is typical of many such beautiful acts that are part of the memory of the expedition. It was the spirit of the men throughout. If only for that reason I regret the structural limitations of the book. And if I have failed to mention the names of any members of the expedition, I hope it will be understood that the omission was not deliberate. They were all worthy.

But, here, the tail has become the head, the groans of the publishers are increasing and I had better desist with the hope that if I have left unsaid anything that should be said, it will be understood that the inexorable limits of space, as publishers measure it, have made it necessary.

R. E. BYRD

Chicago
November 16, 1930
2 A.M.

CONTENTS

ILLUSTRATIONS

LITTLE AMERICA

LITTLE AMERICA

CHAPTER I

NOTES FROM A JOURNAL

1928 was probably the busiest year of my life. So the journal which I had promised myself I should keep, day by day, suffered in consequence. The few hours of quiet and isolation I had, generally came after midnight, on top of an exhausting day; and these naturally found me wanting in the spirit to write; the morrow invariably brought tougher problems. Nevertheless I did occasionally find time to make entries in my journal; and from these I have been persuaded to select the following, in the belief that they may show by reason of their immediacy, some of the difficulties and hopes that attended us as we got ready to go south.

I A.M.
The Owl, en route Boston,
Sept. 28, '28

The time is up. We must be getting southward. The last dollar that I can beg is raised. Four ships, with most of our equipment on board, are already on their way, headed for New Zealand. In their holds and on their cluttered decks are over 500 tons of supplies and material; there are at least 5,000 different kinds of things, ranging from thumb tacks to airplanes; and every single thing is essential, in one way or another, to our unrelieved stay in the Antarctic. I hope that everything is there. There can be no return now. We are going into the largest non-shop area in the world, more than 2000 miles from the nearest human dwellings, and for nine months out of every twelve shut off even from these by the impenetrable pack ice. So we stand or fall according to our preparations here in Manhattan, nearly 10,000 miles away from our Antarctic base. A pity if we should become vitally dependent upon some trivial, forgotten things. Through my brain runs a provoking rhyme . . . "For want of a nail, the shoe was lost. For want of a shoe the horse was lost . . ." I seem to have forgotten the rest, but the moral is clear anyway. No matter. We have done our best; if something is forgotten, some trifle necessary to the support of 82 men, for nearly two years, then it will have to be one of those things with which Providence bedevils humans who reach out for too much. For we have estimated, calculated and considered until heads whirled; we have divided and sub-divided to the nth degree; we have laid out our plans on a cosmic order, setting up, as it were, an ideal scheme—an expedition equipped with the most nearly perfect instruments for gathering information in the most efficient and modern way; and these plans we have painfully contracted into the narrower, more modest limits fixed by the funds at our disposal, surrendering first of all the luxuries, the relatively least essential, until we got down at last to the hard rock level of irreducible minima.

It has been a real fight, this battle of New York. Minor crises fell hard upon major crises. None of us has rested. Nearly all of us are exhausted. We have been stimulated by the knowledge that the battle ahead in the frozen world will be won or lost by the battle of preparation. We are not done yet—not by any means. There is still an immense debt.—I owe more money than I used to think existed.

But debt or no debt, I must have a few days at home, so I am on my way. Merely starting is relief.

Though my mood borders closely on despair there wells up a greater gratitude. My own friends and the American public have been surpassingly generous. Time and time again we felt the weight of our task carrying us sliding down the rope that leads to failure, only to find the burden lightened at the bitter end by the grace of some friendly act.

But enough of this for now. Tomorrow I breakfast at home.

At Home, Boston
Sept. 30, '28
Morning.

Precious moments, these—very little time for note-making. Indeed, for the past ten years aviation, exploration, the Navy and public life have allowed me little time for anything, even home life. And now I am off again; this time on the longest errand of all.

Knowing how often during the long Antarctic winter night my mind will come back to this place, I am cramming it with impressions, snatching them like a glutton. Yet even these last moments are crowded with outside influences, and the hands of the clock seem to be racing around—ticking away seconds that will not come again.

What with long distance telephone calls, telegrams, newspaper reporters, friends, it has been impossible to keep even these last few days to ourselves. For the millionth time I have been pressed to draw my family and home life into newsprint. We do not want to do this. Marie is averse to publicity, and I must say that the reporters have been fair. However much they beg her and however provoked they may become over her steadfast refusal to be interviewed or, as one said, "humanized," they nevertheless respect her attitude; she and the children now bear an almost charmed freedom from the camera. I have had reason on a hundred occasions to note the high sense of fairness and honor among newspapermen. Not a few of them have shared my confidence; none has yet deliberately broken it.

But here's Dickie—he calls me. This notebook immediately becomes nothing. Dickie, only eight, but already a perfect companion.

The rascal has just surprised me with a gift of $4.35. He worked all summer, doing odd jobs, and saved his money, bit by bit. Gravely I told him that his contribution would help. "I'll make some more, daddy, and send it," he said.

We're off now, Dickie and I, for our last romp and play

together—a kite, a boat and an airplane. When I get back he'll be ten.

Oct. 2, 1928
Aboard Twentieth Century Ltd.
En route San Pedro, Calif.

Home is back there now—but no, rather it is two years ahead of me. It is more pleasant to look at it in that way. For then each day must advance me toward it, and not away from it. Yesterday was the last day. There were, of course, no goodbyes. A casual "so long" is so much better. The thing is living with me today, and I have not the will to describe it. Of the three girls, only Bolling seems to have understood that I was going away for a long time, but whatever doubts that knowledge gave rise to were speedily swallowed up in a vaster personal disaster. She cut her finger, and ran up, crying: "Daddy, I'm leaking. Stop me up." Dickie was the little soldier he always is, at the end shoving shyly into my hand his most treasured toy. What a wonderful thing to have come close to the mind of a child! Here is perhaps the most exquisite intimacy, and surely the most tranquil. For Dickie takes it for granted that all fathers adore sons, and all sons adore fathers.

Tonight, as I have done on a hundred nights, I have asked myself: why are you doing this? Can it be that the joy you get out of exploring is the decisive factor in your plans, overpowering all other influences?

This is a time of heart-sinking doubt. I must go it alone for no one can decide the matter for me. My mind knows what the answers are, but there is some obscure, perhaps ancient, voice within me tonight which instinctively interposes others. What a contradictory thing "instinct" is? Half of human instinct drives away from the center, and makes for enlarging the outline of what we know. Half of it drives toward the center, seeking to confirm and make secure the goods that are there. Life is made up of both things, exploring and establishing, a double swing of the pendulum. Sometimes, as tonight, the instinct toward digging-in must have its chance to speak—not a homing instinct, for I am not far enough away for that—but a home-building instinct perhaps.

trying to persuade one that happiness is identified with security, order, and steady work toward making things more perfect. But when intellect takes this instinct by the ears and compels it to listen to reason, it recognizes that security is never perfect, and therefore home-building is never finished, until we know all that is outside that charmed circle. Going away is a part of solid working at the center. And perhaps this is my particular fate, to do my building in this roundabout way. "Man wants to know," Nansen has said, "and when he does not want to know he ceases to be a man."

Oct. 2, '28
On Train en route
San Pedro, Calif.

My suit case lies open on the opposite seat—in it, and opened, is an old newspaper with the following headlines:

Million Dollar Expedition
Has Magnificent Equipment

Costliest on Record

Between the lines the thought lay implicit:—"plutocratic backing, lavish equipment, unnecessary luxuries, and elegant ease where hardships were once considered inescapable."

To the man who wrote the article, an attack on Antarctica with a shoestring would have been the desirable thing. There would then be more high adventure to it, more sport, more drama and so, more news value. I fear we shall pay for that impression.

In polar expeditions of given conditions, the adventure involved varies directly as preparation. There is a saying among explorers that the more the amateur the greater the adventure. Conditions in the Antarctic, however, are sufficiently hazardous to involve risk—which is to say, adventure—even to the most carefully prepared expedition. Faulty preparation must certainly bring a high degree of risk, if not tragedy, were the expedition not even to venture from its main base. Tragedy may follow even with the best possible preparation. A knowledge of what has been going on behind the scenes, as well as the literature on the Antarctic, must have softened that man's humor.

He would then have known of an enormous debt—of creditors pressing us week after week, almost to the edge of bankruptcy, and loyal friends neglecting their own affairs to help us stave off failure.

He would have seen no flock of plutocrats buying luxuries; only a handful of impecunious men collecting necessities with painful economy.

He would have known the mere fact of costs running up into six figures does not mean luxury. If the notion was drawn from comparison with the costs of other expeditions, a moment's analysis must have convinced him that the difference, if anything, would not be against us. The dollar's purchasing power has diminished considerably since the first great expeditions to the Antarctic. The cost of Captain Scott's first expedition (1901–1904) was approximately $460,000, [1] of his last (1910–1913) at least $375,000,[2] and of Sir Ernest Shackleton's second (1914–1916) about $400,000.[3]

Moreover, we must take not only the best in pioneering equipment, but also the most useful apparatus that modern science and industry offers. The unique nature of the expedition, in fact, demands the most expensive kind of transport thus far used in polar regions—the airplane. It requires the services of a highly-paid, well-trained personnel. The pay of the aviators alone will total $35,000, and the extra ship necessary to carry the airplanes and gasoline will cost several hundred thousand dollars to purchase and condition it for the Antarctic and for cost of operation. Ships are very costly things.

No, we are not half so well fixed as this fellow believed.

And there is the added thought that the past expeditions, as large as ours is, were usually supported wholly, or in large part, by governments, or divisions of governments; whereas responsibility for the financing of this one is centered in a single man.

What a debacle if the creditors had forced us to the wall!

[1] "The Voyage of the *Discovery*," i, p. 30.
[2] Hayes, "Antarctica," p. 365.
[3] *Ibid.*, p. 265.

Yet better a thousand times, we told ourselves, to face ruin in New York than accept the dreadful responsibility of starting south lacking a single bit of equipment, no matter what the cost, necessary for the safety of the men.

The raising of money for polar expeditions is always difficult. I have never known an explorer who was not either bankrupt or close to it.

> *October 7, 1928*
> *Hotel*
> *Los Angeles.*

The telephone is disconnected at last. It is quiet here, for the first time in hours. Committees have gone, good-wishers, autograph hunters who flock, like locusts, to the feast. More than five hundred telegrams, most of them wishing "bon voyage," are stacked up on the table. There is no time nor money to answer them, and that hurts.

The devilish flu that threatened to upset everything is almost gone. Fever is down and pulse normal. In fact, I feel quite fit. This is a good omen.

Marie is best of nurses. We have seen more of each other during the past few days than in many, many months. It has made me realize more fully how very busy I have been during the past ten years. Tomorrow is our last day. Then I start south on the *Larsen*.[1]

I do hope they let us get away quietly and without too noisy a show.

> *October 13, '28*
> *Aboard S.S. C. A. Larsen*
> *En route New Zealand.*

Headed southward at last. After years of anticipation and months of preparation.

The moon on the water; the breezes whispering adventure ahead; then the storm, the water boiling; and above the wind the calm sound of the ship's bell striking on the hour, voicing man's indifference to the nature about him that can no longer shape him to its end; the wind slackens again to a whisper and

---

[1] The Norwegian whaler *C. A. Larsen.*

the barely audible chug-chug of the engines feeding man's deep yearning for mobility, carrying us to a new place, where wealth and fame and power count for nothing, and where men will not strut because there are no women about.

October 16

These last few days, I have simply rested and recalled. What struck me most, as the events of the past few years passed through my mind, was the difference between these last three expeditions and the first two. That is, the difference in the magnitude of operations, the methods of financing, and the distribution of responsibility.

In the projected trans-Atlantic flight of 1919 and the MacMillan Arctic Expedition of 1925, of which I commanded the naval aerial unit, the powerful bureaus of the Navy Department shouldered most of the work and most of the responsibility for the hazards of the flying. On the North Pole flight and this Antarctic expedition, the responsibility has been entirely mine. Responsibility for debts, mistakes, plans, execution of work and what is vastly more important—responsibility for the safety of the men involved—has fallen wholly upon a single pair of shoulders; whereas, in the case of a naval or governmental undertaking of the kind, such cares and responsibilities are distributed among 120,000,000 persons. There are more than four score men on this expedition, ranging in age from 18 years to 68, from seamen to scientists. For every one of them I have a deep sense of responsibility. I shall have it with me, without relief, for nearly two years.

This expedition brought me trying problems from the start. Of these, the problem of financing was perhaps the most difficult. The extensive scientific inquiry planned for the Antarctic, which alone could justify our going, required competent supporting forces. The cash necessary for creating the expedition, and keeping it in the field for the necessary period, was estimated, in the Spring of 1928, as approximately $750,000. We had begun to raise this money in the fall of 1927, through public subscription and private contributions; by mid-summer approximately $500,000 had been raised. I knew that meanwhile we had run into unforeseen expenses, the extent of which I did not learn until the last week in September. I was in New York at the time. In seven days I hoped to leave for Boston.

Hilton [1] met me at the office, after a night with his reports. Hilton had been put in charge of raising funds for the expedition. When he spoke, he did not hold his punch.

"I have a final statement to make on our debts," he said. "We have a deficit of $300,000."

I had not expected it to be half as much. The reasons for this were soon forthcoming. The cost and outfitting of the *City of New York* and the *Eleanor Bolling* had amounted to a small fortune—$165,000 for the first, $125,000 for the second. To build new ships would have approximately cost three times what I put into them. There could be no cutting corners in the matter of strengthening the ships for the struggle in the ice: this expenditure was absolutely necessary. I owed a fortune. And here I was, at the bitter end of my resources, dead tired, sustained during the last crowded days by the hope I should have the last few days at home. Well, I had to get that money; though where, God only knew.

While I sat pondering over this cruel turn of affairs, Hilton came at me again. "I have also learned this: an article is being written for a powerful syndicate of newspapers attacking the expedition for lavish equipment."

"Great," I told him. "Now let's have some more good news. I need it."

Only five days—Monday to Friday night—in which to raise that amount of money. It was distressing to be forced to give up those seven days at home. They were more than just spilt milk, not to be cried over.

I am in no proper frame of mind, even at this distant date, to record that struggle here. From early morning until late at night, I was at the most disagreeable job in the world, money-raising, begging it really is. I was fortunate. The debt was reduced to $184,000. The job, I confess, could not have been done alone. Loyal friends went to the bat for me, not once but many times. And to them I give undying gratitude—small recompense indeed for what they have done. They

---

[1] Captain Hilton Howell Railey, manager of expedition affairs in New York City, and personal representative and friend of Admiral Byrd.

made it possible to go ahead and saved me from abysmal bankruptcy.

The day we sailed, in fact, yet another encouraging gift came. It was embodied in a telegram, which I have at hand:

Replying to your request through Edsel Ford, Fisher Brothers are glad to contribute $50,000 to the fund of the great research expedition you are making. Kindly advise where and how funds should be deposited. Best wishes and success to you all in your great undertaking.

L. P. FISHER,
Detroit, Mich.

And so to you, Lawrence Fisher, and your brothers, I also extend my deepest thanks. You cannot possibly know how much your gift has encouraged us.

Still a debt in excess of $100,000. Ahead of us expenses of routine operation that will certainly amount to that much more. In the treasury hardly half enough funds with which to meet them.

Unless we can raise the money, we shall have, then, the humiliation of debts and creditors in a foreign land.

I had determined at the outset not to leave the United States if a large deficit had accumulated. This decision had to be abandoned; the expedition gathered such momentum that it could not be stopped; for another month's delay here must of necessity mean another year's delay, [1] and considerably greater expenditures in the end. But having set my course I shall go ahead with keen pleasure, for these difficulties are part of the problem and they will be met somehow.

The situation nevertheless calls for determination and co-operation on the part of all members of the expedition; and from Nature the most favorable of circumstances. If, for example, we should fail to get our winter base established on the Barrier there can be but one miserable ending—bankruptcy

[1] Time is the principal factor controlling the safety and quickness of passages through the pack ice which lies between the Antarctic Continent and New Zealand. From Dec. 20th on, when the pack begins to break up and drift, a passage through to the Ross Sea can be generally found. Later than the first of March, however. the transit craft faces the probability of being "frozen in" it it can penetrate the pack at all.

and disgrace. In expeditions of this kind success and failure are not nearly as far apart as the antithetical meanings of the words themselves would indicate. Failure of the pack ice to break up at a seasonable date, thus holding us back too long for the complete basing of supplies, or the presence of a speck of dirt in the airplane engines in flight—matters remotely beyond human control—may well bring disaster at the beginning.

The problem of using aircraft to the utmost advantage in the Antarctic has been discussed at length both at home and aboard ship. The use of aircraft in the Antarctic is experimental, and its success unpredictable. Mawson, [1] as early as 1911, proposed to use an airplane in the field, an R.E.P. monoplane, built by Vickers, with a special detachable sledge-runner under-carriage. It came to grief, however, in a test flight at Adelaide, Australia, nearly killing its pilot, and Mawson therefore abandoned the idea of attempting to fly in the Antarctic. [2] The fuselage was converted into a tractor for hauling sledges, in which humbler capacity it also failed.[3] As a matter of fact, pioneering with heavier-than-air craft in polar regions could not have had more distressing circumstances attending it than Mawson found at Adélie Land. Had not the excessively roughened character of the terrain at Cape Denison, on Commonwealth Bay, where he established his main base, been sufficient to preclude the possibility of a take-off, save under the most hazardous circumstances, the ferocity of the winds must have kept his craft permanently under cover. For he discovered the windiest country in the world—"an accursed country." [4] The average wind velocity for the year was placed at 50 miles per hour; for hours on end blizzards persisted at velocities greatly in excess of the maximum on the Beaufort Scale,[5] reaching the phenomenal

---

[1] Sir Douglas Mawson, perhaps the greatest living authority on the Antarctic, leader of the Australasian Expedition (1911–1914) and the Mawson Antarctic Expedition (1929–1930).

[2] Mawson, "The Home of the Blizzard," i, p. 24.

[3] *Ibid.*, ii, p. 10.   [4] *Ibid.*, i, p. 134.

[5] The Beaufort Scale is graduated from zero—a dead calm—up to 12 —a hurricane of 75 m.p.h. or more. The remarkable thing is that the wind pressure increases much more rapidly than the velocity. At 100 m.p.h. the pressure is almost double that at 70 m.p.h.

velocity of 116 miles per hour, July 5, 1913,[1] and maintaining an average of 107 miles per hour for eight hours, jarring even the tightly bolted timbers of their hut. Gusts approaching 200 miles per hour were reported on the anemometer.[2] Such conditions must beggar the mightiest flying efforts of man.

Of course we shall have no problem at our base in the Bay of Whales; although preeminently a windy continent, Antarctica has places of calm, and Amundsen assures me that, if we are eternally vigilant, our planes can be kept safely in flight and on the ice. The principal risks, as we see them, will arise from storms or from the impossible conditions of visibility met unexpectedly in flight, in landings away from the base, upon unknown ice terrain, and from the difficulty in properly securing the ship against the wind in connection with such landings. All three present food for serious thought; the third is perhaps our most difficult problem. A wind velocity of 60 miles per hour is sufficient to give a stationary airplane a true flying speed; at 100 miles per hour a terrific lift; at that speed the wind exerts a pressure of 23 lbs. per square foot, and unless securely anchored, a plane would be instantly hurled aloft and destroyed. Balchen[3] and Smith[4] are particularly concerned with this problem; and they are now working out a system of anchor lines and ice anchors. I have great faith in these splendid pilots. Both have superb records: —Smith, a pioneer pilot in the mail service, one of the four survivors, I am told, of the thirty-two pilots who opened the mail line between New York and Cleveland; he is now only 31 years old. I have yet to learn to know Smith, but I believe in him. When I met his mother I knew that he must have good stuff in him. Bernt Balchen and I have been through much together. He has never failed to meet whatever test has come. Bernt is splendid.

What uncertainty of the future I share centers principally about the matter of attempting landings away from the main

[1] Mawson, "The Home of the Blizzard," ii, p. 149.
[2] *Ibid.*, i, p. 133.
[3] Bernt Balchen, former Lieutenant in the Royal Norwegian Naval Air Force, veteran of two Amundsen-Ellsworth aerial expeditions in the Arctic; the trans-Atlantic flight of the "America" and the Bremen Relief flight.
[4] Dean C. Smith.

base. Our program demands several such landings in connection with the laying of depots for the main polar flight, and for reconnaissance expeditions of the scientists. Each of these landings must be attended with great risk, for conditions of visibility in the Antarctic are notoriously bad, ice surfaces are extremely difficult to judge from the air and there will be the constant threat of unseen crevasses. Even less attractive is the possibility of a forced landing.

All of which gives us much to think about, even on the tranquil Pacific. We plan and discuss matters from early morning until late at night. At luncheon today we discussed merits of seal meat and pemmican as a constant diet. I detected in Parker, [1] who comes from Mississippi, the beginnings of a strong distaste for such food. There is a vast amount of work yet to be done—hundreds of letters and telegrams carried unanswered from the states, and much routine planning for the expedition from New Zealand on. Duties must be allocated continuously, the program for the scientists finally drafted in detail, the plan of the wintering party prepared, and so on, seemingly without end. Lofgren's typewriter seems rarely still. Good old Charlie. He is always an anchor to windward.

I really am not greatly exercised either by our financial problems or by the task ahead. But wherever it can be done, my plan is always to substitute anticipation and preparation for worry. It is the unexpected that messes the plans of an expedition of this kind.

October 27
Aboard S.S. Larsen

Today we reached a most important decision. The original plan to send the *Bolling* and the *City* through the pack together we may now abandon. On the condition we do not delay his own passage, Captain Nilsen has agreed to take the *City* in tow through the pack, and as a result the *Bolling* need not risk her thin metal sides until later in the season, when ice conditions will be less hazardous. The new plan is to have the *Bolling* tow the *City* to the edge of the pack,

[1] Captain Alton Parker, Marine Corps, a member of the North Pole Expedition and a very competent pilot.

where the *Larsen* will pick her up and give her a much needed boost to the Ross Sea. Thus many tons of precious coal will be saved. I have refused to consider the coal situation impossible and here is the solution if it works out. After giving us all the coal we can handle the *Bolling* will return to New Zealand, take on cargo and follow through, probably three weeks later. What excellent luck! We had scarcely dared to hope for this chance! However, there is danger of counting our tows before they are made. Everything now depends upon the speed with which we can get the two ships to New Zealand, loaded and then to the pack. Captain Nilsen expects to enter the pack late in November, and he insists he cannot afford to delay passage on our account: the loss of a day's fishing means a loss of about $30,000 worth of oil.

The question is: can we hold up our end of the bargain? Frankly, I don't know. The odds, in fact, are overwhelmingly against us. According to the latest radios, the *City* is in the doldrums and logging less then fifty miles per day. If the whales get scarce north of the pack early in the season, we are licked, for then the *Larsen* will risk an early passage in an attempt to reach the better fishing grounds south of the pack. But in bending effort to meet her, we have much to lose if we fail and everything to gain if we succeed.

The problem of basing in the Antarctic turns almost entirely upon coal. The vessels used for exploration work in the ice are generally too small to allow of a safe surplus of cruising radius. A large and powerful oil-burner would be just the thing for this kind of work: but where is an indigent explorer going to get the money necessary to build one? The problem we face now almost every Antarctic explorer faced in the past. The round trip between Dunedin and the Bay of Whales is approximately 4,600 miles. The maximum amount of coal we can allow the *City* is 150 tons below decks and another 50 tons on the deck. Steaming all day, she uses six tons, according to Mulroy's [1] latest wireless; and as she averages under steam about 100 miles per day, she therefore has a steaming range of about 3,300 miles. Of course she

---

[1] Chief Engineer Thomas B. Mulroy who was also Chief Engineer of the North Pole expedition ship, *The Chantier*. He acted also as fuel engineer of the Antarctic expedition.

can eke this out with sail; but the danger lies in the fact that power is absolutely necessary in the pack. If we encounter nasty weather in the Bay of Whales, I fear she will be steaming much of the time until the unloading is finished. We shall certainly have to keep up steam for the month we shall lie alongside the ice at the Bay of Whales.

With the expected relay of tows, however, the *City* should be able to enter the Ross Sea with bunkers almost full, and a sufficient supply of coal to see her through.

I cannot begin to describe the many ways in which Captain Nilsen has aided us. This quiet, soft-spoken and amazingly competent whaling master has what is probably the loneliest job in the world. Every August he takes the *Larsen* out of Norway and down and across two oceans to the Ross Sea, an 18,000 mile journey to the last retreat of the whale; and May comes round before he sees his home again. Three months of that time he has the responsibility of the safety of his valuable vessel under conditions that would quickly break the spirit of a lesser man; but he appears to be a man with strength of purpose, a resolute mind and an acquired cunning in ice lore that Nature's violence could not bend aside. His knowledge of ice conditions is very extensive, and it is a pity it is not yet to be found in books.

Attacking the pack is a matter no less involved from a tactical point of view than a military problem. The Continent is the objective, the pack is the enemy entrenched in front of it, and our ships are the forces with which the attack is pressed. "The White Warfare" [1] of the Antarctic begins with the pack itself, when it is first met on the way south, and the outcome is always in doubt until it is traversed on the way out. Thus far man has mastered it provisionally; but though he may run its gauntlet in the summer, he must ever treat it with respect as a dangerous enemy. In the winter it reigns supreme. Probably all the navies of the world together could not batter their way through.

The time at which a passage is attempted and the place at which the pack is entered largely determine the conditions and duration of the passage. The first man to break through it, the distinguished British navigator, Sir James Clark Ross,

[1] Shackleton's "South," preface.

on January 5, at Long. 174° 34′ E. entered the pack and four days later emerged in the clear, sun-lit waters of Ross Sea. Barely eleven months later—Dec. 18, 1841—when he tackled the pack at Long. 146° W., far to the east, it took him forty-four days to struggle through 800 miles of ice.

The first of the many dreadful blows that were finally to overwhelm Scott fell upon him in the pack. The *Terra Nova* entered the pack, December 9, 1910, on Long. 177° 41′ W.,[1] Scott having concluded that the 178° W.[2] meridian offered the best passage, only to be rewarded "by encountering worse conditions than any ship has had before."[3] December 25th, the *Terra Nova* was still in the pack, and Scott wrote in his diary: "We are captured. We do practically nothing under sail to push through, and could do little under steam, and at each step the possibility of advance seems to lessen. . . . Again the call is for patience and again patience."[4] The vessel did not get clear until December 30,[5] after twenty-one days in the pack, and as a result much valuable time Scott hoped to use in preliminary exploration was lost.

This is the record from its gloomier side. The pack is often more amenable. Less than a month after Scott's ill-favored entrance, Amundsen's *Fram* reached the pack on Long. 176° E., and four days later was in open water in the Ross Sea—"a four day pleasure trip," Amundsen described it.[6] Shackleton's *Nimrod* entering the pack on January 15, 1908, at 179° W., gained open water in thirty hours. The only thing about the pack I have been able to learn with certainty is its changeable nature. The danger of the pack is in getting beset and drifted to the Westward into the impossible ice that churns about the Balleny Islands. This is what we will have to watch and prevent.

The sum of the written evidence as I had studied it, indicates quite clearly that the 178° east meridian offers on the whole, the easier passage through the Ross Sea, to the east and the west, apparently, the pack is denser and more tenacious. So, if we fail to make connections with the *Larsen,* we can be

[1] "Scott's Last Expedition," i, p. 15.
[2] *Ibid.,* etc. i, p. 26.   [3] *Ibid.,* etc. i, p. 26.
[4] *Ibid.,* i, p. 37.   [5] *Ibid.,* i, p. 69.
[6] "South Pole," i, p. 166.

fairly certain of getting through the pack unaided toward the middle or the last part of January. Such a delay might very well mean the failure of our program. If the ice has not by then gone out of the Bay of Whales, we shall have a difficult task to unload our stores. There will be no time for flying. Both ships must be sent North before March. If they should become frozen in the pack, we should run great risk of losing the *City* and most certainly the *Bolling*. If the worst comes, I must face the possibility of freezing the *City* in for the winter, a notion neither to my plan or liking.

Captain Nilsen is decidedly pessimistic about our chances of keeping the rendezvous. Generally by the third week in November, both the *Larsen* and the *Ross* are prowling about the edge of the pack, ready to seize the first promising lead southward. If conditions warrant it, he said, both ships will enter the pack at once. Although past experience is overwhelmingly against finding similar conditions, one of the large steel whaling ships forced a passage as early as the middle of November, several years ago, after unusually heavy winds, storms and currents had broken up the pack.

At the risk of being ungrateful to our Norwegian friends, we are hoping that such will not be the case this year. The advantages accruing to the boost the *Larsen* can give us are immeasurable—the saving in coal, the gain in time may well mean the difference between large and mediocre accomplishments. If the pack holds firm until as late as the first week in December, we have an excellent chance.

Aboard the S.S. Larsen
October 30th

It is trying to have the expedition scattered all over the Pacific, in four ships separated by hundreds of miles of sea. This is past helping now. How much better it would be if we could have afforded to build a single ship large enough to do the job. Every man would then have a sense of being part of a whole organization, would come to know the other men with whom he must work during the next year and a half, and, more important, might gain thereby a proper valuation of the job itself. With the exception of the scientists and several of the aviators, I doubt whether a dozen men on this expedition have any idea of the difficulties that face us. It is only natural that they should not. Very few know any-thing about this new world we shall enter into. A good many of them appear to think it is no more than an heroic journey, with opportunities galore for valorous deeds, high adventure and the like. They will have a rude awakening: heroism and coal shovels are not yet identified in common in their minds, but in the Antarctic it is only by prodigious use of the latter and of allied implements, such as the snow shovel, that at-tainment of the former state is possible.

The thought has occurred to me repeatedly that we are strangers. Scarcely a score know each other except by name and reputation. Drawn together by the common wish to participate in the expedition, these eighty odd men have been shoved, with scarcely a pause for introduction, into this lengthy journey, some of them on two highly odoriferous whalers, the rest of them on our own ships, one of them ancient, the other uncomfortable, and both of them small. The differences that separate us have been marked even in the group aboard the *Larsen*. Of the fourteen men with me, only one, Russell Owen, [1] calls me by my first name. It has already been neces-sary to rebuke one man, an officer in the military, for high-hatting one of the men who happens to be in the enlisted ranks. This officer is not to blame. He hasn't had time to learn that special privileges will not obtain on this expedition. An expedition allows of no social differences. "It is the man that counts, here as everywhere," [2] as Nansen says; but especially here.

Where is there another organization knit together as this one? Outwardly it appears to lack the factors that make for stability and cooperation in civilization. There can be no promotion for work well done—no increase in pay. In fact, money scarcely enters into it. Many of the men are either volunteers or else receive only what is necessary to support their families during their absence. None of them could be paid for the service he will render. Nor can there be any lawful punishment for a misdeed or failure. There is no

[1] Mr. Russell Owen, correspondent of the New York *Times*.
[2] Amundsen, "The South Pole," introduction.

brig, with bread and water diet. There can be no court-martial for disrespect, or over-staying liberty, or desertion. There is only one thing holding us together, disciplining us, identifying us from any other collection of persons on the high seas. It is the fact of loyalty. Loyalty not only to a common purpose; but loyalty according to the various ideals we live by: loyalty to family, to country, to men, even to self, and to God. In this affinity I place my hope. There is no other bond on earth save this that will see men through an Antarctic winter night and the other experiences that lie ahead of us.

As a group, the men represent all that I had hoped for. Choosing men for a trip like this is a ghastly responsibility. I know now what Scott, Shackleton, Amundsen and Mawson went through; if I fare as well as they, I shall be lucky. Men are at once the strongest and the weakest links in the chain. The performance of machinery in the face of given conditions can be anticipated with accuracy; but what men will do is past prophecy. The man who Scott thought would outlast all others was the first to collapse.

The idea of selecting men according to their faces alone is one of the most fantastic notions yet swallowed by the race. Whoever claims to be able to judge his fellow men by their faces is an optimist. The face shows certain things, it is true, but you must live with a man for a long time, see him as he stands and thinks in relation to rapidly altering conditions; and even then you have no certainty: only the probability that he will act in the future as he did in the past. I have taken but one man on his face—Captain McKinley,[1] and in his case a very splendid record in the U. S. Air Service more than bore out the first impression. His is the one case in ten thousand where nobility shows unmistakably in his face.

The rest of the men, save for the handful who served me on other expeditions, were taken according to their records and abilities. They come from everywhere, and appear to have done nearly everything. Dr. Laurence M. Gould is a full-fledged professor, with two summer Arctic expeditions in his biography. Dr. Coman was a staff surgeon at Johns Hopkins. During the World War he served four years with the

---

[1] Ashley C. McKinley, aerial surveyor.

French Army. McGuinness, a citizen of Ireland, the mate on the *City,* is an adventurer of the vanishing type. He seems to have taken a very impartial part in the war, having fought both in the English and German armies. When the mood is on him, he talks of occasional anti-social activities such as gun-running. He is hard, courageous and resourceful, able to do a great many things well. He was a General in Ireland and has commanded blockade running ships. Vaughan, Crockett and Goodale—already labelled the Three Musketeers—were at Harvard, when they decided to go south: more than a year ago, they resigned and spent the winter in New Hampshire hills learning to be dog-drivers. At least two young men are the sons of millionaires. The oldest and most experienced man on the party is Martin Ronne, a Norwegian 68 years old, whom I can see from my desk as I write: he is a veteran of several of Amundsen's expeditions. It was a silken tent he made, left behind by Amundsen, that Scott found at the South Pole; and of him Amundsen wrote: "he was one of those men whose ambition it is to get as much work as possible done in the shortest possible time." [1] I have begun to understand why Amundsen recommended him. I doubt if I will ever come across again another man like Ronne where work is concerned. He goes at it with concentration all day long for fear he may waste time by a false move. He is probably the greatest craftsman in polar clothing to be found anywhere. I hope the rest of his countrymen shape up as well as he does. There are seven of them, all splendid men, it seems to me. They are to act as dog-drivers, instructors in skiing, mates and as ice pilots.

Everything more or less turns upon the men. To expect that all of them will come through, nearly two years hence, with untarnished records would be silly; the law of averages alone would argue to the contrary. I can only hope that the man whose misfortune it is to fail will have the manhood to hold himself to blame. Dissatisfaction spread by a single man can infect an expedition as a stone, cast into water, soon disturbs its whole surface. I know a little about every man on the expedition; there will not be many slackers among them, even when the going is hardest. The Antarctic

[1] "The South Pole," i, 135.

is like war in one respect, as Cherry-Garrard has said, "There is no getting out of it with honor as long as you can put one foot before the other." [1]

Thus, the journal, which was thereafter, I confess, too neglected for, and I too busy to give it, more than random impressions jotted down in haste. A sentence often had to do for a day's complicated details; a paragraph for a week's vicissitudes. But now, in the leisurely quiet of the New Hampshire hills, I have had time to go back, to pick up the threads of the narrative; to see things steadily and to see them whole, with all things done and all hopes and fears having run out their sand. From this point of vantage it is possible to see the two years more clearly, with less prejudice and more sureness, through the first planning, then the preparations and, finally, the field work itself.

[1] Cherry-Garrard, "Worst Journey in the World," introduction.

CHAPTER II

THE PLAN, THE PREPARATION AND THE PROBLEM

THE PLAN.—My interest in the South Polar regions dates far back and seems always to have been synonymous with the names of Scott and Peary, of whom I had heard a great deal in my youth. The notion that I should like to go there recurred to mind with greater frequency, in later years, and, as I became connected with aviation, with increasing enthusiasm. But the plan, which I had secretly worked out, was not spoken of until the night of May 10th, 1926. It is a date not likely to fade from memory; for the two men who shared it with me are dead, having later sacrificed their lives in an attempt to aid fellow pioneers.

That night saw the late Floyd Bennett and me at Spitsbergen. A few hours earlier we had completed the first flight by air to the North Pole and back; weary and glad, we had returned to our base, where we were greeted by my friends, Captain Amundsen and Lincoln Ellsworth, who themselves momentarily expected to fly in the *Norge* to Alaska, over our tracks to the Pole and then beyond. We had a splendid dinner that night. Toward the end, Amundsen and I drew together. "Well, Byrd," he said, smiling, "what shall it be now?" Half humorously, half seriously, I replied: "The South Pole." Amundsen's face instantly became serious.

"A big job," he said, "but it can be done. You have the right idea. The older order is changing. Aircraft is the new vehicle for exploration. It is the only machine that can beat the Antarctic. Look here!" And he began to plan; he talked soberly and gravely, as if the fatigue and the buffetings of his magnificent journey[1] were still on him, and

[1] Captain Amundsen was the first man to reach the South (geographical) Pole, attaining it Dec. 14, 1911.

naturally his advice was good. He suggested several capable Norwegian men; he offered the use of some of his equipment; he suggested the ship I was to use—the *Samson* [1]—"the best bargain for that kind of a job you can find anywhere."

Most earnestly he warned me to look to my men. "Men are the doubtful quantities in the Antarctic. The most thorough kind of preparation, the shrewdest plan, can be destroyed by an incompetent or worthless man." In the same temper, but different words, the warning was repeated to me by a distinguished British explorer, an executive officer on Scott's last expedition: "The first man who starts trouble of a disloyal nature deserves the worst death you can think of." Another advised: "The first man who shows disloyalty should be handcuffed and kept so until the return to civilization." A disagreeable procedure, but nevertheless the code of the Antarctic. On expeditions of this kind, a good man is priceless; a disloyal man is soon found out, and his comrades live to damn him and rue the day he was born.

THE PREPARATION.—Actual formation of the expedition was held up until I completed the trans-Atlantic flight for which I had already made arrangements. That accomplished, the work of setting up the apparatus with which every expedition functions was begun. It was some months before we could afford to establish a headquarters. Our first headquarters consisted of a small room on the 15th floor of the Putnam Building, 2 West 45th Street, New York. There was room in it for a desk and typewriter, a cabinet file and a couple of chairs. This was in the mid-winter of 1928. Within a few weeks the expedition had expanded so much that we were compelled to seek larger quarters, taking a suite of rooms at the Hotel Biltmore, the use of which Mr. John McEntee Bowman generously donated. A corps of staff assistants, under the direction of Brophy, whom I appointed business executive of the expedition, began scouring the world for the highly specialized equipment needed. One of my tasks was that of raising money, a beastly job, which I shouldered until toward the end, at which time I engaged Captain Railey, a former army officer and business man, to take over the job

[1] Later renamed *City of New York*.

while I was south. He also acted as my personal representative. A better and more conscientious man I doubt if I could
have picked.

The thing grew and grew; by the spring of 1928 it was a
highly organized business functioning at top speed. It had
to be; our time was limited. August had been set as the
date for the departure of the *City of New York,* September
for the *Bolling,* and the second week in October as absolutely
the latest date for the departure of any unit or supplies from
the United States. As it was, we barely beat the deadlines.

Transport was, as always, the first consideration and the
last. The difference between good transport and bad is the
measure of the difference between great success and failure in
polar exploration. Our plans proposed the enlistment of three
types—sea, ice surface and air. Each had to be selected with
a view to its particular fitness to very demanding problems.

The task of selecting a good vessel was much simplified
by the kindly offices of Amundsen. On the strength of his
recommendations, I purchased the *Samson* by cable at Tromsoe,
Norway, and ordered her sailed at once to New York. She
was a stout vessel, with the spirit and tradition that Conrad
might have loved. She was old, as ships' ages are measured,
but not in strength. Although built in 1882, she was nearly
as strong in 1928 after we reconditioned her as the day she
first put out with the sealing fleet that plies in the pack ice
north of Spitsbergen. When we took her over she was a
barkentine, with yards on the foremast; nondescript sails
rigged on the mainmast, and a fore-and-aft rig on the mizzen.
We re-rigged her, and made her into a bark by putting yards
on the mainmast. She carried auxiliary steam power. So she
was a bit of everything; not beautiful, as square-riggers can
be, but she had the stuff. Though she was very small, the
scale on which she was built was herculean. Her hull was of
thick spruce and oak, of the finest growth. The ribs, which
were also of oak, were so thickly set amidships that a man
could not thrust his hand between them. Inside, the ribs were
sheathed with a layer of heavy planking; outside them lay
another layer of planking, and on top of that yet another
layer of greenheart. Her sides were 34 inches thick, to withstand the direct, encircling pressure of ice; and the garboards

along her keel were 41 inches thick, to give her protection against longitudinal stress in case she might be caught by ice under bow and stern and lifted smartly. She was an ice-ship, in every meaning of the words. Her designers, however, had built into her massiveness full and rounded lines to give her elusiveness in avoiding the crushing embrace of Arctic ice. Like the *Fram* her hull was of a form that offered no particularly vulnerable point to the ice, but would instead convert its horizontal pressure into lifting the ship. Thus she might escape the "squeeze" she could not directly oppose. And thus this tiny old wooden ship could live in ice that could sink the mightiest battleship.

But the *City* had one great drawback—her low horse-power, and, therefore, low speed and small cruising radius. She could scarcely generate 200 horsepower. We were fortunate that an engine built in 1882 would run at all, for we had neither the funds nor the time to equip her with new engines. How much better off we would have been had we been able to install a Diesel engine which burns oil and gives a tremendous radius of action.

On this windjammer, then, the burden of our long-distance transport rested. It was her job to penetrate the immense belt of ice at the gateway to the Ross Sea early in the season, and to get us through in time to have all supplies unloaded before the Bay of Whales froze over.

One other drawback of the *City* was her smallness—a fact vividly impressed on me as the *Leviathan,* one hundred times her size, drew abreast of her the day she left New York, August 25th. Our white little ship, rolling lazily in its wake, her yards clashing, was so dwarfed by the towering black sides of the *Leviathan* that the contrast was painful. Even could she have spared the room, there was no space on her decks sufficiently large to accommodate the fuselage of all our air-craft. The *City* is rated at 515 tons, with a length of 170 feet and beam of 31 feet, and her chunky thickness made her appear even smaller.

Moreover, with advancing age her carrying capacity had diminished considerably. Her dead-weight, for example, was greatly increased as a result of water soaking into the old hull. As a matter of fact, the *Resolution,* one of the ships which

Cook sailed into high Southern latitudes in 1772, had a greater carrying capacity than our *City*.

Without aviation we might have managed with a single ship. The second ship was the *Chelsea,* a freighter of 800 tons cargo capacity. She was not much larger than the *City,* having approximately the same length and beam. Her top speed was nine knots. We purchased her because she was cheap, available and suitable for the job we had in store; otherwise, I candidly confess, she had little to recommend her. She was put in dry dock, where she underwent extensive repairs, principally looking to strengthening the forward part of her iron hull against a fatal blow from the pack ice. The choice of the *Chelsea,* which we re-named the *Eleanor Bolling,* was significant, in that, ours, so far as I know, was the first exploration party to risk a metal hull in or south of the pack.

I came in for much criticism when I announced my intention of taking the *Bolling* to the Antarctic. But I had studied the matter carefully and was convinced that it could be done. The success or failure of the expedition hung upon this point. Captain Gustav Brown would have grave responsibility.

There was, however, prior experience to justify the choice. Steel-hulled Norwegian whalers of the type of the *C. A. Larsen* and the *Sir James Clark Ross,* had made seasonal passages through the pack to and from the Ross Sea without accident. Immense vessels, they can call upon their vast reserve of horsepower to escape from a threatening squeeze, and thus by sheer force avoid the clashing pressure which might sink either of them in a very short time. Moreover, they undertake the passage only when conditions are favorable; when the warming sun and drift of mid-summer have broken up the ice and offer a maze of open leads. Whether our little ship, with its puny engines, [1] could thus play hide-and-seek with the squeeze was the question. There was this difference. The *Bolling* had to get through. For she was to carry the airplanes and equally indispensable supplies.

The cost of outfitting these two ships, including the original price, was approximately $285,000. This work was done at cost, as an act of friendship, by Mr. William Todd at the Todd Ship Yard. This represented a considerable saving.

[1] The engines of the *Bolling* were rated at 200 h. p.

The distinguished naval constructor, Captain Gatewood, offered to superintend the refitting, and he and Mr. Todd's son, Herbert, and engineer, Bill Smith, rendered us invaluable services.

When she arrived at New York, the *City* was in woeful condition. I never believed a ship could be so run down. It was necessary to make new sails, her entire rigging had to be renewed, a new boiler installed, rotted planks in her hull replaced, and the whole ship, from stem to stern, refitted and strengthened. This preparation was costly, but of course it was necessary.

No doubt it would have been better in every way had we seen our way clear to build new vessels, constructed especially with the Antarctic navigation problem in view; but new ships are very expensive, and such advantages are luxuries denied all but a few expeditions. To have constructed new ships for the same purpose to which our second-hand craft were turned would have cost at least half a million dollars, an expenditure which was obviously out of the question.

I confess both ships gave me several distressing nights, even before the expedition really got underway. The stout-hearted *City* came very near ending her days on the Atlantic. Her skipper was Captain Dietrichsen, a sea-going man of the old school, with a love for sail that he appears to have for no other thing. Skipper Isaak Isaaksen sailed the *City* from Tromsoe, her home port, to Oslo. From there Dietrichsen brought her across the Atlantic. She was then under sail and steam; and so long as her screw turned the chief engineer had considerable to do with the running of the ship—more than the skipper cared for.

A few hundred miles off the English coast, the *City* ran into dirty weather; and while straining against heavy seas, her boiler buckled. Why it didn't burst, no one will ever know. If it had the explosion would have sent her to the bottom. Power gone, she came around by the head; seas washed over her incessantly and she seemed ready to succumb to the next wave. A less imaginative man than Dietrichsen might have accepted it as the beginning of a disaster; but he, instead, accepted it as the ordained severance of a disagreeable arrangement. By heroic measures, he fought out the storm and then continued westward—under sail. The engineer had become a supernumerary. The trip consumed nearly three months; having no wireless, Dietrichsen could not report the accident; she was long overdue, and as each day passed without word from her, we began to fear she had been lost. She was finally sighted off Newfoundland, becalmed, and the skipper was replenishing his much depleted larder with fish caught on a hand-made hook.

Dietrichsen's description of his emotions at the time of the accident is worthy of all the traditions of sailing masters. "Worried? Damn, I was so glad those stinkin' engines were stopped I could have brought her back alone. You can't mix sail and steam."

The *Bolling* had a spectacular run from Brooklyn to Norfolk, Va. She put out from the former port Sept. 16, and off Cape May was boarded by a coast guardsman, as a rum-running suspect, an experience that made us feel more than ever for her dowdy lines. The day she left, I took a train to Norfolk, intending to meet her there and superintend the loading of stores assembled there. Most of the crew were volunteers—green men, few of whom had ever been to sea— and I was anxious to see how they would stand up under the trip. She was due at Norfolk the next day, Monday, in the afternoon.

Monday came and went, and she failed to appear, nor was there any radio from her. This was most surprising, as Malcolm Hanson and Howard Mason, expert radio engineers, had assured me they would get messages through.

Tuesday morning—still no word from her. I became alarmed.

About ten o'clock A.M. I was called to the telephone. The caller identified himself as an amateur radio operator. He said he had picked up the *Bolling* and she reported she had a very urgent message for me. Communication, however, broke down, and he was unable to raise her again. He gathered the message was in the nature of an S. O. S.

As if the situation was not already grave enough, a hurricane of great force, one of the worst in years, was reported to have struck the Gulf of Mexico, and was working its way northward up the Atlantic Coast. Tuesday afternoon, it struck our coast with prostrating force. There was no word from the *Bolling*.

The things I could do at Norfolk were painfully circumscribed. There was no way of determining the whereabouts of the *Bolling;* she might have been anywhere along 300 miles of coastline. I ordered an airplane sent south from New York, to survey the coast down to Norfolk; but bad weather turned it back. I stood by the radio for thirty-six hours without a break. I was in constant touch with the Navy Department and the Coast Guard Headquarters at Washington. Neither of them had had word.

Seven o'clock Tuesday night, the captain of a seagoing Navy tug reported that he had caught a glimpse of the *Bolling* in Hampton Roads. She was laboring heavily, he said, but apparently anchored. But whether she was out of commission; whether she was dragging anchor and headed for shoal water, he was unable to say. Thick weather allowed him only a fleeting glimpse. The seas were rough. We could tell that at Norfolk. Water filled the main streets, having been blown up by the storm, and traffic had stopped.

In this crisis, I appealed to Admiral Burrage, Commandant of the Naval District, and within a few hours he had dispatched a tug to the *Bolling's* assistance. They found her in Hampton Roads. She had dragged her anchor some, but otherwise was safe. The next morning she came into Norfolk under her own power. The report of her skipper, Captain Brown, was terse. After passing Cape May, a 70 miles-per-hour hurricane bore down upon her; and in the sliding, whirling, spinning fireroom the greenhorns assigned to stoke the fires either fell violently ill or useless. Despite the efforts of Chief Engineer McPherson, and his assistant engineers, Leland Barter, Elbert Thawley, and John Cody, steam fell rapidly, headway was lost and the force of the wind drove the ship landward. McPherson himself shoveled coal during this time with the strength of a Samson. A great many times this loyal chief was destined to shovel alongside his own firemen. In the crisis, two of the scientific staff, Captain McKinley and Dr. Haldor Barnes, the assistant medical officer, volunteered to take the places of the stricken firemen. Neither had ever handled a coal shovel before; but with great courage and determination they managed to keep the fires going. At this point the breakdown of the generating plant made the radio apparatus effective only for reception. Hanson could pick up my messages, but not reply to them. Making barely five knots, with steam low, the *Bolling* passed Hog Island, made her way to Cape Henry and finally gained the shelter of the Roads. All in all, they were very trying days; and our two "white collar" scientists were very exhausted men.

Affairs like these made our work of preparation in the United States anything but monotonous.

Months of thought and experiment were expended in the building up of our air forces. Our largest plane was a Ford tri-motored all metal monoplane. My selection of a three engined plane for the major transport and investigative operations in the Antarctic was governed wholly by reasons I have repeatedly made public in the past—an ability to maintain flight in the event of failure of one engine, and a lengthened gliding angle if two should fail, conditions of load and wind being favorable. Although such a plane, by reason of an aerodynamic law too complicated to explain here, is scarcely 65 percent as efficient as a single-engined plane of equal horsepower, the added factor of safety, plus the necessity of carrying on every important flight a heavy load of scientific equipment and emergency gear, made this type the essential vehicle. The latter factor was even more important than the former.

It has been our first intention to power this plane with three Whirlwinds;[1] but my friend, Charles L. Lawrance, president of the Wright Company, had developed the more powerful Cyclone engine, which is rated at 525 horsepower. We mounted a 525 horsepower Cyclone in the nose, using two Whirlwinds outboard—that is, under the wings. This gave us a total horsepower of nearly 1,000—200 horsepower more than the stock plane, a top speed of 122 miles per hour, a cruising speed of from 110 to 116 miles per hour, an easy load capacity of 15,000 pounds.

More power was necessary to enable us to meet the problem of hurling this plane, on the main polar flight, over the

[1] The famous Wright J-5 used on the trans-Atlantic flight; nine cylindered, air-cooled, rated at 220 h. p.

passes through the enormous mountains [1] buttressing the polar plateau. Having decided that the aerial gateway to the Pole would be found approximately in the vicinity of the point where Amundsen made his ascent, we knew in advance, from his reports, the approximate nature and dimensions of the conditions with which we must contend. The Ford, accordingly, was carefully redesigned [2] to meet them.

Weight, of course, was the consideration, first, last and always. And because it was apparent, from the day I made my first calculations, there would be scant discrepancy between the total amount of load we should absolutely have to take and the total load the plane could lift, we began shaving excess poundage from the start. We saved in the construction of the plane. By use of a lighter skin, we saved 235 pounds; by using celluloid instead of glass in the cabin windows, 80 pounds; by omitting cabin trim, 155 pounds, and cabin chairs, 94 pounds. We saved 564 pounds in the structure alone.

Two other planes were acquired, for reserve, for use of the scientists in the field, for transport—in short to provide us with a surplus of effective machines to insure the carrying out of the program of scientific inquiry if one, or even two machines were wrecked. These included a Fokker Universal monoplane, [3] with a 425 h. p. Pratt and Whitney Wasp engine, and a Fairchild folding wing monoplane. [4] We carried also a small plane manufactured by General Aircraft. [5]

The experience we had had with the use of skis on aircraft in connection with the North Pole flight was invaluable in the preparation for the antarctic problem. Long before the expedition sailed from the United States, Floyd Bennett and Bernt Balchen flew to Canada and tested various types of

[1] The Queen Maud Range. Peaks in this range are as high as 10,000 to 19,000 feet.

[2] The Ford was a factory transport plane, type 4-AT. Its other measurements were: span over all, 70 ft.; length over all 49 ft., 10 inches; wing area, 785 sq. ft.

[3] The dimensions of the Fokker were: span over all, 74 ft., length over all, 49 ft., 10 inches; wing area, 733 sq. ft. Powered with a 425 h. p. Pratt and Whitney "Wasp" engine.

[4] The dimensions of the Fairchild were: span over all, 50 ft.; length over all, 32 ft., 10 in.; wing area, 332 sq. ft. Powered with a 425 h. p. Pratt and Whitney "Wasp" engine.

[5] This plane failed to reach the Antarctic.

skis on the snow. During the early stages of preparation, Bennett planned the aviation equipment which was used in the Antarctic. His death deprived me of a judgment, loyalty, and determination in which I always had implicit faith. Had he lived, he would have been second in command.

Our surface transport was more in keeping with Antarctic traditions. Our dogs were mostly Greenland huskies, of the breed and blood with which some of the greatest marches in the polar regions have been made. Seventy-nine of these came from Labrador, and were donated by Frank W. Clark, of the Clark Trading Company. Sixteen dogs came from the farm of Arthur T. Walden, at Wonalancet, among them the famous "Chinook." These were heavy draught animals, of his own breed, with a splendid record in transport.

In addition, we proposed the usual experiment with motorized surface transport. [1] The choice, in our case, was a Ford snowmobile. It had a powerful engine mounted upon caterpillar treads, which it was hoped would prove useful in towing sledges to the various depots in the preliminary unloading operations and, perhaps later, in the laying of southern depots.

For the balance of our preparation and supplies, there is space for no more than a summary. The outfitting of the expedition was hard work; for many months all of us had to serve as jack-of-many-trades. We were alternately cartographer, dietician, purchasing agent, fund-raiser, haberdasher, aircraft expert and many other things. In each of these activities I was ably assisted, and often wholly supported, by the men whom I placed in charge of various departments.

---

[1] Shackleton on his first, Scott on his last, and Mawson on his first expedition all attempted to use surface machines. Shackleton used an automobile, with an air-cooled, 4 cylinder Arrol-Johnston motor. ("The Heart of the Antarctic," i, p. 23.) But its wheels repeatedly sank and spun futilely in soft snow. After repeated experiments with rubber tires and cog-like treads, Shackleton was forced to abandon it only a few miles out on his main journey (p. 249). The failure of Mawson's motorized sledge, with propeller attachment, has been described (see footnote, p. 21). Scott took three motorized sledges to the Antarctic. One was lost in the unloading at the base ("Scott's Last Expedition," i, p. 73) when it fell through the ice; and the remaining two, after thoroughly disappointing performances, broke down in the early stages of the Southern Journey—"so the dream of great help from the machines is at an end" (i, p. 311).

The work of Dr. Francis Dana Coman, of the surgical staff of Johns Hopkins Hospital, was especially valuable in the creation of the Commissary. Although biologist and bacteriologist by designation, this brilliant medico took over the job of dietician, and with it the responsibility of keeping the expedition healthy and strong during the stay on the ice. Commissary Steward Sydney Greason did splendid work in the procuring of our food supplies. His wife was a most enthusiastic helper and the expedition owes her much. George Tennant, who was the Chief Cook of the North Pole Expedition, helped to work up the amounts of food required. Food was selected according to its vitamin value; and the considerable advances made in the science of dietetics enabled us to formulate an excellent diet, monotonous perhaps, but wholesome, strength-giving and economical. We had the inevitable pemmican in large quantities. This was made according to Amundsen's formula, and he, in turn, developed it from "emergency ration" prepared for the Norwegian Army.

Pemmican is absolutely necessary on sledging journeys, because of its compressed nourishment. A man engaged in hard physical labor usually consumes between four and five pounds of food per day, of which half is water. The water content of pemmican is less than three percent; the sledging rations of the British Antarctic Expeditions, for example, were 34 ounces per man per diem. Pemmican makes an important saving in weight. The weight of ordinary meat would be prohibitive for long sledge journeys. Our pemmican was prepared for us at Copenhagen; it was one of the last things Amundsen did for me. It came to us in blocks of half a pound, wrapped in tinfoil, and these blocks in turn were packed in unit boxes of 25 pounds. This uniform weight and size rendered it easy to pack and to count out. Pemmican is hardly a food for a fastidious man: it is greasy and rich; but explorers on the march, who are of necessity on reduced rations, soon come to look upon it as food fit for the gods. Nowhere in literature has food been so rapturously beatified as in Shackleton's praise of the ever-thinning "hoosh" that sustained him and his party on their starvation-dash to within 97 miles of the Pole.

We took precautions against scurvy, which had weakened

several Antarctic expeditions. The Insulin Company, at our request, undertook a series of experiments on rats and finally announced the development of a dried fruit powder, containing the vital vitamin C, which, it was promised, would prevent scurvy. We also took large quantities of lime juice, crushed orange juice and lemon powders. As I had hoped, these preventatives proved unnecessary; taking a leaf out of Peary's book, we stocked up with fresh seal meat before winter set in, and got through without a single symptom of scurvy. I want to acknowledge here the debt we owe to those polar explorers who by their suffering and sacrifices taught us how to prepare.

In the selection of radio equipment, the Navy Department and New York *Times* were especially valuable. I suppose this single department received more attention than any other, for our program called for the most elaborate system of communication ever proposed in a Continent where radio conditions are notoriously bad.[1] The necessity of constantly directing the various units of the expeditions in the field—the ships at sea, the dog teams on the Barrier, the aircraft in flight—as well as maintaining communication with the rest of the world compelled us to procure the best equipment available. As we were truly pioneering in this field, there was an excellent chance of acquiring much new information about radio-magnetic conditions in the Southern Hemisphere, especially with reference to the mysterious heaviside layer which does queer things to radio.

In spite of assistance from the Navy, the New York *Times* and several commercial corporations, the radio became very costly. This was another heavy expense with which former expeditions were not saddled. We took with us five radio engineers. Malcolm Hanson was assigned to the expedition by the Navy Department. He is a very capable engineer and a veteran of the North Pole expedition. Mason

---

[1] Mawson experimented with radio between Cape Denison and his base unit at Macquario Island with indifferent success; in summer, continuous daylight limited wireless operations to a few hundred miles at best, and the effective working distance for all times of the day was not above 100 miles ("Home of the Blizzard," ii, p. 36). Scott, on his last expedition, set up a telephone connection between Hut Point and Cape Evans, a distance of 15 miles.

DR. LAURENCE M. GOULD, GEOLOGIST AND SECOND IN COMMAND.

CAPTAIN ASHLEY C. McKINLEY, AERIAL SURVEYOR AND THIRD IN COMMAND.

Captain Gustav L. Brown, Master of the *Eleanor Bolling.*

Captain Frederick C. Melville, Master of the *City of New York.*

had built and used radio sets in the Arctic. Grenlie was another veteran of the Polar expedition. The fourth man was Carl Petersen, a splendid Norwegian with an adventurous nature. Lloyd Berkner was assigned to the expedition by the Department of Commerce. He is an able and enthusiastic radio engineer.

When the minimum requirements for the expedition over a period of two years were finally arrived at, it immediately became necessary to increase everything by half. Upon us, as upon all previous expeditions to the Antarctic, there fell the obligation of providing for a second winter on the ice, in case the relief ships should be unable to get through in 1930. That meant preparing for three years in the field.

As the supplies accumulated, they were assigned to the ships that were to carry them. Everything bought and stored was carefully recorded and indexed, so that the amount and its whereabouts would be determinable. The midnight oil burned over this job was considerable. The loading of the *City* began first. Owing to her low speed, it was necessary that she leave the United States well in advance of the *Bolling;* we hoped—too optimistically, it turned out—she would make the trip to New Zealand in less than three months. With 200 tons of material aboard, and a crew of 33, she put out from Hoboken, August 25th, 1928, and made for the Panama Canal. Her master was Captain Frederick Melville, a sailing man of excellent reputation who, in the face of the times, had not deserted sail. McGuinness was first mate. Frank D. Davies the physicist of the expedition, and Henry Harrison, a meteorologist assigned by the U. S. Weather Bureau, went as ordinary seamen—no easy berth on a bark rigged ship.

The *Bolling,* under command of Captain Brown, put out from Norfolk, Virginia, exactly a month later. She carried 300 tons of supplies and a crew of 28. Aboard her were several of the scientific staff, including Dr. L. M. Gould, the geologist, William Haines of the U. S. Weather Bureau, who proved to be a godsend on the North Pole Expedition, and Captain McKinley, the distinguished aerial mapper.

A third detachment went aboard the Norwegian whaler *Sir James Clark Ross,* which took on Mr. Walden, the dog-drivers, Norman Vaughan, Eddie Goodale and Fred Crockett, and ninety-four dogs at Norfolk, as well as forty tons of dog biscuits. By sending the dogs on this much faster vessel, it was possible to reduce considerably the time they must endure the tropical heat on the Pacific. They would have suffered greatly on our small crowded ships. We owe much to Magnus Konow, the Norwegian whaling director, who generously provided us with this transport. Anticipating the difficulties that the operation of unloading would involve, I wanted to take the dogs to the Antarctic in the best condition possible.

The fourth detachment of the expedition was on the *Larsen*. At Norfolk she took aboard the four airplanes, the aviation gas and oil, about 100 tons of supplies and the aviation personnel. The task of clearing up ultimate details as well as reducing the deficit left me no alternative save to remain in New York up to the last minute. Brophy, Russell Owen, Ralph Shropshire, assistant to the scientific staff, Sergeant Benjamin Roth, assigned by the U. S. Army, Willard Van der Veer and Lofgren, who accompanied me across the Continent, boarded the *Larsen* at San Pedro. October 10th, she put out to sea.

So the second week of October saw all four units on the Pacific, widely scattered, but all hurrying southwestward as fast as their varied speeds would allow, toward the concentration points at New Zealand. I was reminded of a naval force converging for a distant action. The entry in my journal of October 14th, the fourth day out on the *Larsen,* shows that on that day the *City* reported its noon position as halfway between Panama and Pitcairn Island, far to the southeast; still farther south was the *Ross,* making excellent speed; and the *Bolling* had the Galápagos Islands abeam.

THE PROBLEM. Any discussion of the Antarctic problem, except perhaps in scientific circles, soon comes up hard on the question: " . . . but what's the use of it? What's the value of snow and ice so many miles away?" It is sometimes difficult to answer what earthly purpose the great white continent serves. It is not that the answer is necessarily lacking in logic or conviction; more often it is that the asking mind has not turned its thought in that direction; for the most unpracticed student in polar history must soon sense its great significance. We lack, most of us, the universal, philosophical point of view. As is natural in our own crowded affairs, we see things narrowly, especially in a matter such as this, in trite, personal and commercial terms of worth. Antarctica, "a vast wonderland laid out on a giant scale, in which littleness has no place," cannot be judged, or appraised, according to limited values. Vainly did I try to impress this fact upon a well-known American business man. "But where's the money in it? Where's the profit?" he demanded.

Candidly, at this moment the Antarctic is sleeping, so far as we can calculate its value to modern civilization. But no one, except God, can tell how long it will remain sleeping. Cook, over a hundred years ago, returning from his magnificent journeys in high southern latitudes, exclaimed that if a southern continent was ever found, it must remain a continent without a future. "Countries condemned to everlasting rigidity by Nature, never to yield to the warmth of the sun, for whose wild and desolate aspect I find no words; such are the countries we have discovered; what then may those resemble which lie still further to the South? . . . Should anyone possess the resolution and the fortitude to elucidate this point by pushing yet further south than I have done, I shall not envy him the fame of his discovery, but I make bold to declare that the world will derive no benefit from it." [1] But now, in summertime, its waters swarm with Norwegian whalers who annually harvest a revenue of $15,000,000 from their catch. Immense beds of coal were hinted at by Shackleton's discoveries, [2] Scott found copper, [3] there was iron in the "red mountain" that Shackleton climbed in search of a highway leading to the Pole. [4] Economic minerals were found by Mawson's party at Adelie Land, [5] and Scott's Northern Party, under command of Prof. T. Edgeworth David, found titanium on

[1] Mill, "The Siege of the South Pole," p. 85.
[2] The Heart of the Antarctic," i, 327.
[3] At Cape Bernacchi, pure quartz *in situ* with large lumps of copper in it—"the first find of minerals suggestive of the possibility of working." "Scott's Last Expedition," i, p. 411.
[4] "The Heart of the Antarctic," i, 307.
[5] Mawson, "The Home of the Blizzard," i, p. 110. Iron, copper and molybdenum—"The ores were present in small quantities, but gave promise of large quantities in the vicinity and indicated the probability of mineral wealth beneath the Continental ice cap."

Depot Island, [1] a place he described as "truly a most wonderful place geologically, and a perfect elysium for the mineralogist." These, to be sure, are remote possibilities. There is a much richer ore to be mined immediately in *terra incognita.*

Dr. Mawson has said: "The polar regions, like any other part of the globe, may be said to be paved with facts, the essence of which it is necessary to acquire before knowledge of the special zone can be brought even to provisional exactitude. On the face of it, polar research may be said to be specific and discriminating, but it must be remembered that an advance in any one of the departments into which, for convenience, science is artificially divided, conduces to the advantage of the whole. If we ignore the facts contained in one part of the world, surely we are hampering scientific advance." [2]

The fascinating fact about the great southern continent, whose area has been estimated at five million square miles, is that its existence was definitely proved only ninety years ago, and it has been under intensive investigation for only thirty years. "Even now the Antarctic is to the rest of the earth as the Abode of the Gods was to the ancient Chaldees, a precipitous and mammoth land lying far beyond the seas which encircled man's habitation, and nothing is more striking about the exploration of the Southern Polar region than its absence, for when King Alfred reigned in England the Vikings were navigating the ice-fields of the North; yet when Wellington fought the battle of Waterloo there was still an undiscovered continent in the South." [3]

From the Greeks comes the name—*anti* and *arktos,* meaning "opposite the bear," or polar region; and as the Greeks knew the earth was round, it is possible they used the word *Antarctic,* [4] to describe a continent balancing a north polar region of which they knew and thus give symmetry to their conception of a spherical earth. But for hundreds of years the Antarctic problem was no more than a philosophical conception. From the middle ages on, however, the notion of a vast southern continent, *Terra Australis Incognita,* laid hold of the

[1] "Scott's Last Expedition," ii, p. 104.
[2] Mawson, "Home of the Blizzard," i, p. 6.
[3] Cherry-Garrard, "The Worst Journey in the World," introduction, xvii.
[4] Dr. Hugh Mill, "Siege of the South Pole."

imaginations and ambitions of cartographers and explorers alike, and maps of the period show it in grotesque shapes and connections. It was assumed to be inhabited by millions of people, fertile, rich in gold and silver, temperate, and possessing the other qualities which the empire-searching seafarers of the Mediterranean always hoped to find.

They pressed southward, one after another, in their cockleshell ships, ever believing that with the lifting of a new parallel of latitude the mysterious southern continent would come into view. Diaz, pushing toward the southern coast of Africa in 1487, found a living people, a temperate climate, and gave impetus to the quest. But de Gama, rounding the Cape of Good Hope (1497), found to his sorrow an illimitable sea to the south. Drake pressed through the Strait of Magellan (1578); and after being repelled by storm, sailed about Tierra del Fuego with a boundless ocean on his right hand, thus stripping the imaginary southern continent from any connection with America.

One by one the great navigators felt out Australia and New Zealand, New Guinea and Tasmania, and found always the ocean beating on the southern coasts. But hope died hard. "The most celebrated and modern sovereign will be he who gives his name to the southern world," De Brosses, president of the Parlement de Dijon, wrote in 1756. So, as the space it was hoped the continent occupied steadily contracted, and the oceans guarding its approaches were seen to become more fierce, belief in its actual existence began to wane. It remained for the distinguished British navigator, Captain Cook, to hint at its reality and its terrifying nature.

Cook, in circling the globe in high southern latitudes, removed the notion of a circumpolar continent from the realm of fiction and proved that if it existed at all, it must be well south of the 60th parallel. In 1772, Cook sailed from England with two ships, the *Resolution,* of 462 tons, and the *Adventure,* of 336. Cook based at New Zealand. Sunday, Jan. 17, 1773, he crossed the Antarctic Circle at Long. 39° 35' E., the first such crossing ever made. For a month he cruised an open sea, meeting icebergs and drifting pack, until stopped at last by an impenetrable pack. Lest he be beset, he retreated north, returning south again the following December. Twice he traversed the Antarctic Circle, seeking a channel through the pack; but each thrust came up hard upon vast stretches of ice. Captain Cook wrote:

"I will not say that it was impossible anywhere to get farther to the south; but the attempting it would have been a rash and dangerous enterprise and what, I believe, no man in my situation would have thought of. It was, indeed, my opinion, as well as the opinion of most on board, that this ice extended quite to the Pole, perhaps joined some land . . . but if there is, it can afford no better retreat for birds, or any other animals, than the ice itself. I, who had ambition not only to go farther than any one had been before, but as far as it was possible for man to go, was not sorry at meeting this interruption. . . ." [1]

The next half century witnessed efforts of a different character. No longer seeking rich empires, but, instead, the more immediate wealth of fur-bearing seals, Yankee and British sealers, fighting for new and virgin fishing grounds, pressed farther and farther south through the ice in ramshackle and scurvy-ridden ships. The Falklands, South Georgia and South Shetlands were discovered. In this inhospitable vicinity, one misty morning in 1821, the Russian circumnavigator, Admiral Bellingshausen, in search of a continent, came upon the sail of the worthy Captain Palmer of Stonington, Conn., and found, to his surprise, the Yankee master well acquainted with this little known part of the world.

The period of actual discovery found three men—the Frenchman, D'Urville; the American, Wilkes; and the Englishman, Ross,—on the very edge of the Continent within a year. D'Urville was off first, with two corvettes, and after a futile attempt to gain the Continent southeast of the South Shetlands, sailed from Hobart Town in 1840. He discovered Adélie Land, a far-reaching expanse of ice cliffs, on an islet adjoining which his men saw a fragment of rock which scientists hastily broke up for specimens. While off these coasts he met one of Wilkes' ships, the *Porpoise*. Wilkes' expedition was authorized by an Act of Congress, May 18, 1836. It comprised six vessels; two sloops-of-war, the *Vincennes,* of 780 tons, and the *Peacock* of 650; a brig, *Porpoise,* 230 tons; the

[1] Cook, "Voyage Towards the South Pole," p. 268.

Relief, a store ship, and two pilot boats, the *Sea Gull* of 110 tons and the *Flying Fish* of 96 tons. The personnel comprised 345 men, 83 officers and twelve civilian scientists and attachés. The expedition put out from Norfolk, Va., August 18, 1838. After an unsuccessful sortie south of the South Shetlands, the expedition based at Sydney Harbor. December 26, 1839, the squadron sailed to the south ice pack. Despite his ill-equipped ships, Wilkes fought his way to the rim of the Antarctic in 1840 and claimed the discovery of an immense extent of Continental land. Whether he made this discovery is something the British still seem to doubt. Scott [1] and Captain Davis,[2] of Mawson's expedition, have further shrunk his claims. It has always seemed a pity to me that the American government failed to follow up the work of this gallant officer, who had the courage to undertake the great responsibility of this mission. I personally am convinced that Wilkes discovered land. My friend Sir Douglas Mawson, than whom there is no greater authority, has told me that he believes that Wilkes saw land of the Antarctic Continent.

No such doubts imperilled Ross's claims. Under orders from the Admiralty to locate the South Magnetic Pole, if possible, and the Continent, if it existed, he sailed from England, September, 1839. His two vessels, the *Erebus,* of 370 tons, and the *Terror,* of 340, were bombing vessels, and so very strongly built. Ross arrived at Hobart, Tasmania, in time to learn of the discoveries of D'Urville and Wilkes; and "being impressed with the feeling that England had ever led the way of discovery in the southern as well as the northern region," [3] he decided to strike south far to the east, following the 170° E. meridian, rather than to the scene of their discoveries. He sailed from Hobart, December, 1840, and January 5, 1841, he plunged his two vessels into the pack. Four days later he emerged into the deep blue waters of the sea that bears his name. On January 11, the snow-capped peaks of Mount Sabine appeared on the horizon; then the Admiralty Range of

---

[1] "Voyage of the *Discovery,*" ii, p. 392 ". . . once and for all we have definitely disposed of Wilkes Land."

[2] "With the *Aurora* in the Antarctic," chapter xxiii.

[3] Ross, "A Voyage of Discovery and Research in the Southern and Antarctic Regions," i, p. 117.

mountains; and finally the low-set cape he named Cape Adare.
Thus was the forbidding coast of the continent unveiled to
him. He struck a (true) southern course, hoping to hedge
in toward the Magnetic Pole, and on his way sighted a
second range of mountains (Prince Albert) and then an active volcano (Mount Erebus) with a dead crater, only slightly lower, nearby (Mount Terror). He pressed on, and a
discovery of vast importance awaited him. "As we approached the land under all-studding sails, we perceived a
low white line extending from its eastern extreme point as
far as the eye could discern to the eastward. It presented an
extraordinary appearance, gradually increasing in height as
we got nearer to it, and proving at length to be a perpendicu-
lar cliff, between 150 and 200 feet above the level of the sea,
perfectly flat on top, and without any fissures or promontories
on its even seaward face." [1]

Thus was the Great Ice Barrier, which is now known as
the Ross Ice Barrier, discovered; and with it the highway by
means of which two parties of men afoot, and a third by air,
were later to gain the Pole. Ross made two later magnificent
voyages to the south, but the value of his discoveries was obscured somewhat by the public's rising interest in the North,
where the quest for the Northwest Passage and the Pole was
leading to many mad, magnificent things.

Fifty-three years were to pass before man set foot on the
Antarctic Continent; and fifty-seven before Borchgrevink,
apparently in the face of all reason, announced that he would
inflict upon himself and nine companions the dreadful earthly
purgatory of wintering at Cape Adare; by this time science
had taken the place of empire-building in exploration. Storms
buffeted the little hut; the zoologist, Mr. Nikolai Hanson,
died of intestinal complications, the first human being to find
burial on the continent, but, on the whole, the winter was
not as bad as had been expected. The way was open for the
Age of Heroic Discovery, which came in with Scott and is
emblazoned with such imperishable names as his own, and
those of Shackleton, Mawson, Amundsen and the rest of their
gallant companies.

[1] Ross, "A Voyage of Discovery and Research in the Southern and
Antarctic Regions," i, p. 117.

The Ross Barrier.

A Typical Antarctic Tabular Berg in the Process of Decay.

The *City* Takes Green Water over the Windward Rail.

Slowly but painfully, facts concerning the continent were discovered. Scott, on his first voyage, on the National "Discovery" Expedition, 1901–1903, pushed far beyond the limits of Ross's discoveries, adding hundreds of miles to the known coastline of the continent; he discovered King Edward VII Land and the eastern end of the Barrier; with Dr. Edward Adrian Wilson, the chief scientist on his later expeditions, and Mr. Hartley Ferrar, also of the scientific staff, he undertook the first southern sledge journey; he did many things *first,* this gallant Scott, and not the least among them was the manner in which he opened the eyes of the world to the possibilities of a well-organized, courageously prosecuted scientific inquiry into the Antarctic. The traditions he founded, and in keeping with which he died, were sustained and extended by two of his able countrymen, Mawson and Shackleton. What we know about the Antarctic comes largely from them; and if it so happens that the sum total of this knowledge, so painfully and splendidly accumulated, serves largely to suggest the appalling amount still unknown, it is not that they have not done magnificent work; it is only that the problem is so vast.

Prof. David estimated, in 1914, the coastal limits of the continent at 14,000 miles, of which about 4,000 were either discovered or explored. Hayes is inclined to reduce the former figure to approximately 12,000 miles, and advanced the latter to approximately 5,000 miles, as a result of subsequent exploration.[1] Thus, at the bottom of the world there lay, in 1928, a continent, greater than the combined areas of Mexico and the United States, more than half of whose coasts had never been seen, and whose desolate interior had felt only the hurrying feet of the parties under, or directed by, Shackleton, Mawson, Scott and Amundsen, tracing relatively a few narrow paths in its infinite immensities.

We know many things of this continent. It differs from all other land that has come into human consciousness. It is the only polar continent. The north polar regions consist of an ocean encircled by continents. The south polar regions consist of a continent encircled by oceans. Hayes has drawn a singular contrast between its isolation and that of other

[1] Hayes, "Antarctica," p. 308.

great land masses. [1] Europe, Asia and America form only two land masses which are but slightly separated at their nearest points. Europe and Asia are separated from Africa by the Suez Canal; and Asia from America by Bering Strait, with the Diomede Islands in its stream, so that the water jump from Asia to the Island is only 17 miles and from the Island to Alaska only 25. Cape Horn, the most southern continental point, lies 600 miles from the nearest truly Antarctic land, the South Shetlands Islands, and these in turn are separated by 80 miles from the western coast of Graham Land, which is separated from the mainland, having finally been proved by Sir Hubert Wilkins not to be a peninsula. The stormiest oceans to be found anywhere surround Antarctica. And as if these things were not enough, its isolation is made secure by the fact it is separated from the rest of the world by oceans of abysmal depths, soundings showing depths ranging from 2,000 to 3,000 fathoms.

The Antarctic is a continent still in the ice age, similar to that which gripped the northern hemisphere perhaps 50,000 years ago. [2] The greatest ice mass in the world covers the continent, so that only the highest peaks emerge; bare rock is so unusual that explorers, finding it, could hardly seem more delighted if they had come suddenly upon green meadowland. The continent is mainly uplifted tablelands of snow and ice, from 5,000 to 10,000 feet above sea level, and is traversed in places by mountain ranges of extraordinary size and beauty. Inland lie the Polar and South Victoria plateaux—level, vast and elevated—which are central areas of the continental ice sheet; here the depth of the ice cap appears to range from a few feet, where it touches steep mountainous slopes, to from 1,000 to 5,000 feet on the plateaux. From these areas pour moving masses of continental ice, which, propelled by

[1] *Ibid.*, p. 5.
[2] The deglacierisation of the continent is now held to be a fact. The raised beaches discovered by Scott and Shackleton; the finding of moraines and erratics high above the general level of the adjacent surface of glacier ice. Shackleton found the summit of Mt. Hope strewn with erratics at a height fully 2000 feet above the nearest glacial ice, and David and Priestley believe that during the height of glaciation, the ice attained a maximum thickness of 4,000 feet in parts of McMurdo Sound, from which it is now entirely retreated. ("Heart of the Antarctic," ii, p. 277).

vast pressures in the interior, move down the valleys and passes of the encircling mountains in the shape of glaciers and ice falls of a size and grandeur found nowhere else in the world.

Toward this continent we turned; and we approached it with growing humility; conscious of its majesty and its sullen solitudes, and conscious, too, of the large accomplishments of the men who had preceded us. What we hoped to do, and more we could not do, was to attempt simply to extend the knowledge that they had begun to accumulate.

We selected the Bay of Whales as the best place to base because (1) it seemed to offer the likeliest circumstances for flying and (2) because it was surrounded by unknown areas. To the north and east lay King Edward VII Land, first seen by Scott from the deck of the *Discovery,* first and last traversed by Prestrud, [1] and beyond that a wholly unknown coastline and interior. Here lay hundreds of thousands of square miles of territory utterly unknown to geography, a vacuum abhorrent to scientist and cartographer alike. To the southeast lay the supposed Carmen Land discovered by Amundsen on his polar journey, [2] awaiting the inquiry of precise science. Save for the paths of Shackleton, Scott and Amundsen, which at the extreme distance were separated only by 400 miles and thence converged steadily and narrowly upon the Pole, the mysterious plateau was untrodden and unknown. What lay beyond it, between the Pole and Weddell Sea, no one could say. These avenues for pure discovery offered themselves. No less important was the probability of bringing to bear upon these unknown areas, and upon known areas as well, the organized research equipment that modern invention has produced; in the departments of geology, meteorology, glaciology, magnetism and allied divisions, pure science must benefit. And the advantage lay with us in that we possessed three of the most efficient instruments given to the explorer; radio, the airplane, with its wonderful speed and independence of surface obstructions that vex the foot-traveller,

---

[1] The Japanese Antarctic Expedition, under Lt. Shirase, ascended one of the peaks of Alexandra Range in 1911. The exact route followed, however, is unknown.

[2] The South Pole, ii, p. 31, 170, 171.

and the aerial mapping camera, which sees everything and forgets nothing.

We had reason to hope we might accomplish much. But as the *Larsen* forged south, on a peaceful ocean, it was not difficult sometimes, to imagine a very different ending. So many things might go wrong. So many important things that perhaps I had overlooked. So many other things that no one could foresee, save the omniscience reserved at the very end for the reproachful man, when everything is done and past remedy.

CHAPTER III

THROUGH THE PACK

THE *Larsen* docked at Wellington November 5; and the end of the journey across the Pacific was to mean many things, not the least important of which was the discovery of New Zealand's hospitality to Americans. We soon learned that the proximity of this island dominion to the Antarctic was not the only thing that recommended it to explorers. We were to carry from it the experience of having felt unstinted kindness, friendliness and cooperation. Had we been Englishmen, on an English errand, we could not have been better treated. If we, on our side, failed perhaps to show the true measure of our gratitude, it was only because we were of necessity so intent on our work. Dominating our every mood and action was the necessity of making contact with the *Larsen* at the pack. It was a spur that drove us on at top speed.

As for the *Larsen,* on her arrival at Wellington, she immediately began to take on water and supplies: the chasers [1] that were to accompany her south were already waiting at Stewart Island, and Captain Nilsen expected to start within a few days.

Our New Zealand representative, Hon. Harold Livingstone Tapley of Dunedin, owner of Tapley Ltd., Shipping Agents, sent his manager, Jim Duncan, to meet us to discuss the loading of supplies previously sent to Dunedin. Tapley Ltd. was one of the volunteers of the expedition. I have never met a finer gentleman than Harold Tapley; and his manager, Jim Duncan, typifies the words conscience and efficiency.

[1] Chasers are small, tug-like craft, carrying harpoon guns, which seek out the whales and kill them. The *Larsen,* a factory ship, acts as "mother ship" to these chasers and converts the whales into oil on the spot. The chasers are very strongly built and with the proper shape and curves to contend with the ice.

Rest was a word that soon lost personal meaning. We at Wellington took charge of the airplanes and other supplies unloaded by the *Larsen*. We were assisted by our Wellington representatives, Gardiner, Binnie and Halliburton, who were splendid to us. As the days passed, and the *City,* with emptying coal bunkers, dawdled in Pacific doldrums, we almost ceased to watch the calendar and began to count the hours.

November 18th saw the *Bolling* come into Dunedin at dawn, her crew tanned and darkened by tropical sun, her own sides stained and coated with rust, and with a tale to tell of decks that sizzled at noon and fire room temperatures that got as high as 120° Fahrenheit. There was much good natured grousing over the idea of getting seasoned for polar cold in what one member of the crew described as "Hell's anteroom"; but I was delighted to observe that the crew as a whole had come through very well, the greenhorns had become accustomed to their various duties, and Captain Brown's ability was plainly marked in the high morale of his men.

Our plans had meanwhile taken a new turn. Captain Brown had been ordered to dump part of his cargo at Dunedin, to make room, and proceed north to Wellington as soon as possible. There he was to pick up the stuff dropped by the *Larsen,* and return it to the concentration docks at Dunedin, where some of it would be taken aboard by the *City.* This meant a saving of at least a day's time. Just before the *Bolling* got underway, Captain Melville reported that the *City* would arrive in about seven days. She had been becalmed for days, and later driven off her course by storm. She was under both steam and sail and deriving but slight assistance from the Trades. Her arrival, then, would be tardier than we had hoped; and as these precious days ebbed, my hope of meeting the *Larsen* grew fainter.

During the lull between loadings I found that the dogs, which had been quartered at Quarantine Island, about six miles from Dunedin, were in shocking condition, many of them suffering from diarrhea and distemper. The cause of it, apparently, was a new diet with which we had experimented, and the long journey had aggravated their illness. My pity for the beasts was exceeded only by my concern for the future of the expedition. Without dogs we were hopelessly handicapped. We could not transport our supplies from the ships to our base on the Barrier, much less undertake the extensive program of surface geological and glacialogical exploration. Dogs provide the one means of transportation effective under nearly all conditions of polar travel; and as we proposed to pioneer with aircraft, we looked to them especially for assistance in the event of emergencies. To discover them so depleted by sickness, at this late hour, was a dreadful blow. It was too late to have new dogs shipped from Labrador. Unless these could be restored to health, the expedition could go no farther, at least in 1928.

In this serious situation we took our troubles to Dr. John Malcolm, professor of dietetics at Otago University. He worked out a new formula, the ingredients of which were beef tallow, meat meal, wheat germ, molasses, and cod liver oil. To every one thousand pounds of pemmican were added two pints of mixed lemon, which are rich in antiscorbutic vitamins. The problem of making a new food was solved when the Hudson Brothers, of Dunedin, loaned us the use of their chocolate factory at night. A dozen workmen volunteered their services after regular hours, and with their help Dr. Malcolm, Mr. Hudson, and Norman Vaughan started in the production of twenty-five tons of pemmican biscuits. They worked steadily for nearly two weeks, from sunset until nearly dawn, and, for all their lack of practice at the art, they produced a tremendous pile of pemmican. Enough at least, I judged, to see the dogs through to the Barrier, and on the trail. Thereafter fresh meat, both seal and whale, could be had in plenty to feed them at the base. The next day we tried out the formula on the dogs, within a few days they began to pick up and by the time we started south most of them were beginning to get in good condition. We lost only four of our dogs, and it has always seemed a miracle there were not more.

November 24, the *Bolling* returned from her Wellington errand, loaded down with supplies she had taken on there. Probably the neatest trick of that week was Captain Brown's, when he finally managed to squeeze the fuselage of the Ford airplane into the pitifully limited hold of his ship; had the crate been half a foot longer, the trick would have been impossible. When it did fall into place, with a sound that might have been interpreted as an imprecation, all hands cheered. Two days later the *City* came up the narrow passage to Dunedin, and the fo'c's'le was black with men anxious to have foot on earth and asphalt pavement after three months at sea. If they had hopes of a long holiday, they must have been disillusioned when they sighted the docks. At one end was the *Bolling,* from whose open hatches poured an unslackening stream of crates and boxes. Supplies were piled up on the docks higher than a man's head, and this mass was fed constantly by other streams pouring from warehouses. Over this scene presided the indefatigable Brophy directing the flow of each tributary and the activities of half a hundred men with astonishing energy and memory of detail. But I could see that his nerves were not bearing up under the strain and it worried me.

The *City* first stopped at Port Chalmers, twenty miles up the harbor from Dunedin. We came down from Christchurch the next morning and the men from the *City* met us at the train. They were a fine looking group of men. Three months ago most of them were the rankest greenhorns, but now they not only looked like but were real sailormen. Their experience had been far from an easy one. They had had a four-hour watch on duty and four hours off, with work to do while off watch. It was good to see them in their rough clothes and to observe their good humor. They were ready for the contest, I could see.

Precious little sentiment was given the arrival of the *City,* although the incident brought all units of the expedition together for the first time in three months. The conferences with Captain Melville with respect to the taking on of cargo were prefaced by an exchange of derisive remarks from the *Bolling's* crew ashore and even rougher remarks from the men at the taffrail of the *City.* Each implied the other had enjoyed a gentlemanly cruise, which was over, and dirty work was at hand. It was indeed. The *City* went into dry dock immediately, to have her hull scraped clean of the fronds of sea life that such a slow ship picks up on a long journey. The

crew was given liberty for the night, with the strict order
every man was to report for duty early next morning. There-
upon our labors began in earnest, and the adjoining neighborhood echoed to the sounds of unparalleled activity. It was
ever so encouraging to see how every one pitched in; no
one was exempt and no one shirked; every one, scientist and
seaman alike, worked with his hands, trundling boxes and
crates until the back ached and muscles protested. Were
it not for the vagueness of the *Larsen's* movements, this
splendid spirit must have removed my last doubts as to the
ultimate success of our plans.

The *Larsen* had meanwhile sailed south, and was fishing
north of the pack, which she reported was unusually heavy
this year. The radiomen maintained a daily schedule with
her, and the last message from Captain Nilsen reported the
pack was still too dangerous for passage. There was good
whaling north of the pack and we prayed it would continue
so. There was no telling, however, how long the pack would
hold: from hour to hour my mind played with the thought:
perhaps she had already started through. Here was a race of
success against failure. The stakes were large—very large
indeed. I believe that one really lives more at a time like
this.

If any particular memory survives these hurried days, it is
the memory of the appalling number of things that had to be
put into the *City*. How all the things that eventually got aboard
her were squeezed in is worth a chapter in itself; for with an
unsuspected necromancy Brophy managed to find a place for
everything, although the pile of supplies still awaiting a place
seemed always to grow larger and the space of the *City*, pitifully small to begin with, appeared to shrink before our
eyes. The loading schedule had become complicated owing
to the necessity of separating the two ships. Prudence suggested that the *City* be so thoroughly equipped that, if the
Bolling proved unable to get through the pack, the ice party
could not only hold out until relief arrived twelve months
later, but also carry out a substantial amount of the scientific
program. The outfitting of the *City*, consequently, took on
the aspect of setting up a distinct and self-sufficing expedition within an expedition. As a result, the cargoes first as-

signed to the vessels had to be redistributed in large part, a necessity that taxed the patience and nearly broke the backs of all of us before it was done.

The scene that took place on the docks is not likely to be forgotten by most of us. The long arms of cranes rose and fell monotonously, winches squealed, chains rattled, and the wheels of hand trucks slammed and bumped on deck night and day. Sleep was a luxury few gained. In a corner of my memory, whence I can draw it forth when I need to smile, is a picture of two of the outstanding members of the expedition, Professor Gould and Captain McKinley, at grips with a kind of work they never did before and are unlikely to do again—stevedoring. Sweat staining faces and clothes, they struggled with the rest over sacks of coal and boxes of food. With them were Haines, the genial meteorologist, in ill-fitting dungarees, wobbling in the dust under tiring loads.

At last the hold was full: there was room for not another box below, so we began to load the decks. The crated fuselage of the Fairchild airplane was swung aboard and lashed in place amidships, between the main and foremasts. Food boxes and gasoline drums were ranged about it until the waist of the ship became so deep with things that before the mainsail could be set it must first be reefed. Seventy-five tons of coal were stowed away forward; these were for use at the base. Then the dogs, in their clumsy boxed kennels, were hoisted to the poop deck, and their crates ranged in rows; when that space was filled, the remaining dogs found haven on the top of my deck cabin and on the roof of the airplane crate. Here it was believed they would be out of reach of water, which they cannot abide; and the yelps, the growls and squalling with which they announced this change of residence were wonderful to hear. It was a sound we were to know well, for it did not leave our ears for nearly a year and a half.

As the weights of supplies in her mounted, the *City* settled gradually, and before the loading was finished water showed above the Plimsol line. This, with the fact that an immoderately large part of her load was above decks, gave rise to some uneasiness. In fact, the day before we put to sea, an old sailing man, who had been watching operations with a disapproving eye, came up and said: "You're taking an awful chance with that ship. She'll ship green water every roll. You don't know what storms are until you get into the 'Sixties.' I've been there and I know." I assured him we knew what we were doing, but confess that the incident suggested in an unpleasant manner the unhappy wedding guest impaled on the glance of the Ancient Mariner.

During this period the Otago Harbour Board of Dunedin was extremely helpful and generous. It docked our vessels, gave us port facilities and the use of warehouses, and performed innumberable courtesies, for which I was more than grateful.

The late afternoon of December I saw the *City* loaded and ready to put to sea. But rather than start out half-cocked, we decided to postpone departure until the following morning. The delay gave Brophy a much-needed opportunity to check and cross-check the cargo. The night was spent in stock-taking. December 2nd at six o'clock in the morning, the order was given to start. The tug that was to tow us to sea threw us a line, and the *City* followed, with the *Bolling* astern. Even at this early hour many of the new friends we had made in New Zealand were on hand; it was no longer possible to believe we were strangers departing from a foreign land. We slipped down the narrow channel that leads from Dunedin to the sea; and off Tairoa Head the tug cast us loose. Captain Brown threw us a quarter-inch steel hawser, which we took on our anchor winch with a number of turns and then anchored to the foremast. The line ran out about a quarter of a mile and then, as the slack disappeared, a slight shock ran over the massive frame of the *City,* and she slowly gathered headway. So, in this lame, but necessary manner, we began our race to the *Larsen.*

My diary that night carried the following entry:

En route to Bay of Whales
December 2, 1928

I think we may breathe more easily now. The last piece of loose cargo has been securely lashed, and it will take a pretty strong sea to do us much damage. We were lucky to have such a perfect day. Had we run into bad weather earlier we might have lost half the dogs and supplies on deck. There is the barest hint of a swell running, otherwise sea and sky are all we could ask for. With all sails set and under steam, we are making about eight knots under the *Bolling's* tow. If we can keep this up, we ought to reach the northern edge of the pack within seven or eight days.

I am thankful the *Larsen* is still outside. We may still reach her. I have vainly tried to induce Captain Nilsen to set an approximate date for his dash through the pack, even though I knew well he could not do this. Though this uncertainty is trying, the contest is more interesting.

I have just made a trip of survey about the ship. There are fifty-four men aboard, making eighty-three men on the expedition all told. From the amount of congestion, one might imagine there were ten times that number. Below decks, everything is in great confusion. Every bunk is piled high with equipment, which has overflowed to the floor. There is scarcely a place where one can set foot on deck. Supplies of all descriptions so fill the deck that to get from fore to aft it is either necessary to do a perilous balancing act on the rail or else risk one's neck in an alpine assault over peaks and precipices of dog crates and food boxes. How any of us will find room to sleep tonight is beyond me. Dean Smith, who is six feet, four inches tall, and carries a frame to match, looked in at the five foot ten bunk in which he is expected to find haven, and was moved to comment in an emphatic way on the spirit that moves men to explore. I dare say most of the others feel the same way at this moment. It will be days before we get our things stowed away. Van der Veer [1] and Rucker [2] are buried under a mass of photographic gear, and a hasty glance at Hanson's quarters suggests he has taken all the radio equipment in the world to the Antarctic. My own quarters, astern, aft of the smokestack, do not bear comparison: trunks, crated clothing and instruments are strewn about as if discarded by a hurricane. And if this were not enough, the chaos is exaggerated by the mixed harmony of the dogs overhead and the high pitched overtones from the radio machinery next door. The dogs have howled all day

[1] Willard Van der Veer, photographer assigned to the expedition by Paramount News. He was also on the North Pole Expedition.
[2] Joseph Rucker, also of Paramount News.

long, with an unearthly disharmony all their own, and the radio will probably keep at it all night. What few wits as are left to us are rapidly disappearing.

Still, things are not at all bad. Good old George Tennant [1] gave us an excellent dinner, everyone is in fine spirits, and there is a great deal of amusing joking about our lot. We all eat together in the fo'c's'le, officers and men alike. I have decided to permit no social or official distinctions to be drawn during the life of the expedition. The naming of officers will be governed more according to the placing of responsibility and authority than the following of formal service customs with the "aye, aye, Sir" and the complete social segregation of the officers and men. In a sense there are no officers and men. Some merely hold responsibility—that is the only difference. It will be an interesting experiment, whatever comes of it.

We have been under sail for nearly twelve hours. At six o'clock this evening, Mulroy started his engines. It was a wonderful sight, earlier in the day, to see the greenhorns in the rigging setting sail. Most of them stepped about rather timidly, but did what they were told, making up in willingness what they lacked in skill. First mate Strom will have them tough as shellbacks in another week. The men who have made the voyage from the States do their job like old sailormen.

I was rather surprised when Captain Melville got the men together this morning and nominated the starboard and port watches. This means that all hands, with the exception of the cook, radiomen and several other specialists, will have four hours on duty and four hours off. There being much work to be done, besides deck duty, this arrangement must work real hardship; it will be difficult for them to get enough sleep. However, we shall see how it works out. It is my personal opinion that a watch in three would be better. We have enough extra hands to do it. I shall suggest it to the Captain tomorrow, anyway.

The next two days found us pushing southward with refreshing speed. Monday, the wind hauled around to the north and gave us such a boost that we were soon treading on the *Bolling's* stern, with the tow line curved and slack. We were

[1] Also cook on the North Pole Expedition.

sufficiently emboldened to cast off the tow and make our way alone, under sail and steam. We averaged nine knots—luck was with us. Tuesday, the wind veered to the south, and the cold breath of the ice fields was on it. The wolf dogs seemed to sense the ice for their weird howling became almost continuous. We crawled back to the *Bolling's* tow, reefed sail and made ready for a storm that the lowering barometer prophecied. It was a trying day for the amateur sailors. The sea was quite rough, the ship rolled heavily and yardarms were precarious places when hands were freezing and sails were icy and cranky. Bubier, the aviation mechanic, who had never seen a ratline before, much less handled one, came down from a lofty perch with hands blue and teeth chattering from cold. "Give me flying every time," he said. Later in the day, the wind changed again to southwest, and we hoisted the spanker and jib sail.

Slowly we accustomed ourselves to the routine, and as the congestion below was gradually relieved by the sorting out of gear the ship became more habitable. There was still a chill in the air, but Wednesday, the 5th, brought continuing gentle winds and a smoking blue sky. With a few exceptions, all hands were in fine spirits. Among these exceptions were seasick seamen of whom we had an abnormal casualty list. Another was Igloo, who, to my astonishment, developed a real inferiority complex. Igloo is the companion of my ventures, a fox terrier of doubtful pedigree but unquestioned integrity. Neither modesty nor humility, I regret to say, is in his attitude, and until this trip I fancied neither man nor beast could discompose him. He met his superiors, however, in the Eskimo dogs, and in admitting to himself their superiority, his spirit underwent an extraordinary change. He hardly dared venture out on deck alone. His mere appearance brought from the beasts a fearful medley of challenges and imprecations; they hurled themselves at the doors of their crates, and those chained on the deck dashed out at him with fangs bared and a tremendous rattling of chains as he streaked past. Nights, when they began their melancholy singing, which can unseat the composure of an imaginative man, he shivered behind a box in my cabin. Not until the last sound had faded away, as mysteriously as it began, dared he come forth again, and

then only in the lee of a friendly human figure. Poor Igloo,
I did not blame him. Those primitive dogs, who kill for the
sheer lust of killing, would assassinate him on the spot, as
he was shrewd enough to realize. It was he, indeed, who
found adventure on the way south.

Thursday, the 6th, the weather was still favorable, although
the sea was rougher and rising steadily. There was the hint of
a storm in the air. The sky was a deep gray, and the sun
shone through it with paling strength. The wind was abaft
the beam all day, so that we made at times as much as ten
knots, a speed I never dared hope for. But this, in turn,
proved a mixed blessing. Even under favorable conditions,
keeping a taut line on a ship in sail and in tow is one of the
most trying tasks ever wished on a green crew; in the face
of the seas we encountered that day and the next the task
approached physical punishment. As the *City* rose and fell under
the action of the waves, the line would tighten and then pay
off; our progress became a succession of arching rises and
jabbing thrusts, not at all pleasant. The line hummed as it
stiffened suddenly, and I began to wonder when another shock
would break it. We had one nasty moment when the wheel
turned balky, and spun around, with a swiftness and power
that knocked Demas and Bursey from their feet. Before she
could be checked, the *City* swung off to port, and as the strain
increased the *Bolling* was slowed up and the *City* came alongside at a high rate of speed. Under the lash of Strom's orders,
men scuttled up the rigging, sails were hastily taken in and
what might have been a serious crash was avoided at the last
moment. It was a very anxious time.

Toward evening, the wind freshened almost to gale force,
the barometer dropped slightly and all indications pointed to
dirty weather. It came, with the blustery strength for which
this region is famous, and my diary reports:

En Route to Bay of Whales
Aboard City of New York
December 8, 1928
Night

Owing to the bad weather that struck us yesterday, I
made no entries in my log. Thursday night the ship pitched

so, we got little sleep. About five o'clock, the ship was making very heavy weather of it. Seas were breaking over the
taffrail, the wind velocity approached fifty miles per hour,
and the glass dropped sharply. Matters were decidedly serious.
My first fears were for the cargo on deck and the dogs. There
was danger some of the heavy, loose stuff on the deck might
be knocked about by boarding seas, perhaps smashing the
skylights, hatchways and bulwarks. All hands were called out
to make fast dog crates and all gear on deck with double lashings. Fortunately, the gale blew us along the line of our
course. We managed to keep the *City* going with wind and
waves—had we broached into the trough of a sea our decks
must have been swept as clean as a pantry shelf.

The men at the wheel had the worst time. The wheel is
out in the open on the after deck, and, lacking steam power, is
very difficult to control. For this reason, we had two men
on duty all the time, but even against their combined strength
it spun on several occasions out of control. On the morning
watch, McKinley was bowled over by one such revolution, falling with such force that he was knocked out. He came to in
a moment, and save for a severe bruising was unhurt.

From time to time the ship rolled her sides under, but not
enough green water came aboard to cause damage. It was
hazardous work, however, moving about the deck in the
confusion of the cargo, for there was always the thought
that the crate or box that offered lee might in a moment be
torn loose from its fastenings and become a Juggernaut. Believing the towline must presently give way, I went forward
to the fo'c's'le where I had an opportunity to see the play
between ship and storm. A quarter of a mile away the *Bolling* labored heavily in water that rose high enough to hide
her from sight, and she seemed to be rolling her sides under
with every other roll. The bowsprit of the *City* pointed her
out like an entreating finger. Now it rose dizzily to the
horizon, trembled a moment at the top of flight, then plunged
dizzily to the sea, to meet a rush of green water gushing
underneath. Yardarms creaked and groaned overhead, and
at times it seemed the outer reaches of the lower yardarms
were flicking the tops of the waves at the end of a long roll.
The towline tightened and slackened in rapid succession, and

I knew then that it would be only a question of time before it broke or the bridle supporting it on the *Bolling* gave way.

I was writing out orders to radio to the *Bolling* to cast loose the tow line when I saw the port line on the bridle snap. Then the *City* rose on a wave and on the *Bolling* I saw someone race aft, seize a hatchet and cut loose the other line. Almost at the same moment the *Bolling* swerved to starboard, warning us with six toots on the whistle of her intent—a signal we had agreed upon in the event of such an emergency. Smith, helmsman on the *City,* on hearing the blasts, put rudder hard left, and the *City* bore away, dragging the heavy steel hawser across her bows. Had Smith been less quick-witted a collision might have followed.

As it was, we did not get clear unscotched. In the excitement a seaman loosed the main lower topsail sheets, and as the wet sail ran down it bellied out in the storm; before anxious hands could save it there was a series of pistol-like reports, and the sail was in shreds. This fellow's mistake was nothing more criminal than lack of experience, but from the lacing he got from the mate of the watch he is not likely to repeat the mistake.

However, we reduced sail and made our way mostly under steam. The *Bolling* by now was a mile or two to starboard, no doubt alarmed as to our condition. Here the radio proved invaluable. By means of the wireless telephone which Hanson rigged up on both ships, it is possible to maintain excellent communication between the two ships. I lost no time in assuring Captain Brown the *City* was undamaged, and was in turn relieved to hear his voice say that, except for the broken line, the *Bolling* was also uninjured.

We then fell to the job of bringing home the towline, and what a miserable job that was. The *City* had no steam winch on the fo'c's'le, her hand anchor winch was as old as the *City,* and its effectiveness had not improved with age. For two hours Strom and his crew, drenched with spray, pumped up and down, encouraging themselves with stirring chanties. At length we recovered every inch of it, full thirty fathoms in all, but there is scarcely a back aboard ship that can push itself erect.

A trip around the ship showed that everything was in

place, although a few crates had been dislodged by the seas which still fell with smothering force upon the decks. Tennant's galley ran with a foot of water, in which slops and food were commingled on the deck in an unsavory mess. In spite of these difficulties, he managed to keep his fire going and served an excellent hot meal of soup, boiled beef, potatoes, stewed tomatoes and pudding. The dogs took the storm in an evil mood. Their cries never ceased, and with the wind, took on a strange and mournful note, whether because of distress or fear I cannot say. Heaven knows, they are rarely still, but now they howl all day, in the most dismal chorus, with occasional ferocious fighting sounds. Several fell sick, nearly all had their kennels flooded by the higher seas, but otherwise came to no harm. Because they hate the touch of dampness, those which can are standing weakly in their crates, fighting to keep footing against the pitch of the ship.

It appeared, at first, we were in for a spell of bad weather. The whalers farther south reported similar heavy storms, and Haines, our meteorologist, thought the storm might become more intense the next day, at least over short periods. Nevertheless, as the day wore on the glass rose, although the force of the seas did not abate and the sky was unpromising.

Then, about seven o'clock, the wind lessened in intensity and blew slightly to the west; an hour later the rim of the sun showed through a cloud, and the storm blew itself out. It was succeeded, however, by a period of very thick weather, which caused us to debate for a time the advisability of hauling to, lest we collide with an iceberg, the presence of which was suggested by rapidly chilling air. Toward eight o'clock, the sky cleared marvellously fast and we caught sight of the sun in a gorgeous sunset panorama. It came to me with strong force how we appreciate things by contrast. This inspiringly beautiful sunset, falling tranquilly upon a hushed sea after such a storm, gave one the impression of entering an entirely different world.

Saturday dawned cold and clear, with a moderate wind in the quarter. At five o'clock this morning, we gave our line to the *Bolling* again, and were underway by seven, making seven knots. Every one is the happier for the ending of yesterday's travail. At noon our position was Lat. 62° 10' S., Long.

174° 27′ E. We were then 997 miles south of Tairoa Head.

Tonight it is so clear that I can still write without the aid of lantern, although it is nearly ten o'clock. All's well that ends well. The *Larsen* is still outside the pack!

I was to learn, the following day, Sunday, that I spoke too soon. For, as we drew nearer the south magnetic Pole, which was to the southwestward well under 1,000 miles from us, the compasses became erratic; there was a large difference between the standard compass and the steering compass, and the directive force had become so slight we scarcely dared to trust the former. Facing, as we did, the necessity of meeting the *Larsen* which was on the move, the problem of navigation was a difficult one, especially as we spent the last half of Saturday night and most of Sunday poking through thick fog. It shut down so thickly that the *Bolling* was obscured, and opportunities to get a line on the sun to locate our position were few and far between. The *Larsen* for the same reason did not know her exact position. From my point of view, this was one of the most ticklish moments of the trip. The *Larsen* was only about 200 miles south of us; and it was imperative we pick her up without loss of time.

Early Sunday morning we sighted the first sentinel of the Antarctic—a lone tabular iceberg. It was presently succeeded by others, in increasing quantities, until at last they formed an endless procession, stretching as far as the eye could see. They made a striking scene in the half-mist, and the mind suggested fantastic shapes bearing relationship to sculptured forms and faces. We could spare little time for day-dreaming just then, though, for the barometer started to drop with bewildering speed, and the sea developed a long, sustained roll. We turned east, to avoid an isolated section of the flat pack ice dead ahead and made some distance in this direction before turning west. We thus slipped in behind the smaller pack and the larger pack lay somewhere due south over the horizon. Our race against time was almost run.

Monday, the 10th, found us still making our way alongside rafted groups of icebergs, most of them of the long flat-topped types peculiar to Antarctic regions. In the space of a few hours we passed no less than fifty of them, each followed by the inevitable tail of brash ice. On those rare moments when the sun broke through and shone upon them, we had glimpses of enchanting beauty. The light fell softly in the smoking haze, until the sides of the bergs glittered like marbled cliffs, and the blue shadows in the ice glowed as with an internal radiance. In the nearer bergs we could observe the darker shadowed horizontal lines that indicated successive stratification. In the caves worn at the water line we could hear the booming of the sea, and as they struck the waves hurled spray higher, I judged, than our mast. Occasionally we sighted a true derelict—a berg undermined by the action of the sea until it had overturned, and now, with its eroded and hollowed basement in the air, was moving with wind and currents to complete annihilation in warmer waters.

The weather was heart-breaking—moments of glorious sunshine, succeeded by snow flurries, wretched squalls and fog. Nevertheless the Captain did manage to take some accurate sights, and we were so encouraged that at noon we laid a line that went through Scott Island, in the belief that, if our position was correct, we might be able to solve the mystery of this little outcropping of land. Lieutenant Colbeck, of Scott's first expedition had first sighted this "loneliest of islands" and, although whaling ships were constantly in adjoining waters, they had not sighted it and doubted its existence The surprise of every one aboard was no greater than my own when, about five o'clock, the lookout reported land ahead. It was Scott Island, and we passed it abeam about seven o'clock.[1]

What a God-forsaken place it is. Simply two great hunks of basaltic rock emerging in misshapen outline from a waste of sea. One was much larger than the other. It rose, almost perpendicularly, from the sea, and its top was capped with snow. Someone remarked upon its resemblance to an elephant's head, an appearance it did assume from the west. Flecks of brown moss were visible near the top of the peak. The sky overhead was noisy and dark with the flight of thousands of birds, mostly petrels, who nested on its bleak sides. This rock must be at least 200 feet high. The other rock was probably sixty feet shorter in height, but ran about a quarter

[1] Position of the island is Long. 179° 51′ 30″ W., Lat. 67° 25′ S.

mile in a north and south direction. To the south an icefoot descended to the sea. The excitement over this discovery was so great that it was all we could do to prevent the scientists from going overboard to make their first studies of glaciology and bird life.

Leaving this fascinating island behind, we struck due south. A confused, vaguely illuminated grayness in the sky indicated the pack was not far off. Soon the lookout reported it dead ahead, and not long afterwards it could be seen from the deck, a low rafted rampart stretching east and west as far as the eye could see. Reluctant to force the *Bolling* into it, we sought a way around it and saw, to the eastward, a lane of fairly open water. Eight o'clock that night we were only about forty miles from the *Larsen,* but never seemed as far away. The pack ranged all about us, snow flurries from the west struck us continuously, and in the bad visibility we were repeatedly menaced by ice bergs, weighing hundreds of thousands of tons, that lay in our path. It was an eerie experience to see these floating dreadnaughts, propelled by unknown submarine currents, move forward in the face of a headwind, at varying gaits of speed.

All that night and the morning of the next day (it was still December 10—having crossed the 180th meridian we lost a day) we dodged shifting pack ice and bergs, working to the east in search of open water. Weather continued thick and snowy, with poor visibility. During one of these thick spells, the *Bolling* stopped quickly to avoid a berg, her whistle suddenly failed and we nearly rammed her. We went full speed astern and, of course, had just gathered momentum when the *Bolling* went ahead again. The shock tore the cable loose from the *City.* It was our good luck, however, to be free from the task of hauling it up again, so we stood by while the poor devils on the *Bolling* went at it. Then a peculiar accident occurred. They had all but a few fathoms on the drum when I noticed a scurry of men about the winch. The winch began to scream shrilly, I saw the line begin to pay out and flip wildly and serpentinely about the deck and then, with a last scream and a shower of sparks as it struck the metal deck, it whipped overboard. At the same time two men, who I later learned were McGuinness and Kessler, dropped to their knees, barely escaping being cut down in the final contortions of the hawser. It meant the loss of the cable and therefore the end of the towing, but I did not sorrow for that when I learned no one was injured. It was difficult to believe there were no casualties for only a moment before half the crew had been gathered about the winch. The compasses now went completely "haywire." There was one hundred degrees difference between the standard compass and the steering compass. Because of thick weather neither our ships, nor the *Larsen,* knew our exact position. We were heading for a ship of unknown position with our own position doubtful and compasses confused.

In this situation our radio compasses proved invaluable. By means of a series of bearings we headed the ship in the direction of the wireless waves coming from the *Larsen* and thus bore steadily toward her. It was rather a problem, however, trying to keep on that elusive wave and dodge moving masses of ice at the same time.

Once we were caught between the main pack and an enormous field of floating ice, with cakes in it half a mile long, distorted by pressure—a rather fearsome sight, but with a bit of jockeying we avoided dangerous ice. Sverre Strom and Johanssen, Norwegian ice pilots who had come all the way from Norway in the *City,* spent hours in the rigging keeping us out of bad pack. We were greatly relieved when Strom called down from the lookout's barrel on the masthead that they had sighted the *Larsen* on the other side of an ice field. Captain Melville and I studied the situation, and decided that, by making Eastings, we could get into the sheltered bay of ice in which she lay. Here was a perfect ice-locked harbor in the middle of the pack, with upended ice offering a splendid lee. The ice pilots guided us safely around and we stopped our engines a short distance from the whaler. For the moment, at least, our larger problems were solved, and you may be sure we were in a happy state of mind.

However, we found no leisure, for there now faced us the task of shifting 100 tons of coal in sacks from the *Bolling* to the *City,* to replenish the bunkers. Although a very heavy swell was running, we brought the *Bolling* alongside, smashing several davits on the *Bolling* and tearing off a strip of woodwork from the poop deck of the *City*. We had barely started shifting coal when the wind stiffened and drifted us to leeward, and as the sea rose we could see the iron plates of the *Bolling* bend and give as she banged against the tougher wooden sides of the *City*. Meanwhile the barometer plunged to 28.80, which at home would herald the coming of another Florida hurricane. Haines, watching its fall with excited eyes, was moved to say: "I never saw a barometer so low." This position was altogether too precarious, so we cast off, and the vessels separated. About four o'clock in the afternoon Captain Nilsen informed me by radio that he expected to attempt to force the pack that night or early the following morning. We seemed caught between the devil and the deep blue sea. But needing that coal, we decided to take a long risk in getting it aboard. Making our way to the lee of the pack, we found long, slow swells but no rough water. I gave the order to tie up again, and after maneuvering for two hours, Brown with great skill brought the *Bolling* alongside the *New York*, with only minor damage. At eleven o'clock, the *City* was taking on coal, all hands were on deck and the work progressed in the golden haze of the midnight sun. The wind was from the south, a good omen, for it would help to break up the pack. By eleven o'clock the next day, Tuesday the eleventh, the last sack of coal was aboard, ninety tons having been transferred in twelve hours. The weather, fortunately, continued good; and the storm the barometer had suggested had failed, as often before, to materialize. It was a long time before Haines and Harrison got over their amazement at these terrific drops of the barometer that did not bring hurricanes. This was one of the queer things about this new world we were entering.

The *Bolling* immediately cast off and made for Dunedin. There was no use risking her presence in the dangerous ice. Besides, she must make haste if she were to accomplish two more trips that season. We saw her last about noon, her smoke a gray plume in the northern horizon. The men aboard her had done their job well, and Captain Brown proved himself to be a master of skill and courage.

We on the *City* took advantage of the lull to turn in for much needed sleep; during the last three days few of us had

had adequate rest, and the continued solidarity of the pack forced the *Larsen* to delay departure for another twenty-four hours at least.

As a matter of fact, we remained in the bay until the midnight watch, December 15. The delay gave us all a chance to recuperate, and there was enough excitement to keep us on our toes. On the morning of Wednesday, the 12th, we were rather surprised to note that Hanson had been unable to "raise" the *Bolling* on the regular radio schedule, and as minutes went by without word from her we became alarmed. Two possibilities suggested themselves—that the *Bolling,* running fast in thick weather, had struck an ice berg, or the operator was asleep, a thing Hanson held to be unlikely. Ten o'clock came, still no word: most of us by then were gathered in the radio room, our eyes fixed on the glowing tubes and restless pointers. What puzzled us beyond measure was our failure to hear the emergency set: it had been agreed that in case of inability to keep the regular schedule, the emergency signal was to be sent every fifteen minutes. I hesitate even now to describe my feelings during the next hour: I can only say that when Hanson burst into my cabin at noon, with the news he had just heard the *Bolling* and knew it was she because he recognized Grenlie's peculiar way of sending, I was probably the happiest man in the world. The operator, we learned, was so fatigued as a result of helping with the unloading that he had slept through his watch.

While waiting we saw one of the chasers attached to the *Larsen* chase a whale nearby. The gunner dispatched it with two very neat shots from the harpoon gun. When the first shot went home, the crew of the tiny gunboat made the line fast to a bow winch, then the gunner closed in for the death blow. A puff of smoke—a black line snaking out—and another hit was scored. On this the huge blue whale, which seemed at least eighty feet long, hurled its bulk out of water with a resounding splash and expired. Later on, about twenty of us went over to the *Larsen* in a small boat, to pay a social call on Captain Nilsen and his crew. We saw them take a ninety-ton whale aboard, drawing it up through the heart-shaped funnel in the nose and laying it, like a mountainous mass of blubbery jelly, on the forward deck. Ninety tons—180,000 lbs. Think of it! This mighty mammal would dwarf the mightiest pre-historic monsters. Expert cutters went at it, and within an hour the whale was becoming crude oil. It was not a pleasant sight. I had the feeling these splendid creatures deserved a better fate. Nor was it a thing sensitive nostrils would willingly endure. A whaling ship, even when scoured clean, is not suggestive of attar of roses; but in the midst of whaling operations it leaves, as far as smells go, very, very much to be desired.

Weather meanwhile continued calm, but the failure of the pack to break was discouraging. Thursday, the 13th, we had word that the *Ross,* for all her powerful engines, was stuck fast in the pack to the south of us, and as long as she was imprisoned, the *Larsen* was reluctant to entrust herself to the mercy of the pack. It was apparent then that the pack was abnormally heavy for this time of the year, a belief supported by a confidential message I received from the master of the whaler *Nilsen-Alonzo,* Captain H. Andresen, on Friday. He reported a fairly difficult passage through the pack, finding "very hard ice" in many places. "If you can keep to open tracks," he said, "you should have no difficulty in getting through, otherwise I would advise a week's delay, as the ice is slackening day by day."

During these three days we had drifted northeast with the pack to Lat. 67° 48′ S. Long. 177° 59′ W., crossing the meridian 180° and so getting into West Longitude. It was calm, with a smooth sea and sunny, and we made the most of it in checking the compasses. In swinging ship, we found the standard compass virtually useless, but, oddly enough the steering compass moved around fairly well, although with considerable deviation, no doubt from the influence of the local magnetism of the metal aboard ship. We used the sun compass, besides taking azimuths in the regular way, to get the error. They checked fairly well, but not quite as accurately as I had wished.

Noon, Saturday
December 15, 1928
En route to Bay of Whales

We have been in the pack since the first of the mid-night

watch—starting, significantly, on the date of Amundsen's arrival at the Pole, sixteen years ago. It is a relief to be moving,
but the situation is not without peril. The *Larsen* has us in
tow on a 3½ inch single wire cable, and we slide along behind
like a cockleshell in a narrow lane of shattered ice. It is
tricky work keeping in line. A slight deviation to right or left
might bring us up hard against a heavy floe, in which case
something would have to give. The *City,* with her modest
displacement of 500 tons, is just a chip in contrast with the
Larsen, with her 8,000 horsepower and 17,000 tons, and as we
follow behind her we have the impression of being drawn by an
irresistible force. When a collision occurs with a thick solid
ice floe, one of three things must give: the ice; the bow of
our ship; or her sides. Thus far the *City* has smashed the
ice with incredible strength. Were the *Larsen* to hit an ice
mass, at the same speed, she must soon tear a hole in her bow.
The *Larsen* goes at it more shrewdly. She eases up to a
floe, pressing her bow gently against the ice and then surges
forward at full speed. She thus avoids a direct smash, and,
instead of penetrating at a blow she forces her way per-
suasively through. The pack has a tendency to surge back
after the passage of the cleaving hull of the *Larsen,* and we
have the constant feeling that it may come between us altogether. Behind us, the passage has closed down into a slim
ribbon of black water, the edges of which now lip so closely
together it is difficult to believe we got through it. Through
this passage, the tough little chasers are strung out a half
mile behind gingerly picking their way under their own power.

Responsibility for keeping us out of trouble rests with
the mate of the watch, who must be on the job every minute.
We have a watch on the fo'c's'le head, with telephonic communication to the after deck, and a man standing by the
engine room telegraph. Owing to the fact the deckhouse
blocks his vision, the helmsman cannot see ahead. But with
two pairs of eyes serving him (we have a second man in the
rigging) he manages to get along. It is all very trying,
however. For when the *Larsen* stubs her nose suddenly on a
big floe, it is hard to keep the *City* from plowing into her
stern. This old ship has an inertia all her own.

I cannot begin to express my debt to Captain Nilsen.

He trusts us not to ram the *Larsen* and we will not fail him. With all the alertness of which we are capable we will be on the job.

The situation is encouraging. Here we are at the end of the *Larsen's* line, making excellent time, expending little coal and drawing near our base. The presence of our escort is secret. Owen, at Captain Nilsen's request, has not mentioned the fact in his dispatches.

Night,
Same Day.

The pack is still heavy to the south, but our progress has been such as to encourage the prediction we shall reach the Bay of Whales perhaps as early as the 26th, and probably not later than the end of the month. This ought to give sufficient time before winter sets in, in which to accomplish the unloading.

The weather continues clear, calm and warm, and the sky is a light blue which fades out into gray toward the horizon. It is so warm many of the men are stripped down to their undershirts. Actually, the temperature is nearly freezing. The noon sun, however, made heavy clothes seem very uncomfortable.

We sighted a number of seals today, big, bloated looking, lazy fellows, who waked at the noise of our passage, rolled a sleepy eye at us and then, as if dismissing the incident as unimportant, fell into slumber again. From time to time snowy petrels wheeled overhead, hoping to pick up scraps of food, and once I saw an albatross in soaring flight.

The pack is a fascinating place. Those who imagine it to be a bleak waste of ice have no conception of the beauty to be found in polar regions. Midnight is a time of splendor, for then the glory in the heavens descends upon the fields of ice and sky and circumambient air, and they seem to burn and glow with colors in which green, rose, gold, red and blue commingle in delicate tones. Past the up-ended, pressure-ridden masses of ice the low hung sun, wheeling about the horizon, casts long lilac shadows; and the more massive, towering ice forms take on the aspect of architectural magnificence, whose portals, turrets, rounded domes and cornices (of a cosmic disorder no hand could hope to imitate) diffuse a pale coloration.

There is serenity here, disturbed only by the sound of the ice hissing alongside the ship, and the faint grating as the shattered fragments of the pack, lifted by swell and our movement, press their faces together. The sound is not unlike that which one hears in a forest when a slight wind stirs.

Ahead, past the *Larsen,* it is possible to see a streak of dark water reaching south. The southern horizon is mottled, suggestive of an ice-filled but passable sea.

We shall get through. We are truly fortunate.

Monday
December 17, 1928

In looking over yesterday's entry, I discovered that I neglected to say we entered the pack at Long. 178° E. It appears this meridian offers the best passage through the pack. Our noon position was Long. 179° 55′ E., Lat. 69° 7′ S.

Our present position, however, is not very promising. We have encountered a great deal of very thick, old ice, some of it at least seven feet thick; even the *Larsen* is having difficulty forcing her way through it, so we have spent a good part of the day ramming, then backing and filling. It has been very hard on the helmsman. I wish the *City* had more power. On several occasions we came very near plowing into the *Larsen* before we could get her started astern. Still, I cannot criticize the old ship too much. She impresses one with her great strength. All day long, the sharp jagged edges of ice have been stabbing her greenheart flanks below the water line, but to no avail. One can well believe her claim to being one of the strongest ships in the world.

I have been delighted by the way in which the aviators function at the watch. June, Smith, Balchen and Parker have been exceptionally good at this. It seems strange they should be better than sailors at this job. Probably flying sharpens the sense of depth perception and speed. Davies and Adams [1] have also been very good.

[1] Lt. Harry Adams, second mate of the *City,* a retired naval officer with thirty years service and a very splendid record.

We sighted our first penguins today. First, a lone Emperor Penguin, which was nearly four feet tall. In attitude and action, he more than lived up to his reputation as the aristocrat among his kind. This most primitive of birds, which alone of all animals survived the glaciation of the once tropical or semi-tropical Antarctic, was standing erect, when we caught sight of him, and his attitude plainly implied a lordly proprietorship over the wastes he surveyed. His resemblance to man in formal dress was so close as to be positively embarrassing. To see him standing so, dignified, unafraid—did I not also detect scorn?—gave one the feeling that one should address him in carefully chosen speech. Alas, he paid scant attention to us. A scant bow, beak touching the breast, not at all the ceremonial bow for which he is distinguished, then off he went.

Presently we came across a batch of the more gregarious Adelies, and there was great hilarity aboard for a while. These comical creatures came to us unafraid, with friendly waves of the flippers, tobogganing with great speed on their bellies across the ice floes. During pauses, several of the men jumped on the ice and played with them.

Apparently the Adelies took it in fun, for, as I write, three or four of them are following along behind me, swimming like fish through the water, diving under loose floes, and coming up with uncanny accuracy on the other side. Now and then they scramble on a floe and by prodigious use of their flippers race across it as fast as a man can walk briskly.

Tuesday
December 18, 1928

A terrific tussle in the ice today. Captain Nilsen is apparently disturbed. He radioed us this morning that unless we do better work—that is, unless we keep the line taut—he would have to cast us loose. Apparently he fears we shall either collide with him or else the line will foul his propeller. I can scarcely blame him, but I assured him, as forcefully as I could, that we shall continue to do our best. To lose the tow at this stage of the journey would be a real setback. Save for the lane behind us, we are shut in by a solid wall of ice. It would take us weeks to get out under our own power. The ice is very hummocky, and is very much eroded— from the rigging it appears like the surface of the moon when viewed through a telescope.

We have been pounding all day. Down below, in the fo'c's'le, it is like standing in a chamber the walls of which are being pounded with giant hammers. One could not help growing alarmed over the shocks. Can the ship continue to stand them? There would come an impact, the floor would tilt alarmingly, then the ship would sag with groaning timbers and the shriek of cracking ice sounded outside. A good thing for us thirty-four inches of tough planking stand between.

Try as we may, we cannot avoid the thick ice cakes which close in behind the *Larsen*. When she makes a turn the tow line drags us into sharp ice corners. We go by fits and starts. It is a wonderful thing to see the *Larsen* in action, but even she has had to draw upon her immense reserve of power to keep underway. Sometimes it is a matter of forcing a few floes apart. She knifes them at a thrust.

Sometimes she thus gains, at a single stroke, a mile or two of clear water. More often it is a matter of a few yards, when a stubborn floe threatens to resist every charge.

What a fighter this man Nilsen is!

To add to our troubles it has been snowing hard.

Night,
Same day.

We are still in tow, although just a few minutes ago we came very near hitting the *Larsen* again. The only casualty however, was aboard the *City*. In trying to avoid the *Larsen*, which stopped suddenly, we had backed up on a floe, which struck the rudder a terrific blow and spun the wheel so hard it caught Captain Melville, who was standing alongside, and threw him to the deck, knocking him out for a moment. I found him struggling to a sitting position, still quite dazed, with a nasty cut over the eye. In spite of it, he insisted on remaining on deck.

Ice conditions continue bad. How many times we have climbed the rigging to study the situation I would hesitate to say. There was no sign of the dark streaks in the sky telling of open water ahead. Icebergs crept all around us. Some of them were plowing through the pack under considerable momentum supplied by the wind and deep current working together. It would not do to get beset and have one of these monsters bear down on us. It was exciting to stand in the rigging and feel the give and take of the ship; and hear the rumbling of ice under her bow and the hiss of it pressing along the side. Though the delay involved in this struggle is irksome, there is in it a savagery and doggedness that is exhilarating.

For most of the men the situation has lost its seriousness —familiarity does breed contempt. From the fo'c's'le comes the lilting tune of a Norwegian folk song—Strom is entertaining them with his accordion. It is a very comfortable scene there, with a few lanterns throwing a pale yellow light into the darker shadows; and the faces of the men lolling in the bunks, or crowded about the mess table, stand out sharply in the glow. Ronne is bent over his sewing machine in the forecastle, his nimble fingers flying faster than the tune. I have never seen such a man. Let the world about him turn gay or melancholy, Ronne is unaffected; he works all day without a pause except to eat, and seems to find great content in it.

The snow storm has passed, and out of a gray indefinite haze the sun stole back, to give us an enchanting midnight display.

Thursday, Friday and Saturday were much the same. No relief from the interminable pounding, the slowest kind of progress and a baffling mixture of sunny and stormy weather. We had hoped to get through the pack in two or three days, and were in it more than eight. We fought our way through the areas of very hard ice, once coming across vast trackless fields full of volcano-shaped structures, the cones of which sometimes attained a height of ten feet. Other fields were jumbled masses of caked ice that gave every appearance of having been subjected to terrific pressure. The one solace our position offered was comparative immunity to storm: the pack effectively dampened the sea, despite the snow squalls that beset us, and the swell was the longest I ever witnessed.

We ceaselessly scanned the southern sky, looking for open water: but only the eternal high-blink of ice, ice everywhere. But at last a change came. On the morning of Sunday, the 23rd, there was the merest suggestion of increased movement in the ice, and from a distance came the muted sounds of some disturbance. A black line, that grew larger as we watched, spread across the southern sky. Open water!

The last fifty miles were the hardest, probably because the proximity of escape made us impatient. Still, I think we took our most violent pounding then, for we struggled through a rampart of floes that repeatedly snuffed out our motion and ground us to a halt. We stubbornly made our way past ice which was as high as the poop deck, and the walls were so clean and smooth as to suggest they might have been cut out by machine. Then, to the south, we described a vast battlement of flat-topped bergs, stretching from east to west, with thin streaks of open water showing in between. It was the southern edge of the pack, and the gateway to the Ross Sea. We hurried on, making better time, as the floes became more scattered and the ice a mushy, coagulated mass hardly more resistant than soup. At eleven o'clock we had the swell of the Ross Sea under foot, a fact that speedily undermined the false sense of security several of the men had built up in quieted seas of the pack, and with a blue sky overhead and the tow line taut as a bow string, we continued due south.

The *Larsen* towed us until two o'clock, when the appearance of whales compelled Captain Nilsen to turn to a more lucrative occupation than acting as escort. His final gift to us was a pile of whale meat, young whale for the men and older whale for the dogs, which we hung in the rigging to dry. There was little time for amenities. Time was as precious to us as it was to him. We bade goodbye till another fourteen months to this excellent friend, then with all sails set and under steam we drove south, for whatever fate held in store for us. A last glance backward showed the *Larsen* in the shadow of the ice, and a chaser spurting madly, with white showing under her bow, after a plunging whale.

CHAPTER IV

WE ESTABLISH A BASE

On our second Christmas Day (we had two because we recrossed the 180th Meridian) an imperceptible brightening in the southern sky—"barrier blink"—suggested the proximity of the Barrier. As the second was the official Christmas Day, I sacrificed a ton or two of coal for sentimental reasons, in speeding up engine revolutions, hoping thereby to make the Barrier before the end of the day. I felt that a glimpse of this mysterious Antarctic rampart which we had fought so hard to gain would be an exciting gift to the men. The Ross Sea was smooth as a mill pond, and the air so fresh and pure that breath was a delight. For all the anxiety with which we anticipated landing, we went forward with our celebration. It was a most excellent affair. Tennant served a fine dinner, Lofgren as toastmaster kept things humming, and our physicist, Taffy Davies, took the part of Santa Claus as only a Welshman can. With journey's end so near, our happiness was sincere and infectious. In the midst of this, Strom's voice from the crow's nest—"Barrier on the starboard bow"—fell with the especially abrupt swiftness that long awaited news always assumes. There was a clatter of dishes hastily dropped or pushed aside, the race of footsteps up the companionway and a wild crowding of men on the fo'c's'le head and in the rigging. The thing we had come so far to see was before our eyes, a far-flung reach of lifted ice, stretching east and west as far as the eye could see. In the distance it appeared low and flat, not yet impressive, but there it was, the mysterious Barrier. Simultaneously excitement laid hold of the crew: they cheered enthusiastically and pounded on one another's back.

The *City* drove slightly to the right, to avoid a large pack of ice which stood between us and the Barrier. The course was then laid for Discovery Inlet. In the back of my mind was the idea that, if we should be unable to base in the Bay of Whales, we might find a base in Discovery Inlet. The Barrier grew steadily before our gaze, and we saw that its sheer white cliff rose eighty or ninety feet from the sea at its foot. Awe seized one with the realization that this towering rampart, which extended east and west for more than four hundred miles, and south for an equal distance, was, except in the few places where it apparently touches land, floating on the sea. If the high cliffs which show above the surface are majestic, how much more majestic must be the mass submerged? Five or six to one would be a conservative estimate of the proportion below sea level. This immense moving, water-born ice sheet is the last retreating remnant of a colossal sheet of ice which, during the period of maximum glaciation, completely covered the continent and lay on the floor of the Ross Sea. With this creation of an ancient ice age before us, inspiring reverie, it was rather shocking to find that the provocative sounds which the ear was trying to pick up came from the loudspeaker in the fo'c's'le—a jazz band broadcasting from a radio station.

We reached the Barrier at Long. 177° 25′ W., came alongside and cruised all night and part of the next day almost in its shadow. Caution stifled our curiosity, and we rarely ventured nearer than a mile from the base. The scarred and jagged wall commanded respect; one had the fear that an overhanging cliff might let go with scant warning. For here were the breeding grounds of the icebergs, and deep wounds in the Barrier walls told of the labor that brought forth the bergs that prowled the Ross Sea. Near the water's edge, the Barrier in places was honeycombed with caves, of bewildering shapes and sizes, which, when the sun struck them at just the right angle, blazed with a rich blue coloration. We took soundings every hour, and they showed an average of 250 to 300 fathoms of water. Davies and Quin Blackburn, the surveyor, were meanwhile busy with their pencils, sketching the Barrier as it paraded past.

We made out the mouth of Discovery Inlet shortly after eight o'clock in the morning, and three hours later were inside. We found ourselves in a long narrow harbor, running east and west, imprisoned between cliffs which rose, perpendicularly in places, 100 feet above sea level. These walls were smooth for the most part, but here and there were shattered and cracked as by some great disturbance. Even though it was mid-summer in the inverted seasons of these polar regions, we found the harbor filled with bay ice for more than three quarters of its length; a minor wall, it curved crescent-like between the precipitous sides of the Barrier, effectively halting our advance. As we prepared to moor off its edge, the aviator Parker made a flying leap ashore with the cry: "The Marines are always the first ashore." A dozen more tumbled after him; in a moment the silence of the bay was broken with their shouts. Plankings were hastily put to use as gangways, a bunch of the dogs were let loose for much needed exercise, and a number of the men, who had been instructed in skiing by the Norwegians, made ready to try their luck under polar conditions.

The need for haste, which was always with us, reasserted itself; and Balchen, Braathen, Strom, Petersen and I set out on skis to the eastward, in search of a possible landing field; meanwhile another group of men started out to explore the fascinating caves in the Barrier. Our trip proved worthwhile from a geographical point of view, for it greatly extended the known size of the Inlet. Instead of running east and west and ending about ten miles from the mouth, as shown on the charts, we found there is a general curve from the east to the south. At the beginning of the curve, the inlet narrowed down into an inner bay, on the western side of which we observed two snow-covered ice hills rising forty or fifty feet above the Barrier, which was very nearly 150 feet high at this point. These little hillocks (relatively) were fissured by pressure, a most interesting discovery, for it suggested an explanation as to why this harbor keeps its shape: beyond a doubt land lies underneath, holding the Barrier intact at this point. Beyond these hillocks the bay widened slightly, continued in a southerly direction for several miles and appeared to end in front of an enormous boulder-like formation of ice, behind which we saw a wide crevasse extending four or five miles.

In making this survey, we found a place about three quarters of the distance between the ship and the end of the harbor where the Barrier fell in a gentle slope to the bay ice, and up this we made our way: we managed to climb 150 feet, and yet did not attain the level floor of the Barrier. From this eminence, however, we had a fine view of the inlet and the mysterious hinterland beyond, stretching empty and rolling to the south. I wished I might have spent more time exploring this glaciological perplexity, but we had already been out several hours and I was anxious to get on to the Bay of Whales. We found no good landing field. So we turned back.

For the first time, we had to cope with the extraordinary visibility with which the Antarctic baffles all travellers. An impalpable haze took possession of the atmosphere, in which the eyes became uncertain and the relative distance of objects confused. We stumbled across little rises in the snow we did not see, and breathlessly plunged down declines before we knew we were on them. A hump of snow that seemed under our noses turned out to be fifty yards away. It was all very confusing, and we were tired when we reached the ship. We had covered about twenty miles on skis, a lengthy journey for those of us who were not used to them. I must confess that I was a lame duck on the journey.

On reaching the ship, we found her rising and falling on a strong swell. The ice where she lay was broken up and had already begun to go out, and several large floes were bumping her sides. Realizing that a storm might be a serious matter under these conditions, I gave orders to have all men brought aboard and to put out at once. A warning blast was sounded on the whistle, and a moment later the last stragglers came dashing across the ice.

Midnight
Dec. 26, 1930
En route to Bay of Whales

We're at sea now, coasting along the edge of the Barrier, heading for the Bay of Whales. We're under sail alone— trying to save coal. We now have constant daylight. At midnight it is scarcely less bright than at noon.

The City of New York in Pack Ice.

The *Eleanor Bolling* in the Pack.

Getting the *City* started was a job. The men who had been ashore came back exhausted, and after dinner were asleep in their chairs. Scarcely enough hands could be mustered into action to get sail, and the second watch is still on duty—sixteen hours of work for them. This must not be allowed to happen again. Until we know more about this region, we must be constantly alert.

Every one commented on the penetrating quality of the cold. For all the heat of the sun, the light wind cut through light clothing like a knife; and on the Barrier especially, it was so cold that one could not stand still for more than a few seconds at a time.

My mind as to the men is now made up. Gould I have made Second in Command. A splendid fellow, competent, a brilliant geologist, and popular with men. He has proper respect for the seriousness of the job. Naturally, he is greatly interested in the scientific results, and this is most important in the Second in Command. He will do well, I am sure, and I am fortunate to have him. I am now casting about for a Third in Command; McKinley, I think, will be the man. He is one of the most delightful and charming men I have ever known. Reserved to the point of reticence, he nevertheless is outspoken when the proper time for speech comes. He is a former army officer, with years of experience in handling men, and seems to possess that tactfulness and sympathy that makes for efficient leadership.

Picking the senior in charge of the aviation unit was a more difficult thing. For here I had the job of selecting a man from four specialists, each with his special qualifications and claims, and all of them unusual men. I had selected them from hundreds. In the end my choice was Balchen, because of his service with me in the past, his knowledge of polar conditions and, above everything else, his great loyalty to whatever cause he serves. It was the latter quality, I think, that moved me most. We have been through much together—Bernt and I—and I know him. His service alone entitles him to the senior post in aviation. I cannot speak too highly of the manner in which Dean Smith, June and Parker took the news. With such splendid fellows with me, I can await the future with untroubled mind.

Brophy, however, has begun to worry me. The tone and wording of his radios indicate that something is decidedly wrong. His messages are verbose and erratic. The job of getting the *Bolling* ready [1] seems to have vexed his patience, and now I find myself compelled to make decisions on the loading of a ship more than 2,000 miles away. Such matters have kept me up most of the night for nearly a week. Brophy was on the verge of a nervous breakdown when we left, and it may be that he is seriously ill. I must ask him to be frank on this point.

Twenty-four hours now will tell the story. Shall we be able to get into the Bay of Whales? Shall we find a low place in the Barrier where we can unload supplies? Our fate turns upon these things. But I am too exhausted to bother. The sound of the wind in the rigging, the soft slap of the waves against the sides of the ship are an irresistible suggestion to sleep. Cheerio.

It was only a cat's-nap, however. I was up and about in time to see the *City* round the eastern portal of Discovery Harbor at about four A. M. The four to eight watch proved so drowsy, however, it was hours before we had all sails set. I urged Captain Melville not to use the engines except when absolutely necessary. Drawing near the end of the journey, I saw the need for greater caution, and took advantage of the time to prepare a number of safety rules, with the assistance of Gould, which I caused to be posted on the bulletin board. It was natural that the men should have little respect for ice conditions, none of them, with the exception of Ronne, having been in the Antarctic before: and Ronne had remained only a few weeks. My own knowledge came largely from our two Arctic expeditions, Antarctic literature and discussion with explorers, still it was sufficient to instill in me a great distrust. The danger of falling down an unseen crevasse or floating away on a piece of bay ice that suddenly detaches itself from the main body is always present: and the last thing I wanted was a casualty.

[1] The *Bolling* reached New Zealand on Dec. 20th, and was then making ready for a trip to the Barrier.

So I announced, that the regulations restricting the movements of landing parties would be strictly enforced.

These regulations said, in part:

"Crevasses in the ice barrier and floating bay ice, and getting lost in storms are, it appears, the biggest hazard that the expedition (other than flyers and trail parties) will encounter.

"Fortunately, the Ross Ice Barrier, except in the proximity of land, has, so far as we know, very few crevasses. However, men out on unknown terrain should keep constantly on the alert for crevasses.

"Except in cases of extreme emergency, travelling over unknown areas shall be done by not less than three men, and whatever party sets out should use Alpine rope and bamboo poles.

"Frequently there is no indication on the snow to warn of a dangerous crevasse. If Alpine ropes are used, together with the bamboo pole or skis, there will be little or no danger.

"Some crevasses, of course, are not covered by a snow bridge. Some that are so covered show a slight rounding of the snow above the level of the Barrier area. Whatever crevasses may be near the base should be inspected by every member of the expedition so that he may familiarize himself with their character.

"The first scouting party to leave the ship for the proposed base will use special care in searching for crevasses. Skis distribute the weight in such a way that, in passing over a snow-covered crevasse, there is less danger in falling through. Snow shoes also distribute the weight, and long snow shoes have been provided for the reason they distribute the weight more widely than shorter ones.

"The ship will probably unload alongside the bay ice. Cracks may appear in this ice at any time, and therefore every man should be on the watch for them. The weather is fairly cold, and frequently a man falling into cold water in heavy clothes cannot drag himself back onto the ice. Where practicable, therefore, men should travel over the bay ice in pairs or groups.

"To prevent casualty from getting lost in a storm, parties should not go any distance from the base without having a competent navigator along. There is considerable variation in the compass in this district—about 106 degrees from true.

"It is very easy to lose one's way in a snow storm. Storms here may rage for days. On a number of occasions it has happened that men on exploring parties have lost their lives by losing their way only a few miles from base. I wish to emphasize this point especially.

"There are two competent weather men on the expedition, and weather predictions will always be available at the base.

"Special parties going out from the ship shall be designated Nos. 1 and 2, and will respond to the following signals:

"1 blast on ship's whistle: Party No. 1 returns at once.

"2 blasts on the ship's whistle: Party No. 2 returns at once.

"3 blasts on ship's whistle, or flag on mainmast: Storm warning, and all hands will return to ship at once."

As the day wore on, and we busied ourselves preparing for the manifold tasks that would attend landing, an air of uncertainty descended upon the *City*. So much did depend upon what we found! Even the dullest men sensed the magnitude of our problem. If the ice in the Bay of Whales had not gone out, we faced the heart-breaking tasks of sledging several hundred tons of supplies over miles of treacherous ice. Even with favorable conditions, the operation would be difficult and perilous; if conditions were bad, it might be impossible. Leaving the dog men to their duties of overhauling gear and sledges for the first dash, I returned to the library, to refresh my mind for the last time with the limited information about this place that I now knew nearly by heart.

What would we find at the end? Shackleton passed the Bay of Whales in January, 1908, and James Murray, his biologist, described it thus:[1]

"The desolation and lifelessness of the Antarctic were fully realized as we approached the great Ice Barrier. There was no living thing in sight as we steamed eastward, tracing the line of this immense glacier. Towards midnight there opened suddenly on our sight a scene of abounding life.

[1] Shackleton, "Heart of the Antarctic," ii, p. 233.

The cliff of the Barrier terminated, and a wide bay opened up, extending far to the south, and partly filled by fast ice of one season's growth. Away to the eastward the cliff recommenced. This bay, which we afterwards referred to by the appropriate name of the Bay of Whales, was teeming with all the familiar kinds of Antarctic life. Hundreds of whales, killers, finners and hump-backs, were rising and blowing all around. On the ice groups of Weddell seals were basking in the midnight sunshine. Emperor penguins were standing about or tobogganing in unconcerned parties. Skua gulls were flying heavily, or sitting drowsily on the ice . . ."

But the spectacle that delighted the eyes of the biologist Murray did not have the same effect on the explorer Shackleton, in search of a place for a base, and harassed by the pack ice menacing his ship. He recognized it as the place where Borchgrevink landed in 1900, and believed that Scott's *Discovery* expedition, of which he was a member, passed the same inlet in a fog two years later. [1] But he saw that something colossal had meanwhile happened. Miles of the Barrier had apparently calved off, in a magnificent, unseen demonstration, the inlet was swallowed up, leaving a long wide bay joining up with Borchgrevink's inlet, and the whole "was now merged in what we had called the Bay of Whales." [2] To Shackleton, the discovery of this change was a great disappointment, and complimenting himself upon having escaped a terrible fate, he sped the *Nimrod* out to the Bay, with the thought in mind that this disturbance might have occurred while his party was there: "(it) made me decide then and there that under no circumstances would I winter on the Barrier, and that wherever we did land we would secure a solid rock foundation for our winter home." [3]

It was this decision which, more than any other factor, defeated Shackleton's ambition to be the first to the South Pole and vitally affected the whole course of exploration in the Antarctic. For until a man, with shrewd eyes, indomitable spirit and the will to risk when risk was necessary, started to analyze things, the idea of wintering on the Barrier was held to be madness.

[1] Shackleton, "Heart of the Antarctic," i, p. 72.
[2] *Ibid.*, i, p. 75.   [3] "Heart of the Antarctic," i, p. 76.

The man was Amundsen. He carefully studied all information bearing on the Barrier, and it recommended itself
to him as a base for the reason it was the farthest south
one could go by ship "a whole degree farther south than
Scott could hope to get in McMurdo Sound." [1] And from
Shackleton's discouraging report he drew the startling conclusion that this "peculiar formation in the Barrier is nothing
more than the selfsame bight that was observed by Sir James
Clark Ross—no doubt with great changes of outline, but
still the same. For seventy years, then, this formation—
with the exception of the pieces that had broken away—had
persisted in the same place. I therefore concluded that it
could be no accidental formation. What, once, in the dawn
of time, arrested the mighty stream of ice at this spot and
formed a lasting bay in its edge, which with a few exceptions
runs in an almost straight line, was not merely a passing whim
of the fearful force that came crashing on, but something
even stronger than that—something that was firmer than
the hard ice—namely, the solid land. Here in this spot,
then, the Barrier piled itself up and formed the bay we now
call the Bay of Whales. The observations we made during
our stay there confirm the correctness of this theory." [2]
Amundsen, who had a great respect for Shackleton, has told
me that if Shackleton had based at the Bay of Whales, he
would have been the first to reach the South Pole.

We knew we would find security in the Bay of Whales, if
we based near Framheim. The fear of the Barrier disintegrating and carrying our base out to sea was therefore
a minor possibility. It was a chance worth taking. The
thing that vexed me was the possibility we might find the
bay entirely locked in ice, which would force us to stand
idly by, using up coal which was now precious as gold, until
it broke up. Time was fleeting, and the task of unloading
and setting up a base would take weeks.

What did history show? In February, 1900, and February,
1902, Borchgrevink and Scott, respectively, found the Bay
open. [3] As late as January 24, 1908, Shackleton found the

[1] Amundsen, "The South Pole," i, p. 47.
[2] Amundsen, "The South Pole," i, p. 49.
[3] Hayes, "Antarctica," p. 376.

Bay full of ice. Amundsen, years later, January 13, found the Bay open, with the ice half gone and moving out rapidly. The following year the bay ice did not begin to go out until the third week in January; and when Captain Larsen took the *Ross* in, in December, 1923, and January, 1924, Captain Nilsen had told me, he found the Bay completely ice-locked.

The record was clear on one point: our chances of finding the Bay swept clean of ice at this early date were decidedly slender. Nevertheless, short odds or no, it was a gamble we had to take.

As we cruised along its lee the Barrier constantly changed its outline. It is by no means the formidable uniformity we believe it to be. Its structure varied in height from 70 to 125 feet, small inlets and fractures marked its profile, and scarred cliffs reflected the sun, in chill blue and white, like great reflectors. The instability of the Barrier was forcibly impressed upon us. Occasionally there came from the distance a boom as of remote thunder—the sound of ice cliffs crumbling; and once, as I watched, the face of the Barrier miles away tore loose and fell in a showery cataract of ice. The sea when we drew near was littered with debris, in which several minor icebergs floated proudly in the newness of birth. Not very pleasant, really. This process is called "calving."

During the morning watch, December 28, we sighted the western gateway to the Bay of Whales, and stood off the entrance some time later. West and east the northern portals of the Bay, which we knew were about twenty miles apart, were shrouded in a drifting haze, so we could see no more than a few miles in either direction. But as we crept within sight of the western wall, gingerly feeling out our way, a glimpse of the full stature of the cliffs was occasionally had: it was with awe that we realized over 100 feet of steep, sheer tightly packed snow lay between water's edge and summit. I strained with all my might to make out something in the mist shadows ahead; hoping against hope for clear water, then hearing the slap of waves against ice.

The Bay still held in its bosom a solid wall of ice that the power of half a dozen vessels of the *City's* power could not bend aside. It was a disappointing finding. We changed course sharply, veering to the right, but progress in this direction brought no improvement. When wind brushed the haze aside, we saw that the bay ice, which in places was so heavily crossed and ridged by pressure as to appear impassable, stretched solidly from West Cape to the eastern wall of the Barrier. At least eight miles of it lay between us and the place where we hoped to establish our base. There was no doubting the fact the ice was far north of the point where Amundsen found it, [1] I realized there was much dirty work cut out for us.

We moored to the edge of the bay ice with ice anchors, which were hammered into the ice some distance from the ship, and hastily made ready for a trip of inquiry. Our great need at the moment was to find a suitable place for a base: worry over getting supplies to it could come next. By seven o'clock we were ready to start. Two dog teams were ready, Walden's and Vaughan's. On one of them Petersen had packed a portable radio set, and with him, Balchen and Braathen, our ski experts, I started across the ice, striking for the eastern wall of the Barrier, where it sloped to within thirty feet of sea level.

To the south the bay ice was criss-crossed by pressure ridges: near the Barrier massive blocks had been forced up; these we avoided carefully, picking our way round-about over fairly smooth ice until we neared the place where the Barrier descended to the bay ice. Here we found the whole eastern edge marked by crevasses, which had been partly drifted and closed by snow. We found a way through them, and gained the Barrier via a gentle snow incline. Before we ventured any farther, I insisted the party be roped together, lest an incautious traveller find himself plunged suddenly into a crevasse. In this manner we made our way up the Barrier, which rose steadily, and presently we saw stretching before us, provocatively indefinite in the haze, the smooth roof of the Barrier stretching south. Our goal was Framheim, but though we knew that by then probably all trace of its existence had been obliterated, each of us, I think, had in his mind the thought that perhaps some quirk in Nature had left part of it exposed. We followed the Barrier's edge for five or six miles

---

[1] The *Fram* was moored 2.2 geographical miles from Framheim. "The South Pole," i, p. 182.

and came to a place where the Barrier sloped gently into a kind of valley, but could tell very little about its shape. There was an extaordinary baffling condition of visibility in which it was broad daylight and not foggy, yet we could see only several hundred feet and inequalities on the surface took on weird shapes. We had an oppressive, shut-in feeling—a strange feeling on the vast stretches of the Barrier. Westward this basin continued to descend into an inconspicuous inlet.

We judged then that we were in the vicinity of Framheim, and the eagerness of the Norwegians, Balchen, Braathen and Petersen to locate the camp of their countrymen, was infectious. Petersen and Balchen skied to the southward to inspect a haycock which they thought might cover the house Amundsen left behind. Braathan and I went to the westward and descended the slope which fell into what was apparently a small bay. We scanned the scene for the sight of the two great pressure blocks that Amundsen told of, Mounts Nelson and Ronniken, but saw not a trace of them. Braathen shrieked, "I see a peak,—there is Mt. Ronniken"—which he took to be about 75 feet high and some distance off. He made for it as fast as he could propel his skis, only to be greatly chagrined to discover the "peak" was no higher than his shoulders and almost at the end of his nose. Such, at times, are the confounding properties of Antarctic visibility.

It may well be, as I concluded then, that these ridges, which Amundsen described as huge, "raising their highest summits over 100 feet in the air," [1] have been entirely drifted over during the intervening years. Certainly nothing that approached his description of them was visible. We continued on about a mile to the end of the bay, for such we saw it to be, and found that it debouched into the Bay of Whales amidst a chaos of pressure ridges that in the dimness looked like pre-historic monsters. We selected a camp site on a level piece of ice that was nearly surrounded by chaotic ice shapes. The others followed our tracks and soon joined us and we pitched camp; the first members of an American expedition to sleep on the Antarctic Continent. My diary reports:

[1] Amundsen. "The South Pole," i, 173.

Midnight
Dec. 30, 1928
Camp on the Bay Ice

It is as quiet here as in a tomb. Nothing stirs. The silence is so deep one could almost reach out and take hold of it.

A moment ago I stepped outside the tent and was impressed anew with the deceiving effect of the Antarctic on the eye. Try as I could, screwing the eyes, I could not make out the distance of things from us, nor their shape. Skiing, it was the same. We glided smoothly over a surface and then all of a sudden came to a cropper on a slight upward slope we failed to see. We sighted a mountain of snow, miles off, and it turned out to be a haycock twenty yards away. We strove to reach a pressure ridge close aboard and found it still miles away. Just as I wrote the last sentence there came a sharp cracking noise directly under us and a rumble from not far away. Pressure is working in the ice and no doubt creating wide cracks in the Barrier. However, this is no cause for alarm.

I A.M.
Jan. 1, 1929

We made an unsuccessful exploration trip today to the southward in an attempt to locate a base. We sledged over the bay ice close to the Barrier cliffs which rose sheer on our left hand to heights of 50 to 75 feet. The bay ice at its foot was rolling in thick, heavy ridges and cracks. There was no way up. As I was so inexpert with skis that I could not keep up with the Norwegians, I had to go without them, with the result that I fell through three or four cracks, thinly roofed over by snow. Each time I saved myself by spreading my arms. The others, however, slid over these easily with their skis.

After travelling two or three miles south we came to a place where the Barrier descended to the bay ice in a long easy slope. Here the snow had filled in and provided a ramp to the Barrier. Petersen and I began to climb up. Just as Petersen reached the top, the fragile covering of the crevasse gave way underneath him and only his skis saved him from a nasty fall. A moment later Walden's heavily loaded sledge nearly went to the bottom of the sea through a slush hole in the ice, and Walden came within a hair's breadth of falling in while trying to save the sledge. His famous leader, Chinook, showed the greatest concern while watching his actions, and one had the feeling that he was determined to prevent his master from taking what he judged to be a foolish risk.

On our return from this unsuccessful mission, Petersen and Balchen prepared the evening meal—pork and beans, bread and butter, peanut butter, biscuits and canned apple sauce for dessert. Few meals ever tasted better. I have forgotten to mention that this is New Year's Eve and we drank the New Year in with tea.

Petersen has put up a bamboo pole to serve as a mast for his antennæ, his radio set is assembled and he is now working the key. Messages are flying between our camp and the ship. New inquiries have been relayed from Brophy in New Zealand, with respect to the loading of the *Bolling*. The radio beyond doubt has ended the isolation of this ice cap. As a practical thing, its help is priceless. But I can see where it is going to destroy all peace of mind, which is half the attraction of the polar regions. Our external difficulties must always be with us.

The dogs have delighted me beyond words. They are so lively and strong one would never think they have been cooped up for more than a month. Terror, Vaughan's leader, pulled today until he could hardly stand. The love these Eskimo dogs have for their work is quite wonderful. As we are about to start out from the *City*, one of the dogs appeared to be so lame that we decided to leave him behind, but he broke from the hands that held him and staggered to his place in the team. He seemed heart-broken, really, when we went off without him. We were off with a rush and a great flurry of snow, the dogs' feet padding the snow with a soft noise and the sledge creaking and slamming on the unequal surface.

We can see now that the wisest thing we have done was to insist upon bringing a great many dogs. We were assured that half the number we demanded would serve our purposes. But now, with the problem of unloading confronting us, we can use every one, and many more for that matter.

Jan. 1st, 1929

Tonight I may sleep with the certainty that the second phase of our operations—reaching the base—is concluded in satisfactory fashion. The third—unloading and creating the base—may perhaps be the most difficult task of all. It is a river we shall cross, however, when we come to it. We shall surely find a way across.

Having failed yesterday to find a suitable location for a base to the southward, this morning Bernt and I returned to the bay we had followed when we glided down from the Barrier, and found that the slope at its head was a very gradual ascent to the Barrier. We climbed it. Visibility had slightly improved and we found ourselves in a kind of a basin. We recognized instantly that here was an excellent place for our base and named it Little America. It is splendidly protected by a high snow rim from the winds in all directions but west, and accessible from the point of view of loading operations. We have named the inlet Ver-sur-Mer Bay after the village that was so hospitable to us when we landed in France at the end of our trans-Atlantic flight.

Today we returned to the ship, taking a circuitous route through the pressure ridge in the bay. Farther to the south we found the bay ice badly ridged by pressure. Beyond, the Bay ended against the Barrier, which rose, in a series of terraces, to considerable height.

The dogs, refreshed by long sleep, fairly raced back to the *City,* and my hurrying thoughts preceded them. How best to accomplish the job of unloading tons of supplies in a single month allowed us? Balchen had remained in the tent we set up at the base, and I made up my mind to send Gould in at once to take charge of the temporary camp, and with it the responsibility of putting up the houses and getting the camp ready for winter. McKinley is to have charge of supervising the transport of supplies from the *City* to Little America. He will have a very difficult task to keep them moving on schedule. George Black, another member of the

North Pole Expedition, has been made supply officer. In that capacity he will keep track of all supplies.

We have decided to unload the *City* directly on the bay ice. This was a decision over which I hesitated for some time, knowing that however firm the ice seemed to be it must presently break up, perhaps with scant warning and with attendant risk to supplies and personnel. It is true that patience is one of the strongest weapons with which man can combat polar regions but there inevitably comes a time when the long chance is the most wiser one. This seems to be such a time.

There was much excitement aboard ship when we broke the news we had found a site for the base, and instantly preparations were begun to unload. The *City* was edged slightly to the east, to bring her nearer the Barrier and reduce the length of the trail by a few yards. Planks were run from the deck to the bay ice, and down this a stream of boxes, gasoline drums, crates and other articles commenced to pour in noisy confusion. As fast as these things touched the ice, a second party of men moved them back some distance from the edge, to minimize the risk of loss in case the ice started to break up. There was a great to-do as the dog men got their teams ready, for the dogs seemed to realize their enforced vacation was over and lively work was at hand. They rolled in the snow, dashed about in insane circles; and a number of them, at some fancied wrong, sprang at one another's throats. There was serious work with the handle end of the whips before peace could be restored. But in time Walden, the Three Musketeers, and Jack Bursey had five teams in harness, eager to go, and before lunch they started for Little America, sledges heaped high with supplies. An excellent way to start the New Year. They made a pretty sight snaking across the bay. The dogs' tails waved like plumes, and the drivers hurried behind, cracking their long whips and chattering incessantly in the mad monologue that passes as language between driver and dogs. We kept them in sight until they moved up the low slope on the Barrier, and then lost them behind a ridge. Some time later Gould radioed the ship that he had found the site, that several tents were up and that Little America, the most southern American community, was formally colonized.

We ran our teams thereafter with some attempt at railroad precision. Perhaps we erred on the side of caution: I do not think so, for it is my experience that in the polar regions the most careful way of doing things is often the fastest. First of all, we marked out the trail between vessel and base with red-orange flags, so chosen because of their relatively high visibility. These would serve as sign-posts in case a storm caught a driver on the trail. A lookout watch was permanently assigned to the crow's nest, to follow the teams across the bay ice and watch for cracks in the ice. Besides this, the departure of every team from either terminal was reported by radio to the other end: the absence of a team that ran into difficulties, perhaps in crevasses, must soon be noticed. No team was allowed to travel alone.

We drove, now, as if our lives depended upon it.

Tuesday, January 2, we sent off seven teams, each fully loaded, to the base. On this day, an evil-looking crack opened up in the ice, cutting across the old trail, so the teams had to detour a mile to the westward to get around it. This made the sledge journey to the base a total of *nine miles*—or *eighteen* miles for every load. Wednesday, we sent off eight teams. They had barely departed when a huge field of excessively roughened and jagged ice bore down on the ship from the eastward. To save the ship, we hastily got up steam and put out to sea, warning the base party of our departure by radio. We hoisted sail but dared not drift with the wind, as that would have driven us against the Barrier, so tacked about all night long, trying to conserve coal. It was a miserable night, for we collided with pieces of scattered pack continually, and the men were on duty nearly the entire night.

Realizing how important now was the need for haste, to compensate for the loss of time that must result from recurrence of the same situation, we impressed every free hand and every dog that could move its bones into the service of transport. Men who were not on watch on the ship volunteered to man-haul supplies to a safe place on the bay ice, where they could be picked up by dog teams sent out for the base.

Dogs that were ignored in the first picking, because they had not been broken to harness or were less strong than the others, were welcomed into service like thoroughbreds. Saturday, the 5th, we had nine teams on the trail, and several of these made an extra trip to haul up the 4000 lbs. of supplies that nine men had laboriously hauled to the cache on the bay ice. That day we moved five tons to Little America.

Sunday
January 6, 1929
Bay of Whales

Worked like devils today—and a miserable four tons ashore to show for our efforts. We must do better. With the time at our disposal before the *Bolling* arrives, six tons per day is the minimum we can allow for: Ten would be more to my liking. But how to do better, is the question.

I am delighted by the way in which the green drivers are handling their dogs. In a few weeks they will be veterans. Blackburn, de Ganahl and Siple are doing especially well, in view of the fact they never drove dogs before. Of course, the Three Musketeers and Walden are our mainstays. They have worked so long together that they know exactly what to do. Several of the new drivers, however, are having difficulty and today one of the teams broke loose half way between the ship and Little America, escaped from its driver and came running back to the ship. The driver came in much chagrined.

The idea has been in my mind that we may have to freeze the *City* in for the winter, if we fail to land all supplies before the middle of February. The *Bolling* ought to reach here within a month; and she must be unloaded— absolutely! "Freezing in" the *City* would complicate matters terribly and would also be dangerous. It must mean increasing the winter party by at least twenty men, with attendant over-crowding, besides enlarging responsibility. I shall not like it. However, let us see what another week brings. The *Bolling* presents an equally trying problem. No matter how much we rush, unless the ice goes out much farther to the south, I doubt whether we should have time to unload her before the bay begins to freeze over late in February. She cannot possibly survive even a slight squeeze. Moreover, I am reluctant to unload the airplanes on the bay ice. A sudden break might drop them all to the bottom of the bay. Our only hope is to force the *Bolling* to the Barrier, unload her there, cache the supplies nearby and haul them to Little America after the ships go north. If we can get all the supplies on the Barrier during the next month, they will be reasonably safe there until we find time to move them to the base. From the rigging of the *City* we can see a place where the height of the Barrier drops to within 20 to 30 feet of the level of the bay ice, and what appears to be a tightly packed ramp of snow leads up to it gently. This would be just the place, but unfortunately at least two miles of thick bay ice lie between us and it. We must find a way to get in.

A big lead opened up in the ice about four o'clock this afternoon, not far from the ship, forcing us to move our berth a quarter of a mile to the west, which means a longer journey for the teams.

We tried breaking the ice this afternoon in an attempt to reduce the distance to the base—backed the *City* and charged it, full speed ahead. Gave it a number of fearful wallops, but with no success. The force of each charge carried the *City* well up on the ice, where she poised a moment, every yard clacking and loose things pounding in the ship, and then fell back, her screw protesting and churning the water at her best speed. The impact was enough to throw an unwary man to the deck.

We had to give that up. Using too much coal. The best we did was to chip off a few slivers of ice.

Now we pray for a storm, whereas a few days ago we begged to be delivered from one. A walloping storm from the north would make waves that would break up the seaward edge of the bay ice, and we could make our way to a low place in the Barrier to the eastward.

We have had a really severe epidemic of influenza; about forty percent of the men are suffering, with varying stages of severity. Doc Coman believes the germ was spread by the dogs.

Everyone is dreadfully tired.

City of New York at Discovery Inlet.

Barrier in Background.

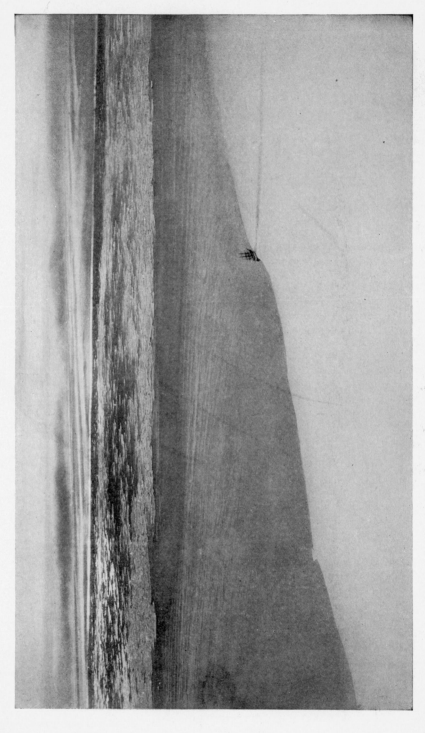

AERIAL VIEW OF THE *City of New York* BERTHED ALONGSIDE THE BAY ICE IN THE BAY OF WHALES, WITH PACK ICE CLOSING IN.

Next day there was some improvement. Part of the bay ice to which we were moored separated itself from the main pack under the gentle persuasion of a swell. We are able to make a new berth about half a mile to the south. By lightening slightly the weight of the loads, we found that four of the teams were able to make two round-trips in the same day. We now had ten teams on the ice, and I confess that even then I had my eyes on the last of the dogs, "the lame, the halt and the blind." Dogs which everyone believed were wholly useless did excellent work. Chris Braathen made a splendid lead dog out of a motheaten husky that was blind in one eye. He calls him Moose-Moss-Mouse.

Tuesday, the 8th, the lookout reported a lead running north and south had opened up to the eastward. We forced the *City* into it, and battered our way through a mass of drift ice to a position two miles nearer the base. With that our prospects brightened: if we could hold that position, all the teams ought to be able to average two trips per day.

"Let's go," someone yelled. And instantly the discouragement seemed mysteriously to fall away. Fatigue that a moment before seemed overpowering was brushed aside. Instead of seeming as distant and inaccessible as the South Pole, Little America came magically nearer within reach. We had a pretaste of victory, and it made all the difference in the world. I have seen the same thing happen to football teams, one moment in the slough of despond, and the next, owing to a fortuitous turn of fortune that brought them suddenly within striking distance of the goal, vividly infused with the psychology of victory. Here, on this forsaken tableland of ice, which Nature implacably refused to bend to our wishes, the thing was an interesting experience. We were close—closer than I care to remember—to humiliation, only to be carried ahead by a word we have, in the triteness and cynicism of our language, cheapened—the word *faith*.

CHAPTER V

THE BATTLE TO UNLOAD

WE did not lack for company. For all the tumult that accompanied unloading, the penguins continued to pay us formal calls, and it was not unusual to see as many as a score of them on the edge of the bay ice, watching operations with an unfeigned curiosity. The Emperors were in session most of the time, with the pompous gravity of state dignitaries. Standing three or four feet high, weighing 70 or 80 pounds, very handsome in their black coats, yellow waistcoats and orange-stained beaks, they strutted to and fro, giving voice every now and then to trumpet-like commands. When hunger moved them, they dived into the frigid waters in search of shrimp, swimming with astonishing grace and speed by rapid oscillations of their flippers. Seeing them waddle clumsily on land and swimming with the ease of fish, it was difficult to believe that these most primitive of birds once had the power to fly.

The more comical and smaller Adelies were our constant companions. Their curiosity was insatiable and the undoing of many of them. Although we tried to frighten them away, from time to time one or two would insist upon investigating the dogs. Sometimes they came stealthily, heads cocked to one side; but other times they came impetuously, squawking dire threats and waving their flippers in a military manner. Such visits generally ended in a funeral. When the dogs struck, they struck hard. There were many such tragic episodes, for the Adelies, shrewd little creatures though they seemed to be, could not quite get it into their pin-shaped heads that where the dogs lay, there also lay death. I once saw one little fellow attack single-handed a team of nine huskies. We plucked him from their jaws just in time. He showed no gratitude. When we set him free at a safe distance, his cocky attitude said plainly that he had certainly put it all over those strange beasts.

The Adelies were absolutely without fear, which seemed strange in creatures so wild. Its absence, I think, is due to the fact that for centuries no surface animal, except the swooping skua gull, which attacks the penguin chicks, has been their enemy.

The bay ice abounded with seals. These dull-witted creatures had none of the attractive qualities of the penguins, for they spent most of the time sleeping beside open leads. Two types were common—the Crab-eater and the Weddell seal. The Crab-eater's coat is a light brown color, and in the younger seals has a rich sheen. The coats of the old bulls were quite white. They were from 6 to 8 feet long. The Weddell seal has a thick coat, with black and gray markings, and is much bigger than the Crab-eater. Both are rather stupid and uninteresting, but as they served as a food supply both for dogs and our own table we were constantly alert for them.

They, too, had no fear of man. When approached gently, the Weddell seal simply opened sleepy eyes, stared at you a moment, then returned to slumber. But sometimes, on being prodded with a ski stick, they uttered an intimidating bellow, which so disconcerted some of our hunters that they retreated hastily, until they learned that this was just a hollow threat masking a craven heart. With that single show of force, the seal would make off in blubbery, undulating haste. The Crab-eaters were more courageous, and I came across one of them in a death struggle with two Eskimo dogs. It was sorely beset, but undismayed. It maneuvered swiftly, and feinted with rapier-like deftness, drawing its head in to escape a slash from a dog and darting it out again to deliver one in retaliation. The Crab-eater's coat was quite badly torn, but the dogs had not come off unharmed. They were bleeding from half a dozen wounds.

During the summer months, the Bay of Whales was truly a recreation ground for whales. It was not unusual to see schools of from 40 to 50 sporting in the bay, sending up long, plume-like vapors and thrashing the water with their tails.

Several times the vindictive Killer Whales were seen. They aroused dread, with their ugly snouts and ominous, triangular fins cutting the water, but they did not trouble us. Many deep and half-healed lacerations on the bodies of seals, however, showed how narrowly some of these ill-protected creatures had escaped annihilation.

After a two-day interruption due to a blinding snow-storm, the unloading proceeded at top speed. The storm itself was a trial, as it blew with such strength as to test severely the five anchor lines we had on the ice. We were constantly menaced by ice fields creeping into the bay from the northeast, and once or twice heavy bergs were carried off by submarine currents just when it seemed they must crash down upon the *City*. The storm ceased, however, as quickly as it had come; a clear sky appeared and presently the dog teams, which had lain snugly in the tents at Little America, came dashing across the ice, eager to renew the job. The drivers brought the news that the walls of the main building had been put up, and had withstood the storm. The roof, they said, would be put on that day, the 12th, and the American flag hoisted over the structure. Come what might, we had in that house shelter for thirty men. It was gratifying to know that. Gould, Balchen, Hump Creagh, McKinley, Davies, Teddy Bayer, engineer of the *City*, Jim Feury, a fireman, and Chips Gould, the carpenter, comprised the working force in Little America at the time. To Bayer and Feury had been given the disagreeable job of erecting the three 65 foot radio towers. This involved much handling of iron work with bare hands at punishing temperatures.

We were then principally unloading the scientific gear. This material was bulky and heavy, but as the objects of the expedition were scientific, I was determined to get this stuff ashore at all costs. To the aviators was entrusted the task of getting the Fairchild on the ice and in flying trim. June was put in charge of this operation, and on Sunday, January 13th, he had the crate on the ice. In a few minutes they were ripping it apart with hammers. "We'll have it in the air within forty-eight hours," he promised.

That same day we inaugurated a programme of economy. The so-called luxuries, butter, sugar, jam, etc., were there-

The Dogs, Bless 'Em, with One of Their Best Friends, Paul Siple, Boy Scout.

A WEDDELL SEAL AND CRAB-EATER SEAL HAVE A SLIGHT DISAGREEMENT.

(Courtesy Paramount.)

after rationed out, according to schedule. We had more than enough food to see us through, but I foresaw the possibility of running short in these items, if reckless use were permitted. Although we had fresh meat in plenty, Tennant continued to serve both whale and seal meat at the mess, and with some the food was popular. Although my own tastes were catholic, I confess that the meat of old whale and old Weddell seals has a very strong taste against which a sensitive stomach may rebel, but the meat of young whale and Crab-eater seal is quite good, and not unlike steak. Some of us regarded penguin a delicacy. It is a very dark, rich and gamey meat and tastes like nothing that we have in civilization, although it did remind me of the meat of small Auks that are found far North in the Arctic.

To save coal, which was still a pressing concern, we closed the refrigerating plant on the *City*. We simply hung the meat on the rigging. It seemed absurd, suddenly, to continue to operate a little plant when the world's largest cold storage plant was alongside.

Sunday, we broke our unloading record—we put seven and one-half tons of stuff ashore.

The following day we received word that the *Bolling*, loaded to the guards with supplies, including 7,500 gallons of aviation gasoline, had left Dunedin and was on her way south.

She was about to undertake a significant experiment. Could so small a steel ship, even at this advanced stage of the season, safely run the gauntlet of the pack?

Tuesday
January 15
Bay of Whales

We feel repaid tonight for all the difficulties we have had in our 9000 mile journey from the United States. Today we made seven short flights in the Fairchild, and actually inaugurated the programme of discovery.

I cannot speak too highly of the men. They have worked like dogs for the past three days getting the plane ready. The crate in which the ship rested was lifted by winch and swung thwartship, so that it rested half on the bulwarks and half on a block of timbers built up on the ice. Then, laboriously, it was let down an incline until it rested on the ice. The wings were carried down on the shoulders of a dozen men.

It was hard work, for the weather was quite chilly, and it was necessary, while unscrewing bolts and making adjustments, to work with bare hands. But at last the sides of the box fell away, exposing the ship, the wings were bolted into place and Demas and Bubier, the mechanics, greased, oiled and otherwise anointed the engine. They were ready to start the engine at 2 A.M. this morning.

In the midst of this, a snow storm came up, the bay ice began to disintegrate and there was a large possibility that, unless we quickly moved the plane to the Barrier, it might be swept out to sea on a broken floe. While we were debating this move, the sky was swept clear of the snow clouds and everything was serene once more.

A bit of warm oil in the engine, the stimulation of a torch, a few whining turns on the inertia-starter—in a moment the engine was purring under Balchen's hand on the throttle.

Balchen ran the plane up and down on the ice a few yards, to test out the skis, and then turned over the controls to Parker, to whom had been promised the privilege of making the first flight. And because I felt that the mechanics, on whom every flight depends to large measure, are too frequently overlooked, I let them go as the first passengers.

Sergeant Roth, of the Army, accompanied Parker on the first flight. Smith took Sergeant Bubier, of the Marine Corps, and Demas, on the second flight. The ship got off the ice each time very fast—in 15 seconds according to my stop-watch. Then Balchen and June took off for a slightly longer flight, to test radio and flying performance. They reported the plane in perfect trim.

With such fine weather at hand, it seemed a pity not to take advantage of it, so I instructed June and Smith to make the plane ready for a short flight of exploration. (I forgot to mention that Balchen took Owen and Teddy Bayer for a hop on the fourth flight.)

We took off at 3.45 o'clock. Air clear, visibility about 50 miles. The few inequalities in the surface of the bay ice caused the skis to bang a bit, but the 425 h. p. engine lifted the light load clear with a rush. We were instantly on the threshold of the unknown.

The first glimpse of the rolling Barrier to the south was a fascinating one. Snow, snow everywhere, as far as the eye could see, save behind, where the blue-green Ross Sea shimmered and glistened in the sun. The *City* was a toy ship with a black toothpick for a mast stuck against a curving crescent of flat ice. The orange sides of the house at Little America were just visible above the snow. And the trail, a thin, irregular line worn by dogs and sledges, twisted across the Barrier from the camp to the ship.

The vagueness wrought by the effect of light on snow was quite disturbing. Instead of an horizon there was a curious dappled effect. Not an easy line to fly a ship by.

Within five minutes we were looking down upon areas never seen before by man. The rolling slopes of the Barrier had hidden them from the eyes of Amundsen and his men.

We sighted a new harbor, about three miles deep, on the west side of the Bay, not far from Floyd Bennett Harbor. Our compasses then, owing to our nearness to the magnetic Pole, began to swing badly. This started a flow of recollections. It recalled the difficulties that Clarence Chamberlin had had with his compasses at the beginning of his flight to Germany, and nothing seemed more fitting than to name this harbor after him—Chamberlin Harbor.

We struck out due south, the Barrier below and stretching endlessly to the south. Some miles to the left—I hesitate to state the distance exactly, owing to the difficulty of judging distances from the air—we made out an extensive pressure ridge trending across the Barrier. It seemed to be twenty miles long, at least. More evidence, then, of the submerged land that impedes the northward movement of the Barrier.

A glance about the cabin showed how crowded we were. Smith's huge frame seemed to fill half the forward part of the ship. June sat at the radio, bulking large in his fur suit, communicating with the operators on the *City*. The floor was piled high with gear—a hand sledge, sleeping bags, enough food to sustain three men for one month, a small primus cooker, an emergency, hand-operated radio set. All essential precautions in case of a forced landing. But they made it

deucedly cramped in the cabin for an explorer who was trying to take in everything.

After flying south for a few miles, we turned to the
westward and flew approximately 15 miles parallel to and
south of the Barrier's edge. Perhaps 30 miles west of Little
America we observed an inlet running north and south. We
flew over it and found a beautiful formation in the Barrier.
The cliffs to the east and west of it at its mouth rose, we
saw, in vertical whiteness to a height of at least 100 feet
from the water. Here, the inlet appeared to be about 1,500
feet wide. A mile beyond the entrance the bay ice began, and
from our altitude seemed to be as smooth as a billiard table.

A few miles beyond the edge of the bay ice the inlet
narrowed a trifle and bent to the southwest. As we banked,
the more closely to study the formation, we caught sight of
hundreds of seals lying alongside a pressure ridge. Our
engine must have made a fearful racket, for we saw them
tilt their heads, as if by unanimous agreement, and stare up
at us. For a moment the bay was alive with black shapes
scattering and hurrying in every direction, many of which
rolled off the edge of a black lead of open water and disappeared. But the rest, after seeing that nothing untoward
happened, lay still and no doubt returned to sleep. At least
they no longer gave us as much as a glance.

The inlet curved again to the south and terminated in
a wedge-shaped formation a few miles farther on. The inlet
here was filled with great blocks of ice, cracked and broken
as if some mighty hand had used them as missiles. Far to
the south the Barrier rose higher and higher, until it appeared
to reach a height of 200 to 300 feet.

Just then we made out an unusual cloud formation which
was so similar to a cloud we had seen on the trans-Atlantic
flight that I was astonished. At first glance this cloud
appeared to be high land; and on the Atlantic flight we had had
a moment of panic when we saw a similar formation, for
navigational reckoning supposedly placed us in the middle
of the ocean.

It was impossible to recall the flights of 1927 without
thinking of the man who was the first to cross the ocean

alone. I marked the position of the inlet on the chart, and named it Lindbergh Inlet.

There was a great temptation on this flight to continue on and on, seeking new things. The real joy in exploration by flights comes from the speed with which discoveries come—a new, perhaps greater finding seems always to be impending in the advancing horizon.

But the polar regions are won only by patience. Disturbed somewhat by the violent oscillations of the compasses and deciding that it would be well for the pilots to have more experience in dealing with the eerie conditions of visibility before undertaking a longer flight, I suggested to Smith that we turn back.

Halfway back to the base, the engine stopped dead. Smith worked the throttle without effect, and then headed the plane in a long glide toward the Barrier. None of us, to say the least, anticipated the landing with pleasure. The surface was quite rough, and if we cracked up the walk home would be a dreary affair. And what a stupid thing, I thought, to jeopardize the unloading at this critical period by necessitating a rescue.

Smith decided one of the wing tanks had run dry, and quickly turned the proper valve. The velocity of the dive was sufficient to turn the propeller over, and the motor took up its steady, reassuring hum.

As we approached the bay, I saw that conditions of visibility were much worse. A drifting haze—sea smoke—obscured the surface of the bay, and the shifting light playing on the snow made it very difficult to judge our altitude.

Smith, however, very neatly measured his glide with respect to the water lapping the edge of the bay ice, levelled off at just the right moment and landed with scarcely a jar.

All told, it has been a fairly good day's work. An airplane has been taken from temperate regions on a long voyage through the tropics, assembled, tested and flown in the polar region without accident. Twelve hundred square miles of unknown areas surveyed within a few hours—it would have taken foot travellers weeks to learn the same things.

I do not altogether agree with some of the authors who

say that aviation can accomplish nothing in the Antarctic.
I am more than ever encouraged in my belief that it can
accomplish a great deal.

Eastward lay a greater, solid reality of discovery. Beyond
the rocky outposts of King Edward VII Land and the dim
shapes of the small Alexandra Mountains which Scott had
seen from the deck of the *Discovery,* in 1902, before the
onrush of the ice pack had driven him back, lay thousands
upon thousands of square miles that no man had ever seen,
much less trodden. What lay there was perhaps the most
fascinating geographical enigma yet left unsolved. It held
the answer to at least half a dozen of the unanswered major
mysteries of Antarctica. Here was the thing we had come
to the Antarctic to find—a sight of things denied to man
since the beginning of time. Both Shackleton and Amundsen
had later hurled their ships into the massive ice fields guarding the coast, only to be driven back before the blows of the
pack. "The forces of these uncontrollable packs are stronger
than human resolution," [1] Shackleton said, and that admission
coming from one of the most resolute men who ever accepted
Nature's challenge, is indicative of how fiercely East
Antarctica guarded its secret. Now we were eager to try
our luck against it, and were emboldened by the faith we had
in our vehicle. In the heavens, we were sure, lay the road
to discovery. I was impatient to show that aircraft could
succeed where surface craft had failed.

The next day, Wednesday, January 16th, we flew the
Fairchild to Little America. I was reluctant to risk its presence any longer on the shifting bay ice, which, under the
warmth of the sun, was beginning to break up. Affairs were
humming at the base. Two houses were up, a third was
started and about the place was a suggestion of security and
coziness. Gould and McKinley had the job well in hand. The
boxes of supplies were neatly assembled in orderly piles, and
the exact whereabouts of every item was recorded. Haste
had not been allowed to destroy efficiency. The dog teams
were then averaging two round trips per day, carrying from
700 pounds to 1000 pounds per load. Only a person who knows

[1] Shackleton, "The Heart of the Antarctic," i, p. 81.

dogs can appreciate what that means. Knud Rasmussen once said, "I bless the fate which allowed me to be born in an age when the Arctic dog sledge was not yet out of date." And after seeing them race into Little America, team after team, while the drivers fought top-heavy loads which threatened constantly to tip over into the snow, I could exclaim with him. Had it not been for the dogs, our attempts to conquer the Antarctic by air must have ended in failure. On January 17th, Walden's single team of thirteen dogs moved 3,500 pounds of supplies from ship to base, a distance of 16 miles each trip, in two journeys. Walden's team was the backbone of our transport. Seeing him rush his heavy loads along the trail, outstripping the younger men, it was difficult to believe that he was an old man. He was 58 years old, but he had the determination and strength of youth.

Our sledge transport was not at all uniform. In size the teams ranged from Walden's, which was the largest, with thirteen dogs, down to four. The weight of the load hauled in each sledge varied according to the number of dogs in the team. As a rule the load averaged approximately 150 pounds per dog. The following teams, with the following leaders, provided the surface transportation during the operation of unloading:

Driver	Leader
Quin Blackburn	Holly
Chris Braathen	Moose-Moss-Mouse
Jack Bursey	St. Lunaire
Frederick E. Crockett	Quimbo
Joe de Ganahl	Terror
Edward E. Goodale	Blizzard
Paul Siple	Pete
George Thorne	Tickle
Norman D. Vaughan	Dinny
Arthur Walden	Chinook

Arthur Berlin alternated with Blackburn and Siple. Of these men, Blackburn, Braathen, de Ganahl, Siple, Berlin and Thorne had never before driven a dog team. The dogs were scarcely more seasoned. Three of the leaders mentioned above had never led a team before.

The strain of loading was so great that I had feared the dogs could not continue to stand up under it, and therefore requested the New York office to send 20 additional dogs. These, we were told, would be sent from Alaska under the care of Mr. Alan Innes-Taylor, a veteran driver. They were expected to arrive at Dunedin in time to catch the *Bolling* before she started her second trip south.

Because the arrival of the *Bolling* would compel us to throw all efforts into unloading her, I decided to try to squeeze in the eastern flight before she appeared. Thursday, Balchen and June went over the Fairchild from stem to stern, checking structure, engine and radio in preparation for the flight. Weather permitting, I intended to take off within 48 hours. Haines, our weather man, shook his head. "You'll be up to your ears in snow," he told us.

His prophecy was as good as his word. Friday, the 18th, it blew a gale all day long; but in spite of it, dog transport never slackened. The teams floundered through the smother of drift and deposited seven tons at the base. They had then moved more than 100 tons since December 31, without the loss of a single package.

This period was marked for us by two incidents.

Captain Brown reported by radio that the *Bolling* was laboring in very heavy seas, and taking much water over the decks. The night before the sea ran so high he feared he would lose his whole deck load. He requested an emergency 3 A. M. radio schedule with us. Before the hour arrived, however, the weather moderated slightly, and he reported that the immediate danger was past.

The second incident, perhaps the saddest during our whole stay in the Antarctic, was the loss of Walden's famous lead dog, Chinook. Chinook was Walden's pride, and there was no doubting the fact that he was a great dog. He was old when brought to the Antarctic, too old for hard, continuous labor, and Walden used him as a kind of "shock troop," throwing him into a team when the going turned very hard. Then the gallant heart of the old dog would rise above the years and pull with the glorious strength of a three-year-old. The affection between him and Walden was a beautiful thing to see: one sensed that each knew and understood the other

Who, Indeed, but the Emperor Penguins!

ALL IN A DAY'S UNLOADING.

Note how supplies were protected by canvas boxes.

perfectly, and it was Walden's rare boast that he never needed to give Chinook an order: the dog knew exactly what had to be done. A few days after his twelfth birthday, Chinook disappeared. We searched the camp for him, without success; in the trampled snow about the ship, it was impossible to find his tracks. No doubt he made his way alone. Whether he walked out alone to die, because his days of service were done, is something I cannot vouch for: this was the romantic theory advanced by several of the men. At any rate, his body was never found. A clue to his disappearance was suggested in the following spring when Davies, during the course of a scientific investigation of the crevasses in the vicinity of Little America came across the marks of a dog's feet on the shelf of a crevasse, some thirty feet below the Barrier surface, about half a mile to the eastward. The traces were half covered by falling crystals, but Davies believed that the dog had lived there for several days. The walls of the crevasse were scored by small furrows, such as might have been made by a dog scratching, and some of these reached as high as a man's shoulder. Whether these were made by Chinook or another dog, we never learned. All this was a deep disappointment to Walden, who wanted to bury Chinook in his harness.

Saturday the storm continued with undiminished strength, whipping the snow into the face and numbing the hands. Nevertheless the dog drivers pluckily maintained their schedules. They carried 11½ tons of coal, in sacks, to the base, which is, I believe, a record of its kind. I watched the weather apprehensively, praying for sun. Really cold weather would not shut in before April. This fact had a definite bearing upon two "ifs" in the flight equation. *If* we could make the Eastern flight within the next few days, and *if* we should have a forced landing not more than 200 miles from base, we might still be able to walk home without suffering undue hardships.

The impending arrival of the *Bolling* brought up bothersome planning. One thing was certain: We could not unload her by the same process by which we were unloading the *City*, and still expect to have her to complete a second round trip between Dunedin and Little America. Even ignoring the time limits set for her stay, it was doubtful whether the dogs and men could continue to stand up under the strain of 32 miles per day with very heavy loads.

The alternative was to force the *Bolling* to the Barrier's edge, by some determined action, and unload her there. This I hoped to do, if the operation could be accomplished without too great a risk.

Sunday night, shortly after 10:30 o'clock, the weather clearing somewhat, we decided to make an investigation of the low edge of the Barrier. Some distance south of the northern edge of the bay ice, the Barrier sloped to within a few feet of the bay level, and a lead, perhaps a mile long, had opened between. The ice, however, was still much too thick to risk the *City* in it, so we reconnoitered in a small motor boat. With me came Owen, Strom, Paul Siple, the Boy Scout, and John Sutton.

It was still snowing a bit, and the atmosphere was quite thick. With the outboard motor arousing a medley of echoes in the Barrier cliffs, we cruised along the edge of the bay ice, making to the east. Submerged tongues of blue ice licked out at the hull and large floes of loose ice floated on the wind and tide, making navigation quite exciting. Carefully we steered between them and presently were able to make out the Barrier cliffs, smoking in the haze, and the stratification lines of scores of snows which ran through them like darker levels. The hacked surface showed where large pieces had broken away; and in places undershot cornices hung out at dangerous angles, suggesting impermanence. I was reluctant to approach nearer, not knowing when the Barrier might greet us with a shower of ice brickbats, and turned the boat to the south. We followed a lead for about a mile until we were stopped by the wall of thick bay ice. Half a mile away the Barrier sloped almost to the level of the bay ice. Here it could be approached by an incline formed by drifted snow, which had packed hard and rose in a gentle slope to the edge of the Barrier. If we could get the *Bolling* in that far, here would be an excellent place to discharge cargo. But how to get her in? A cursory examination showed conclusively that the ice which lay between us was much too hard and firmly set to be broken by the charge of either ship. We must wait until nature saw fit to move it.

Just then the motor, which had been kicking up wickedly, gave a final splutter and died. Siple and Sutton worked over it for some time, without success, and, there being nothing else to do, we unlashed the oars and began to row back to the ship. This proved so tiresome that we were soon persuaded to give it up, in favor of making further experiments with the engine. This time we were successful, and with the motor humming attractively, we made for the mouth of the lead.

About the time we gained it some one saw a whale sound about a quarter of a mile ahead. I turned in time to see half a dozen waterspouts rise in grayish vapor above the water, and fall hissing; then a long, white and ebony body lunged out of the water and sank in a curving movement. Then another, and another, and still another, until I had counted about ten.

There was no mistaking the identity of the ominous, black triangular fin; the ugly heads and the sickly yellow patch under the jaws. They were Killers. I do not consider myself a particularly imaginative man, nor am I impressed as a rule by the legends that accumulate about the habits of certain animals. Yet I confess candidly that the sudden appearance of these ill-reputed creatures had a disturbing effect: and we became most sensitively aware of the flimsy character of our boat.

The others, I am quite sure, drew no enjoyment from the situation.

I was at the tiller at the time, and deciding that discretion was the better part of valor, edged the boat toward the bay ice, looking for a protruding shelf of firm ice where we might land. Meanwhile I kept one eye on the approaching whales, whose slow deliberate movements fascinated one as a serpent is said to fascinate its victim. Always they drew nearer, with a showing of glistening, oily backs. The measured progress was intimidating but I was reassured when I saw that if they remained on their course they would pass astern; but, when fairly close aboard they rapidly changed course and headed directly for the motor boat. I sincerely believed that they had seen us and doubted very much if their intentions were good.

Having no desire to make their acquaintance, in scientific observations or otherwise, I hastily looked about for a place we might land the ship. The nearest ice edge was 300 yards away, and very ragged. At that moment, however, any kind of firm ice looked good. It was not necessary to order Sutton to open the engine at full speed. We raced for the ice, and the Killers, which seemed to be travelling twice as fast as the boat, gained rapidly. The thought was in my mind that one of them, coming up after a long dive, might capsize the tiny boat. Each porpoising lunge brought them nearer, and the short dash to the edge of the bay ice took a long time. The hull scraped over an undershot tongue of ice and banged violently against the edge. I am sure that no boat was ever so quickly abandoned as this was. As we faced around the Killers came up not more than 15 feet from where we stood. Another dive would have brought them up with us. We had drawn our revolvers—a foolish gesture, I concluded later, for a battery of 75's would not have stopped them if they had meant business. They dived underneath the bay ice and we did not see them again. We waited quite a while after they disappeared before we put out again, and the journey to the ship was completed without incident. Serious as it was at the moment, the episode presently yielded its lighter side, and by supper time was subject for many a good laugh. It was Siple's unfortunate fate to have been appointed assistant to the scientific staff a few days before, with the duty of studying animal life in the bay, and his introduction to this particular department was the cause of much jesting.

Each day seemed to develop its particular excitement. Monday, about noon, a swell came from the north and before long had hammered to pieces the ice about the ship. At the time seven dog teams, several of them heavily loaded, were grouped on the ice near the ship. So rapidly did the ice begin to break up it appeared doubtful whether they could be driven away in time. Meanwhile the ice on which the dog crates were placed began to crack. Several empty teams were dispatched to retrieve them, the loaded sledges were ordered to race for Little America, a radio message was sent to Little America to hold up the departure of all teams until the danger passed, and a group of men were sent ashore to take up our ice anchors, of which we had four out on the ice. These operations were directed from deck by megaphone, and were executed, it appeared, none too quickly. For the *City* was in the grip of a very powerful swell, and pounding violently on sharp ice. The strongest vessel ever made could not endure that kind of thing for very long.

With the ice anchors aboard we steamed to the west, hoping to take on the dog crates, only to find the water much too rough to risk coming alongside. We then turned east, to find that two sledge teams, which had started before our message reached the base, were waiting for us near the berth we had quit an hour before. By this time, a considerable amount of ice had gone out, and finding comparatively smooth water to the leeward, we edged in and anchored to the ice again. The teams were loaded and hustled off to the base, but before the other teams returned, the ice began to drift out anew, the *City* shivered under several nasty wallops, and we hastily stood out to sea.

This time we steamed to the east, entering the lead we had explored by small boat the night before, and found haven there. The ice was none too thick nearby to suit me, but as the position brought us half a mile nearer the base, we prepared to make the best of it.

Bay of Whales
Wednesday
January 23

A dull day. Nothing except the usual unloading operations. The *City* is now practically discharged, and the men are allowed to let up a bit, pending the arrival of the *Bolling*, which will mean very hard work for every one. The *Bolling* entered the pack Monday, and is apparently getting through without trouble. Splendid.

Bay of Whales
Thursday
January 24

Captain Brown radioed today that there is a possibility the *Bolling* will arrive here the day after tomorrow. We simply must find a place where she can unload on low Barrier.

The ice has turned quite soft, and we have had to seek a new berth. The drivers frequently went up to their waists in soft snow, and several sledges sank on settling cakes until nearly submerged. They were saved after some difficulty. A suddenly tilting cake flung Vaughan into the freezing water. He clung to a piece of ice until his chum, Goodale, could get him out.

Altogether, I think we have been fortunate in getting through this day without loss of personnel or supplies.

Melville and Strom made a gallant attempt to force a way to the ice foot at the edge of the low Barrier. Our position this morning was about a quarter of a mile from its edge, and the lead in which we lay having widened slightly, to within a few hundred yards of the low Barrier, we determined to smash aside what ice lay between. We steamed south down the lead, parallel to the Barrier, and from the rigging the bay ice at the end was seen to be traversed by a number of radiating minor openings, several of which appeared to lead directly to our objective.

We directed the *City* at the most likely looking of them, and let her crash into the ice with her utmost force. The ice gave only slightly. We backed up the old ship, gave her the gun and rammed the ice again, still again, and yet once more. We kept at this pounding all day, and with each blow the *City* seemed to roll more wildly, and there was real danger of unseating her masts. The man in the crow's nest, who acted as lookout and directed the attack, bore the brunt of it; for in his lofty perch each shock was intensified and every roll of the ship was lengthened.

On one occasion we were very nearly caught. An immense floe of old ice simply refused to break when we came crashing down on it: it folded up well aft of the bow, and so impetuous was the *City's* charge, she rode well into the floe, and could not get clear on the recoil, even with the screw turning full speed astern. We put a number of men on the ice, and by prodigious work with axes, saws and poles managed to set the ship free.

In the midst of this assault, the dog teams returned from Little America. We paused long enough to reload them and send them back. Bursey's team fell through an unseen hole in loose ice. He saved his sledge, with its precious load of coal, by throwing his body in front of the runners, bracing himself precariously between the sledge and the edge of the hole. If the weight of the sledge had been greater, Jack, dogs and load would probably have been pulled under. Jack hung there for some time, nearly exhausted, and his companion driver, who for some reason believed that he was joking, continued on. Fortunately, the lookout stationed on the *City* saw the team go in and sent out a rescue team. Bursey was shivering with the cold and could not have held on for much longer. For failure to observe the order requiring that the dog teams remain together on the trail, his companion driver was removed from dog duty.

The end of the day's push found us within a hundred feet of low Barrier. A ridge of ice, lifted and distorted by pressure, at least 25 feet thick, with 15 feet of blue ice below water, lay between. We hit this fortress a dozen terrific wallops and then gave up. I don't believe we gained two feet at each stroke, although we opened a crack to the pressure ridge which might allow it to go out with the tide. It was a difficult task trying to wriggle from this position. We dared not back out, lest we ruin the propeller on heavy pieces of ice, with which the water abounded. We charged, and smashed and bore away, over and over again, nibbling a widening circle to starboard until at last we had room in which to turn.

Measured in terms of coal, it has been a costly day. But I do not think we have erred. The ice is so cracked, now, that a strong blow from the south should very nicely clear out what remains.

Bay of Whales
Friday
January 25

I am anxious to undertake the flight to King Edward VII

Land. The Fairchild is ready, but it would be silly to attempt it until the weather man gives the word.

We further tested the radio today, and Hanson managed to "speak" with Fred Meinholtz, chief of the radio staff of the *New York Times,* and the operator at the Mussel Rock Radio Station of the Robert Dollar Company, San Francisco. Signals were sent out on a wave length of 34 meters.

Few things are more vexing than waiting on weather. Everything for the flight is ready, men, equipment and planes. Only good weather is lacking. The *Bolling* will be here soon; and if we don't get off within the next 48 hours, we shall not have another chance to make the flight for some time. Anxious as I am to start, I cannot overturn the convictions of a life-time. Good weather and visibility are absolutely necessary. The decision is in the hands of Haines, who has never failed me.

Bay of Whales
Saturday
January 26

Bolling due tomorrow.

Haines is optimistic—believes we may undertake the flight tomorrow. This is good news.

CHAPTER VI

DISCOVERY BY FLIGHT

Bay of Whales
Saturday
January 26, 1929

IT has been a real experience, lying here alongside the bay ice week after week, with the opportunity of watching the changes and caprices of this frozen world. It is not the rigid and immobile world that we imagined. All is movement and change. Day after day, hour after hour, the contours of the Barrier and bay ice change as fragments break off and float northward. The wind, the sea, the sky and the visibility change with bewildering swiftness; the penguins and the seals are here in large numbers one moment and gone the next. I fancy that in Little America it will be the lack of change that will be striking.

But what take my imagination are the regiments of ice fields and icebergs that drift past the mouth of the Bay of Whales. They come from the mysterious unknown area to the eastward. Sometimes these regiments pause at the mouth of the Barrier until a northerly wind starts the invincible mass in the direction of the *City*. We watch it carefully, for if it should catch and grind us between it and the bay ice, the good old *City* might be crushed into pulp. Several times we have had to fight our way through these moving fields to the open sea beyond. But these scrimmages have given us a chance to observe how varied are the forms of the bergs and the pack that come from the land we are so impatient to enter.

Eastward was mystery, and at 2:53 o'clock, on Sunday afternoon, January 27th, we took off in the Fairchild to try

to see with our own eyes what lay there. We had planned
originally to carry a gross load of 6,000 pounds, but shortly
before departure reduced this by 300 pounds, to lessen the
strain on the skis. Balchen was pilot, June the radioman.
The sky was a cloudless, pervading blue, and the temperature
a few degrees below freezing. Exactly the kind of a day we
had wished for. Haines looked up from his charts and with
one of his rare smiles said, "We ought to have good weather
here for at least twelve hours." What was brewing in the vast
unknown reaches of ice to the east no magic could fathom;
for Antarctic weather is a thing of sudden, violent and unpredictable changes, which appear to occur contrary to all
known laws and systems, and more than one meteorologist
has thrown up his hands in disgust before its caprices. But
if there is anything in which I have abiding faith, it is in a
weather prediction by Bill Haines. When he said you *may*
go, I knew then that we *could* go.

A run of 30 seconds lifted us clear of the snow, and a
few minutes later Little America had fallen from view
astern.

Almost immediately we were gazing down upon untrodden
areas. To the left we had the curving coastline of the Barrier
trending north of east: on the right we had the inner spaces
of the Barrier rolling unbrokenly to the horizon. Visibility was
about 40 miles.

Let us pause a moment to glance about the cabin. In the
after part of our small cabin crouched June, using a sleeping
bag as a seat, tinkering with his radio. Balchen was forward,
at the controls, gradually putting the ship on its course as
the compass sluggishly settled down. The cabin was so
crowded with gear I could not stand up. I found myself
sitting on a primus cooker, in lieu of a seat, while working
at my charts.

On the instrument board were the usual instruments—
bank and turn indicator, altimeter, tachometer, pressure
gauges, etc. At Balchen's right was a radio key: in an emergency, he could also communicate with the base. Fixed on the
back of his seat was another compass: we had found this to be
the only position on the plane comparatively free from local
deviation.

In all, we carried 700 pounds of emergency equipment, for use in the event of a forced landing. These impedimenta fairly filled the cabin to overflowing. There were two hand sledges, two sets of man harness, one primus cooker, three sleeping bags, 1 pair of snow shoes, three pairs of skis, 2 pairs of crampons, 60 feet of alpine rope, an ice axe, spade and snow knife, bamboo poles, a tent, a portable emergency radio set, an engine repair outfit, two medical kits, a funnel for draining oil from the engine, a blow torch and funnel for heating the engine, as well as enough food to sustain three men over a period of three months.

A liberal supply of cold weather clothing was provided. This included mukluks, with sennagrass, fur mittens, underwear, socks, windproofs and the parkas which we wore.

There was also my navigational equipment. This included several charts (which could be of little value, owing to unknown character of the area we proposed to investigate) a sextant, drift indicator, a sun compass, earth inductor compass and a large magnetic compass. It is my practice to leave as little as possible to chance. Each of these instruments could be used the one to check the other. As long as the bright sun held, the problem of navigation would be comparatively simple: for I could then check the magnetic compass with the sun compass and be certain as to my course.

I laid my course directly for Scott's Nunatak, which was, as we flew, nearly 200 miles away.

Just before the Bay of Whales disappeared in the lengthening perspective, I glanced back, hoping to make out the masts of the *Bolling* against the horizon. But nothing moved on the blue waters of the Ross Sea, which glittered like a vast tray of diamonds tilted in the sun, except a column of ice bergs, deployed like a regiment on the march.

Twenty minutes out, we sighted a bay in the Barrier to the left, and to the right ran a long deep fissure and pressure ridge. An interesting discovery. No doubt the Barrier here had grounded on land, which opposed the thrust of the ice to the sea and maintained the formation of the bay.

The Barrier edge constantly enticed our eyes from the hinterland. Its high, steep cliffs (from our altitude, however, they seemed relatively a few inches of beautifully carved alabaster showing above gray-green water, which lay as softly as velvet about their foot) trended to the northeastward with few variations in structure; but here and there a large floe on the open sea, with edges neatly matching an indentation on the Barrier, explained the manner in which the Barrier disintegrated and, in a measure, the source of supply of some of the bergs that had marched steadily past our berths in the Bay of Whales.

We were flying at 3000 feet, and visibility was excellent. Oddly enough, the packs that had beset the ships of Amundsen, Scott and Shackleton, when they attempted to push eastward, were not to be seen. Except for a few scattered fragments and an occasional iceberg standing in solitary grandeur on a blue-green carpet, the Ross Sea was clear and open as far as the eye could see. A southern wind had blown the ice temporarily to the northward.

At our altitude a hustling tail wind gave us a splendid boost. We averaged well over 120 miles per hour at cruising revolutions.

About an hour after the start of the flight we passed over a beautiful bay [1] in the Barrier, the mouth of which was several miles wide. A long, curving tongue of ice formed its westward side. The bay appeared to be four or five miles deep. From our great height it was no more than a modest, rather exquisitely carved indentation in the Barrier. But actually it was a stern and rugged thing, with 150-foot ice cliffs, sheer and perfect as if cut out by knife, as its walls. Flying does deprive an observer of much of the awe that seizes the surface traveller. I could not help but feel, as we flew over this bay, that had we come upon it suddenly from the deck of the *City*, we must have marvelled at its dimensions. But the vastly lengthened perspective that the airplane provides substitutes a different measurement. With so much to see, the things on the earth tend to diminish to their true cosmical proportions: and that which lifts itself above the rest and impresses must, of necessity, be truly striking.

Not long after passing the bay, I saw many miles to the right a few black peaks protruding from the snow, and beyond them a single peak which invited speculation. On

[1] This bay was named Hal Flood Bay.

consulting the charts used on this flight, I find that I wrote in the corner of one of them: "Small peak to the right—land may show—looks like it." I decided to investigate this peak later on.

By this time the Barrier surface on the right had begun to rise in a rolling movement of grand dimensions. There was land underneath, beyond a doubt. Between our position and the coastline the Barrier, on its march down to the sea, was riven and cracked until an area at least 20 miles in length became a mass of crevasses. These were of a character so fearful as to suggest no foot traveller, however stubborn, could long exist in them.

Presently a snow peak lifted its white head dead ahead —an inconspicuous mound dancing slightly over the head of one of the cylinders. A patch of bare rock showed on the northern side. It was Scott's Nunatak. Since he first saw it in 1902, three men, Lieutenant Prestrud, Johansen and Stebberud of Amundsen's Expedition, had fought their way to this lonely spur, in December, 1911. It gave one an odd sensation to rush at a rate of two miles per minute toward the spot which he and his companions had struggled weeks to gain; to be over it and gone in a very few minutes, whereas they had lain, shivering and wet, in a tent, beset by snow storms, while Prestrud, to pass away the time, conjugated Russian verbs.

From a point a little beyond the Nunatak, we flew over land never before seen: and at the given speed of the plane, we were exploring snow-covered land to the right at the rate of 4,000 square miles per hour.

To the south of the Nunatak a chain of rather small mountains, trending to the southeast, lifted snow-capped peaks from the surface. This was the range which Scott named Alexandra Mountains. It is doubtful whether any of them exceeded 1500 feet in height. I was surprised to observe that several of them exposed bare rock on the northern slopes. Prestrud, when he observed them from the more modest eminence of the Nunatak, reported that "only on the most easterly spur was the rock just visible." [1]

[1] "The South Pole," ii, "The Eastern Sledge Journey," 247.

These few bleak crags were, then, the first real land we
had seen since we re-discovered Scott Island.

From the Alexandra Mountains the snow-covered land
(for land undeniably lay underneath) descended quite rapidly
to the sea. The slopes were distinguished by well-marked
terraces, and these in turn were traversed by large numbers
of crevasses.

These terraces fell into a slope which met the sea. The
Ross Sea was solidly frozen over here, for miles to the north,
and in the pancake smoothness we noted a number of odd-
looking ice islands, the rounded domes of which were mostly
split and broken, like tarts which had been toyed with. These
domes, however, stood at least 100 feet above the general
level of the sea ice, and their bottoms must have been well
grounded. We also made out a lone glacier discharging its
stream of pale blue ice into the sea, and around it, oddly
enough in this hard frozen waste, lay a pool of open water.
There were many indications, such as the lack of pressure
ridges and the smoothness of surface, to show that the sea
ice here rarely breaks up: and the theory suggested the
possibility of land to the northward which held it anchored
in this place.

I had envisioned this as a probability, and peered ahead,
over Balchen's shoulder. In the gray opacity where ice met
sky a dark, provocative ribbon held my eyes. Land, I was
sure, lay there and beyond to the northeast. But before I
could exclaim, Balchen lifted his hand from the wheel and
pointed a gloved finger to the east. The whole sector of the
horizon had disappeared in a thickish haze. We were catch-
ing up with the storm that had passed over Little America
the day before.

So near a perhaps important discovery, we were not easily
to be turned aside. We flew on, at a slightly increased rate
of speed.

We now could make out the dim outline of snow-covered
land to the east and south, and presently came to a typical
Antarctic mountain formation—a mountain entirely snow-
covered, as round and uninteresting, at first sight, as the
upper hemisphere of a billiard ball. We approached it at an
altitude of 3,000 feet, and with some wonderment observed

that a hollow depression, perhaps a channel, appeared to separate this peak from King Edward VII Land. Whether this channel was at sea level was, of course, impossible to determine.

Behind this peak lay a slightly uplifted, island-like formation, and between them ran a second channel. We examined this channel as carefully as we could, and though little could be judged by the naked eye, we were certain of at least one point: the ice to the north of the formation was sea ice.

Further inquiry was halted by the onrush of snow squalls. Actually, our rush of speed carried us into them; but the lack of things rapidly sliding past which we associate with motion gives the aerial traveller rather the impression of things advancing upon him. We saw long fingers of gray shadows stretch and feather along the snow; here and there a darker shadow blotted out the surface, and its restless, rapid rotations identified it as a "whirlie." The atmosphere about us thickened, the horizon was swallowed up in a gray indefiniteness and the impression we had at the moment was like nothing so much as flying in a bowl of milk. How very easy, I thought, for a careless or intimidated pilot to fly his plane straight down into the snow. There was no point on which to pin the nose of the plane for steady, level flight. Only a milky, trembling nothingness.

Balchen, undisturbed, attended to the minor oscillations of instrument fingers and from them evoked a true flight path. He dodged between several squalls, and, finding clear sky to the north, swung out over the Ross Sea. As we turned, we saw the sun, a red disc glowing in a rising murk.

We were reluctant to leave this fascinating area, for ten minutes more of flying, I believed, would have shown whether or not King Edward VII Land was an island cut off from the land to the eastward, as the conditions seemed to imply, or even a peninsula. There was no alternative, and we were compelled to turn back. So again this area had guarded its secrets—had added us to the long list of those whom it had turned back from its frontier's north, east and west.

We flew well over the frozen surface of Ross Sea, noticing a number of rather large ice islands. Visibility to the south seemed to be good, so I asked Balchen to steer in that direction. We set our course toward the first small peak we had seen on the way to Scott's Nunatak.

The air turned very bumpy. One shock caused us to drop for 600 feet, and the gear in the plane was wildly tossed about when the wing met a rising column of air. It was quite like meeting a solid obstacle.

June handed me a slip of paper. It was a message from the operator at Little America. "*Bolling* sighted." Receiving this encouraging news at this time, nearly a mile high above and in the midst of this unknown area was one of the most exciting incidents of the flight.

Balchen suddenly turned and beckoned to me to come forward. I looked out over the nose of the ship, through the shimmering play of the propeller. Far ahead, but perfectly distinct, was a splendid mountain peak, with the slate gray of bare rock showing. Then as we advanced a second peak, then a third, and more lifted their summit above the southern horizon until we had counted fourteen.

This was our first important discovery. I had never seen Balchen so delighted. His splendid face was one long smile.

I could not help but think, as we approached them, what an immense advantage the airplane gives the modern explorer. Prestrud's sledges passed within a few miles of this range, yet in the restricted visibility had failed to see them.

We approached the mountains at an altitude of 4,000 feet. Here was no jammed-up, continuous range, but rather a group of highly individualistic mountains, solitary and stern, many of them with patches of gray rock showing on their northern profiles, their spurs and crags clothed in snow. They lay in the shape of a crescent, and the northernmost peak we judged to be approximately 50 miles from Scott's Nunatak, in a west by south direction. We were impressed by the surprisingly large amount of bare rock exposed, in contrast with the Nunatak and the Alexandra Mountains. As we drew nearer, the gray overtone of the rock was modified, and some of it had an interesting brown and black coloration. I knew then that when he learned about this discovery, our geologist, Dr. Gould, would insist upon flying to these mountains to make a special investigation of their structure.

Anticipating, as I was, the making of a preliminary aerial reconnaissance of the range, I was quite disappointed when Balchen handed me a note saying that fuel was running low, and suggesting we return to the base. We could not afford to extend our journey: in flight, gasoline allows of no compromise; so we pointed the nose of the plane for Little America, and raced home.

For a long time the peaks of this range danced across my vision, gradually growing smaller while the bare rock diminished to mere pin points, and I found myself wondering what we should name it. The names of several of the men who had befriended the expedition came to my mind; and foremost among these was that of John D. Rockefeller, Jr. And it occurred to me that his true inner life is as little known as these peaks which we had just seen. His character is in keeping with that of these austere mountain masses. He stands, steady as a rock, in the chaos of life, and the great power he controls is directed wisely and unselfishly for the betterment of the world.

I could do no better than to name this range after him —Rockefeller Mountains.

To two of the peaks I decided to give the names of two of the most loyal men I have ever known. One of these is "Chips" Gould, carpenter on both polar expeditions. It can be said of him that when there is anything to be done he never stops working during his waking hours. The other is George Tennant, the cook, also a veteran of both polar expeditions. I have never forgotten that he offered his meager pay, on the completion of the North Pole expedition, to help pay our deficit.

My musings were interrupted by June, with the news that the *Bolling* had come alongside the *City* and was now tied up to her. Another river crossed. And a larger task—the unloading—to face.

We drew within sight of Little America about eight o'clock, and from our lofty platform saw the two vessels, tiny and still, moored to the bay ice. I noted with pleasure that even during our short absence some of the ice had gone out.

Down below I saw a dog team making its way across the Barrier, and I recognized it as the team which I had asked Strom, Braathen and Erickson to take out in search of an easier and safer trail between the low Barrier and the base, which they were to mark with flags.

The scene, as we spiralled down, was one of wondrous beauty. An unbroken stillness, save for the hum of the propeller. The Barrier cliffs and slopes diffused the most exquisite colors, which changed and shifted as we watched. The lofty arch of sky was a clear blue, with friezes of perfectly stationary cloudlets, some rose, some mauve. A few icebergs glittered on a sea washed with gold; and in the west a range of the most beautiful mountains I have ever seen lifted purple peaks in tantalizing mirage.

A trembling, impermanent delicacy had taken full possession of this rugged immensity of ice. How still, how lovely, how perfect! One could understand, after this, why Scott, Mawson and Shackleton returned to this continent. The shock of the skis on the snow was an alien note snapping the thread on which the spell hung suspended.

Now we hustled. Nature, after begrudging us our needs so long, relented a trifle, and during the flight sped out the ice between the ships and the low Barrier until only a few feet of ice remained. Our hours of ramming with the *City* had not been wasted. Captain Brown brought the *Bolling* into action, and with the aid of her sharp steel prow and superior horsepower she attacked the remaining ice and sheered off 150 yards of it. This gave us a fine pier on the ice foot about 50 feet from the Barrier. Directly opposite, the Barrier descended in an easy slope to the ice foot, and near its northern end the snow was firm enough, and the incline sufficiently easy, to justify hauling stores up to the Barrier by means of a block and tackle which could be operated by the *Bolling's* winch. To the right and left the Barrier rose steeply to heights of 60 feet or more. This place was exactly suited to our needs. We were then only five miles by trail from Little America. Unloading operations were resumed at once.

Monday
January 28th,
Bay of Whales

Things are humming once more. We have a block and tackle rigged up, and this is hauling stuff up to the Barrier at the rate of two or three sledge loads every half hour. As they arrive, the sledges are towed a safe distance back from the Barrier edge, and the loads dumped, to await the arrival of the dog teams. If we can continue at this speed, we shall have the *Bolling* unloaded within five days. But for the life of me, I cannot see how she can accomplish a second round trip, unless we get exceptional breaks.

I am slightly concerned as to the permanence of this ice foot to which we are anchored. I examined it very carefully, and am most certainly of the opinion it will break up soon. I was apprehensive enough to order all hands to remove to the Barrier the materials deposited on the ice foot. Among these was the heavy crate containing the two outboard engines of the Ford.

Captain Brown must have had a real battle in the ice. He says that when the *Bolling* bucked the pack her sides vibrated and bent as the ice closed in. It is a wonder he did not lose a couple of plates. I like the way Brown does things. He may be given to taking long chances, but I feel that he can be trusted to get through, no matter what the difficulties. At any rate, he will get through or bust —but just at this time we don't want anything to bust, especially the *Bolling*.

Tuesday
January 29, 1929

It happened, after all. This morning, at 9:30 o'clock, the ice foot to which we were moored broke without warning, and some of us are lucky to be here tonight.

We were not caught unprepared, however. Last night, in the midst of unloading, a squall blew in from the northwest, forcing us to call a halt. We rode out the storm, though

not without misgivings, for constantly we heard the reverberating, long-sustained echoes of the Barrier crumpling to the
west and north, and the sharper, more piercing reports of
splitting bay ice.

Toward morning, the wind abated and shifted to the
south. The temperature fell to several degrees below freezing. The blow filled the Bay with loose, broken pieces
of ice. A vast amount of destruction had been wrought
somewhere, to cause this.

We resumed our unloading at once. The one change in
our surroundings was the discovery of a widening crack near
the Barrier's edge, and this, while seemingly not cause for
alarm, caused us to proceed with greater care and to work
as fast as possible. Among other things on the ice foot were
part of the structure of the main house and the center section
of the Ford wing, which had just been put ashore. The
Fokker had just been hauled up the slope.

A number of men were working on the ice foot. Bubier
and Balchen had just started up the slope, with Goodale
behind them, and June and Demas were working on the ice.
Suddenly Demas noticed a crack appear in the ice literally
between boots, and before he could get the words, "The ice
is breaking," out of his mouth, the crack was several feet wide.

How things flew then!

The crisis came in an awful silence. The silence was the
most striking thing about it. Without so much as a groan,
our dock split open near the Barrier's edge and then the
whole area rose and swayed and disintegrated before our
eyes. Then Goodale fled racing down the slope, yelling at
the top of his lungs.

The entire slope fell like an avalanche into the sea. It
tore out part of the Barrier, and the ice foot broke into
three huge pieces, riven by cracks that ran parallel to the
Barrier.

That portion which was nearest us rose under terrific
pressure until it seemed it must reverse itself and fall against
the ships. Brown's whistle piped shrilly, and all hands were
ordered to don life belts and shift the lines holding the
Bolling to the Barrier. When this strain was relieved, the
ice settled back into the water, and the immediate danger

Dog Team on the Bay Ice, with Pressure Ridge in Background.

The Crew of the *Eleanor Bolling.*

passed. The center section of the Ford lay on the broken fragment, nearest the Barrier, and this floe was tilting more and more as the crack between it and the ice nearest the ship widened gradually. I have never seen men work so fast. They planked the gap between the ice blocks with the sides of airplane crates, which had been broken open, and managed to haul the center section to the ice block nearest the ship just before the first ice block tilted at an angle that must have dumped it into the sea. It was a close call.

Meanwhile another floe, on which rested cargo quite as valuable, began to tilt, ever so slowly, and the up-ended edge hid the boxes from view.

Men were rushed out to retrieve them.

The tumult gradually subsided, all the gear and the houses were saved and it is difficult to realize that our only loss was a sack of coal and a few crates.

We're back alongside the Barrier now, slightly to the south of the old position, still unloading. The Barrier here rises as high as the *Bolling's* bridge, and as we rise and fall on the slight swell, the *Bolling's* superstructure occasionally chips off a small piece.

Our position is far from being a safe one, but where else can we go?

We are racing to get the fuselage of the Ford unloaded. A block and tackle has been rigged, and stuff is going ashore at a furious rate. As the supplies accumulate we are moving them about 100 yards inland from the Barrier's edge, where the dog teams can pick them up later. We are simultaneously discharging from the *Bolling* to the *City*.

I do not care to have the *Bolling* remain in these dangerous waters any longer than is absolutely necessary.

The bay is simply full of broken pack and small bergs.

We continued to work the 24 hours around, using two shifts. Balchen taxied the Fokker plane to the base. We then had two planes safely at Little America. With considerable difficulty we landed one of the Ford wing tips. Wednesday, January 30th, we had two block and tackles operating, which greatly simplified our problem.

We worked feverishly for fear the Barrier might let drop another berg. I issued rigid orders to the men that every man working near the overhang where we lay should wear a life line. The fear did not leave me, even after a day and night of security.

Wednesday night, about seven o'clock, shortly after supper, I was in conference with McGuinness in my cabin. Suddenly I felt a jar, followed by a succession of terrific shocks and then a tremendous explosion. It had happened after all. The Barrier had broken. We had taken the necessary chance and lost. Was the *Bolling* sunk? For a moment my heart stood still and my brain raced with self-condemnation. Ships and men lost. The *City* heeled sharply to port—so sharply I thought she must capsize. As I flung the cabin door open I saw the *Bolling* heeling in the opposite direction to starboard. I was sure, for a moment, she was capsizing, for I saw her keel and she was still leaning. No words can fit the horror of that moment. At such a time the mind sees a long story in an instant.

But as I watched, the *Bolling* reached the peak of her heeling movement, standing almost on her beam's end, and then swung back. At the critical moment the lines from the *City* maintained the balance and offset the overbalance of the masses of ice and snow on her decks.

As the *Bolling* rolled back to port, Captain Brown, who had been on the *City,* made a flying leap from the rail to his bridge. It was a very daring leap, but no more than one could expect from Brown. His own ship was his place in the crisis. Tons of snow lay on the starboard deck and gave the *Bolling* a heavy list.

Huge blocks of the Barrier floated in the water, which was still boiling from their impact, rivulets of ice were still streaming down the face of the cliffs, and falling, with a hissing noise, into the sea. The break, then, had come at a point where the Barrier attained a height of about twenty-five feet, and very near the point where we had landed the Ford fuselage a few hours before.

Only part of the iceberg, I noted, had fallen directly upon the *Bolling's* deck. She had escaped the main stream of the avalanche by a few feet. Thousands of tons had fallen,

enough to obliterate her.   An iceberg had been born almost on
her deck.

High up on the Barrier was a man clinging to a thread of
rope, his feet dangling helplessly in empty space.   I recognized
him as Harrison.   And in the water, clutching a small piece
of floe, which was menaced by the newlyborn icebergs, was
another man.   It was Benny Roth who, I knew, could not
swim.   He had grabbed a piece of ice and was holding on to
it for dear life, but it was round and slippery and he could
not get a firm hold; it spun continually in his hands.

Were there any others in the water?   No one knew.   Both
Melville and Brown had already begun to put the first boats
overboard.   While men on the *City* and *Bolling* set out after
Roth, several men who had been working on the Barrier,
notably Dr. Coman, Davies, Frank McPherson, E. J. Thawley,
and Boehning set out after Harrison, who was clinging to a
slippery line with bare hands.   It did not seem possible that
Roth could be saved.   The disturbance was rapidly sweeping
him sternward and I did not believe he could possibly hold on
much longer.   When the first boat was lowered, too many men
jumped in it.   Hanson, who was in the bow, made a very
heroic and quick-witted move.   Realizing that the boat was in
danger of capsizing, he dropped overboard, in the chilling
water, and begged the others to start out at once after Roth.

Roth by then was near the end of his strength.   He had
meanwhile grabbed a second small cake of ice, and had one
under each arm.   But his head would go under every now
and then, as his numbed hands slipped and his heavy clothes,
which had frozen hard, dragged him down.   He called out
that he could not hold on much longer, but he remained very
calm.

De Ganahl came paddling past the *City*, astride a plank,
which had carried down with the avalanche from the Barrier.
He had seized it when it floated past the *Bolling* and was paddling fiercely in the direction of Roth, through the debris.
When the life boat beat him to Roth, he scrambled aboard a
sluggishly moving floe, sat down, carefully removed his shoes,
and with arms folded about his knees, calmly watched the
rescue.

Were any other men still in the water? Lofgren was assigned to call the roll and as man after man was accounted for, it was an indescribable relief. I am sure I was the happiest man in the world at that moment.

Harrison's rescue was accomplished when Coman, with real coolness, dropped a looped rope to him, in which he could put his foot and so relieve the strain on his hands. Then Thawley, with a line tied to his ankles, which the others held, crawled out on the overhang, into which Harrison's line had cut several feet, so that he could not be pulled up, reached down, secured a firm hold on Harrison's wrist and lifted him, unhurt and unruffled, to the top.

The whole incident took no more than twenty minutes, but it seemed hours.

When the second party came aboard I ordered the ships to tie up to each other, and we discharged the *Bolling* directly into the *City*. It was a very fortunate thing that the unloading was nearly accomplished when the break came. I would never again tempt fate by trying to unload on the Barrier. We moored at our old berth on the bay ice.

Saturday, February 2, we finished unloading the last of the *Bolling's* 440 tons of supplies into the *City*, while the *City* discharged more slowly on the bay ice. The same day, the *Bolling* put out for New Zealand, with the U. S. Mail Flag flying from her mast, carrying the first mail from an American colony in Antarctica. She went with our most sincere, but none too confident, hopes of seeing her again, with the last of our supplies, before the end of the month.

Bitter days followed.

With twenty-seven dogs hauling, we managed to move the Ford fuselage to Little America. Seven more dogs carried in the radio transmitter, which weighed about 1,000 pounds. And another group, using two teams hitched to a sledge, transported the second wing tip. We had the polar plane at the base at last.

Sunday, February 3, a severe wind from the north and a heavy swell which set the immense ice cakes clashing and grating, forced us out to sea. Beset by encroaching ice, it was necessary to force our way astern, a very risky maneuver, as it exposed the propeller to contact with ice. The whole ice-littered surface near the edge of the bay ice was then in the throes of tempestuous motion, and the friction of many pieces of ice made an ominous noise. Time and time again, large cakes of ice, lifted by the swell, smashed down upon the propeller, and the wheel spun with such force that three men could not hold it still. We finally broke into clear water, and spent the night cruising at sea, with the engines at full speed to prevent us from being hurled back by the gale on to the Barrier. Many times I wished for greater power and speed.

Next day we berthed again on the bay ice, and resumed unloading.

Wednesday
February 6
Bay of Whales

Two large fields of ice, at least ten feet thick, drifted down upon us last night. I was up most of the night, on guard lest they threaten to catch our rudder and smash it. The rudder has taken a terrific pounding. It is a good thing that we had the foresight to put in a massive rudder before we left the United States, but for all its great strength I am not eager to expose it more than necessary. This morning, a small berg drove toward us, and we had to abandon our berth. The wind was so strong it took us three hours to come alongside the bay ice again.

This is indeed a place of chastisement. And of change.

A visit to the base was encouraging, but I am afraid that I did not make myself popular. Work had progressed amazingly well under Gould's direction, and my sole objection was that the foundation for the Administration Building had been dug quite near the edge of the Barrier and smack against the mess hall, which is already up, and is only 100 yards from the rim. I have no desire to place any building nearer than that. The houses must be separated because of the fire hazard.

It may very well be that this is undue caution, yet I did not feel like surrendering my convictions. Consequently, it will be necessary for the men to dig a new foundation 200 yards inland. Not a very pleasant job.

The performance of the snowmobile is gratifying. Arnold Clark is doing a good job with it. It is nothing more than a Ford chassis, fitted with skis in front and double caterpillar treads behind. It has attained a speed as high as 25 miles per hour on the smooth Barrier surface, and, in hauling loads from the Barrier cache to the base, has equalled the work of five or six dog teams. I wish we had another.

We shall have a very snug camp this winter. Gould and McKinley have made the most of the material.

Thursday, after supper, the menacing movements of a large iceberg, that was propelled by a strong wind, expelled us hastily from our berth, and we passed the night drifting about the Bay. We returned, early the next morning, to renew the discharging of cargo, but the wind stiffened nearly to gale force and we had to desist, although we remained anchored to the bay ice until late in the evening. By that time our situation had become so precarious, we had to depart quickly, losing two ice anchors.

The weather turned very thick, and the wind being from the east, we hugged the eastern cliffs of the Barrier, in search of lee. We were unpleasantly close, and could hear the seas crashing against the cliffs.

The wind blew with increasing force, and it required the full horsepower of the *City* to keep her head into it. Four or five times we were thrown into a mass of drift ice which had piled up against other masses of bay ice; and the pounding to which the wooden sides of the vessel was subjected seemed more than any ship could endure. As we struggled to get clear, the consolidated masses rose and fell with the waves, grinding against the *City* and testing her sides severely. We finally fought our way to the mouth of the Bay. Visibility was reduced to about twenty yards, and for a moment we were uncertain as to our position. We made a slow and cautious easting, until we saw the Barrier cliffs dimly through the driving snow; and by means of these occasional glimpses and the smashing of the waves, Melville and Strom guided the ship during the night.

Saturday
February 9
Bay of Whales

Sea quieting today.

We are cruising alongside the bay ice, seeking smooth water for landing. Time is precious.

A short time ago a vast explosion came from the Barrier—like the sound of big guns firing. More of the Barrier has apparently disintegrated.

City jogging along under jib, staysails and spanker.

Last night was a tough night for amateur sailors. It was bitterly cold. The crash of ice against the vessel—the rumbling of disintegrating Barrier and the soupy mixture of fog and snow were a disconcerting experience.

Several times we nearly collided with Barrier cliffs, but we came about smartly, with rattling stays and flapping canvas.

What makes waiting hard is that we could complete the unloading if given forty-eight hours of good weather.

Sunday
February 10
Bay of Whales

Managed to tie up to the bay ice today after spending another night at sea in storm. The dog teams started out with loads after supper. The weather is very thick, snow soft, and the pulling very difficult. The dogs were up to their bellies in snow.

Gould, in a radio from the base, reported the weather quite bad there and urged the departure of the teams be postponed. But we cannot afford to continue to postpone unloading, even if the weather is not all that we might wish for.

Monday
February 11
Bay of Whales

More dirty weather. Soon after the dog teams put out, the sea roughened and drove heavy fragments of bergs against the ship. We had to put out to sea again. Drove into the bay ice again this morning, and radioed Gould to send out the dog teams. He reported conditions were bad at the base.

At 9:30 P.M. the sea is calming, and arrival of the dog teams is promised in the morning.

Such delays are distressing.

Tuesday
February 12
Bay of Whales

The teams arrived, as promised, but a shift of the wind to the north, which repeatedly jarred the *City* against the ice, forced us to dump our load on the bay ice and make for the open sea. In turning at full speed, the stern sheets came within a few feet of the ice—quite the closest shave we have yet had.

The continuous, strong northeasterly winds have so choked the mouth of the bay with pack that no safety can be found there. As any increase in wind would have driven this mass straight down on us, we dodged our way through it and stood for the Ross Sea.

All day long we have been under steam and sail, dodging ice and trying to prevent the wind from blowing us far to leeward. As it is, our strongest efforts seem pitiful: we have drifted at least eight miles and more likely ten, through a narrow lane of water between two packs.

There seem to be no signs of let-up in this storm. The barometer is rising slightly, but that does not necessarily mean anything down here.

Wednesday
February 13
At Sea

The storm seems to be over at last. The sun shone this morning, the wind has shifted to the southeast, and though the sky is overcast a line of blue can be seen in the southern horizon.

We punched a hole through the pack defending the entrance to the bay, and made for our old berth. It was so cluttered up with bergs and drift that we could not tie up.

Piles of this stuff were rafted tightly against the bay ice from the east to the west walls of the Barrier.

It was then decided to attempt to make a trip to King Edward VII Land.

We are now in an extensive field of loose, but heavy, floes, and about 20 miles northeast of the Bay of Whales. Under sail and steam combined, we are making about 5 knots—a merry gait for the old *City*.

First signs of winter darkness tonight—a faint darkening in the southern sky.

The sea is full of bergs, of various sizes. One mighty fellow was at least a mile long, and 40 feet high.

Thursday
February 14
Bay of Whales

This eastern sortie came to a quick end about five o'clock this morning. An impenetrable pack was sighted dead ahead, stretching from the Barrier to the north as far as we could see.

I gave orders to steam northward, in search of a passage, but the solid front of the pack remained unbroken. At six o'clock, no way through having been found, it was decided to return. There was little to gain by continuing, and much to lose if we became trapped in the ice.

We took soundings on the way back.

Returning to the Bay, we found a fairly good berth slightly to the west of the old one. A radio summons brought out the teams, and a heavy load was sent to the base.

Our own difficulties in the Bay of Whales were not the only ones that troubled the expedition. On the way back, the *Bolling* ran into frightful weather. A radio from Captain Brown on the 11th disclosed she was running before a wind of Force 8—a wind of hurricane force, and listing 56°. The chart house, he reported, was awash at times, and there were moments when he thought the ship would capsize, as she carried very little ballast. But she defeated the gale, and on the 15th reached Dunedin, having taken four days to make the last 150 miles.

On the same day, the Fokker completed three successful trials. Our unloading was nearly done, and the situation was sufficiently promising to cause me to attempt a second flight to the east, in an effort to reach the land from which we were turned back twice by sea and once by air. Accordingly I gave orders that the two planes, the Fokker and the Fairchild, be checked and made ready for a seven-hour flight.

Sunday, the 17th, I went into Little America by dog team. The sun was swinging low in the west, and the whole sky was a pool of gold. In a rainbow arc there trembled a number of mock suns. The richness of the radiance fell in a golden torrent on the Barrier, rendering a scene of ineffable beauty. A gorgeous setting for a flight of discovery. However, before we reached the base, the sky turned misty and the air became full of snow crystals. On Haines' advice, the take-off was postponed.

CHAPTER VII

DISCOVERY OF A NEW LAND TO THE EASTWARD

BOTH planes, the Fokker and Fairchild, took off on Monday, February 18. The Fokker was off first, and the Fairchild took and held a position about twenty yards astern. In the Fokker with me were Balchen, as pilot, and Berkner, as radio operator. Parker and June comprised the crew of the Fairchild. The temperature was 14° above zero, [1] and we were warmly dressed. We laid our course for Scott's Nunatak, as before.

We flew high, the engine at cruising revolutions. The Ross Sea now lifted a face marked by infinite desolation. Its surface for miles was littered with grayish patches of pack, sometimes consolidated, sometimes scattered, and through its interstices the water cut dark and irregular patterns. It suggested a mosaic laid by a madman.

It was apparent that while we strove to find a passage with the *City* the pack had disassembled somewhat, and a bold assault might now carry its outworks. At any rate, I decided to make the attempt on return.

To the north a dark water sky, of decidedly threatening appearance, indicated the Ross Sea was open. The extensiveness of this darkness appeared to influence the horizon ahead, for, as we advanced toward it, the cloud sheet was suffused with a uniform, milky gray color, utterly lacking in shadows. The horizon slowly disappeared, and the ridges and depressions in the Barrier, never too distinct from the air, were blotted from view. Again, we had the sensation of flying in a bowl of milk. Nevertheless, we pressed on, hoping that conditions would improve.

Just before we sighted Hal Flood Bay (we had then been

[1] All Temperatures are recorded in Fahrenheit.

flying about an hour), the sky ahead was swallowed by a mass of heavy, low hung clouds, which stretched directly across our path. These were definitely snow clouds, and probably meant a storm was raging over the very areas we hoped to reach.

We rose steadily and surmounted the first layer of cloud, but above these there was no improvement. A still higher mass lay ahead.

I conferred hastily with Balchen, and we were agreed that to continue to the east would be not only very hazardous but unprofitable. We could see nothing. We therefore changed course to the southeast.

This change of direction soon brought us past the Rockefellers, and we swung by them ten or fifteen miles to the westward, at a height of about 4,000 feet. I saw now, as we traversed them, that the mountains were more extensive than they had at first appeared, and began to count them until the profusion of peaks rendered the task confusing. I judged, however, there must be at least twenty-five mountain peaks in the group, most of which showed patches of bare rock.

The highest eminence did not appear greatly to exceed 2,000 feet above sea level, and the lowest perhaps not more than 500 feet. The great ice sheet had folded over them, burying all but the highest peaks and filling the valleys to overflowing. Deep depressions had been smoothed out until they seemed to be no more than shallow basins. It was a scene of extraordinary beauty and simplicity. One could not resist the impression that the peaks were struggling to lift their heads above the eternal snows. And over a span of centuries, the same struggle had been going on: the warfare between the earth's crust fighting to keep itself clear and the forces of the ice age which would engulf it.

Wherever we glanced, the peaks and ridges were deeply covered with snow, except for the patches of nearly vertical rock on which the snow, owing to the vigorous eddies and currents of wind which played about the mountains, could not gain foothold. And always at the base of each mountain, to the leeward of the prevailing wind, the currents had built up a long mound of snow, perhaps 100 feet wide, which gave it a wonderful stream-line effect. The valleys appeared to be a mixture of ice and snow, which so softened and masked their outlines as to rob them of striking character. Blue glints in the ice near the lower mountain slopes caught the eye, which led me to believe that the foothills approaching the mountain masses were largely encased in ice, no doubt the result of summer melting. These frozen pools, of striking blue, stood out quite distinctly from the white that surrounded them.

Such melting, even on a continent where the temperature only rarely rises above freezing, is not uncommon in the vicinity of mountains. All explorers in the Antarctic have reported similar phenomena. It is due, of course, to the fact that the dark faces of the rocks catch and hold the sun's heat, and, radiating it, melt the adjoining snow which, on passing out of its influence as water, cools rapidly and forms ice.

We searched in vain for evidences of wide movement in the snow and ice about these mountains. Save for a small area to the eastward, where we passed over a minor plateau which was crevassed and irregular in spots, the Barrier rolled about their feet unbrokenly. This, then, is an area of slight change.

With the Rockefellers thus spread out before us, I suddenly remembered my debt to Captain Nilsen. I picked out a prominent peak, marked its position on my chart, and scribbled a message for June: "Have just passed Mt. Nilsen." By radio he sent it to the *Larsen*, which was still fishing in the Ross Sea.

While passing the southern end of the Rockefeller Mountains we saw a superb peak, the resemblance of which to the Matterhorn was so striking as to suggest comparison instantly. Only its peak showed above the clouds. I believe we had sighted this same peak on the first eastern flight. I wrote a message on my chart, which I passed to Balchen. It said: "I see land to the East. Let's try it." So we headed for the peak.

We had risen to an altitude of 4500 feet.

The character of the surface began to change subtly and one could pick out where the snow lay deep and soft and where it had been hardened by wind into a firm crust. Once or twice we could make out where rough sastrugi ran over it, like ruffled water suddenly frozen into stillness, and we saw as well several odd little mounds. But for the most part the surface appeared quiescent and undisturbed; it is doubtful whether there has been any movement here in ages.

We had our eyes glued on the mountain, and to our chagrin it did not appear to draw nearer, although both planes were advancing toward it at the rate of about 100 miles per hour. The peak must, therefore, lie close to the 150th meridian, the eastern boundary of the Ross Dependency claimed by Great Britain and I realized with some satisfaction that the land that lay to the east could be claimed for the United States.

But as to the nature of that land, the size of the mountains which no doubt traversed it, we could not say then, for, as we watched, masses of clouds spread over the whole eastern horizon, blotting out Matterhorn. The sky was still clear to the southward and we, therefore, bore due south.

We flew south 60 miles to Latitude 79° 30′ S. By this time we had penetrated far enough to hope we might be able to see the mountains and the "appearance of land" which Amundsen reported in Latitude 82°.[1] This land and mountain he had taken to be a southern prolongation of King Edward VII Land and a definite link to the mountains trending northward from Carmen Land. No peaks arose to break the monotony of the Barrier, but far to the south we saw a dark streak flat on the horizon, tantalizingly vague. Could this be Amundsen's land? It was so far away we dared not risk sending both planes toward it, as a satisfactory excursion must bring them rather close to the limit of the fuel supply, so we set our course to the northwest and headed directly for Little America.

The surface of the Barrier continued unchanged with rolling hills and valleys of snow and an occasional pressure ridge.

To the stretch of land running south of the Rockefeller Mountains, and east as far as 150th meridian, I decided to give the name of the man who, more than any other, awakened the modern world to the importance of the Antarctic—Captain Robert Falcon Scott.

Both planes landed at Little America after a flight of four hours and 15 minutes.

McKinley then asked permission to make a photographic mapping survey of the coastline between Little America and

[1] Amundsen, "The South Pole," ii, 170-171.

Hal Flood Bay. This was readily granted, and the Fairchild was refueled and made ready for a second flight. Smith was to pilot it, and Berkner was to serve as radio operator.

Because I was eager to attempt another assault on the pack to get over to the northeast, I hastened down to the *City* by dog team, and ordered Captain Melville to put out to sea as soon as possible. Just as I reached the ship, the Fairchild wheeled overhead in a parting salute and sped off across the Barrier. The sound of its passage filled the Bay and echoed for a long time in the Barrier cliffs.

I went at once to the radio room and there had an experience which is one of the most thrilling I have ever known. From the loud speaker attached to Hanson's apparatus came a steady, throbbing roar—the sound of the Fairchild's generator pulsing with a beat corresponding to the cycle of the engine. As the engine increased its speed, the roar deepened and filled the whole ship; and as the speed slackened, the sound tapered off. It ceased entirely when Hanson broke in to send a message, then would resume when Berkner fastened down the key. It was a comforting sound; for as long as it persisted, one knew that all was well.

The Fairchild reached Hal Flood Bay about an hour later, and reported heavy clouds to the east. I was rather surprised, therefore, when McKinley radioed, a short time later, that he had the Nunatak in view, and requested permission to fly over and photograph it. I could not understand how the Fairchild had managed to cover the intervening distance in so short a time, but nevertheless gave him permission. More than any other I might cite, the incident illustrates the great advance in modern exploration. An airplane flying at a rate of two miles per minute at an altitude of 6,000 feet in exploratory flight could be directed and governed by radio from a point miles away. How very different from the conditions that prevailed on this same continent scarcely two decades before; when exploring parties set out on their lonely journeys and remained in the fields for months on end, with no communication with their bases; and when Scott and Amundsen, with scarcely 450 miles between them, patiently waited out the winter to begin their competing dashes to the Pole, the one as ignorant of the other's movements as if they had been separated by the Poles.

The contrast was heightened during supper when we heard, from the loud speaker, the sounds of Berkner "talking" with the *Bolling* and a short-wave station at San Francisco.

We had much fun at McKinley's expense when a message, rather humbly worded, confessed that the outcropping of rock which he had taken to be the Nunatak was none other than the northernmost peak of the Rockefellers. He reported that he was flying high above them, for a photographic survey.

Some time later came a more exciting message. Far to the eastward, fifty miles or more from their position, he saw a mountain ridge headed by a high peak. This we took to be the Antarctic Matterhorn.

So, for the second time that day, the land we had discovered earlier was exposed to human gaze.

Beyond it lay what is, to all explorers, the true Promised Land of Discovery. I was eager to get over it; but at this advanced stage of the season, I deemed it prudent to defer any further extended flights until the following spring.

After mapping the Rockefellers, McKinley swung north again, then west, to make an oblique strip map of the coast-line. Soon we heard the Fairchild overhead. It dipped low in greeting, then headed for Little America. We lost sight of it as it disappeared, in a curving glide, behind the Barrier; but were immediately assured by radio the landing had been accomplished without mishap.

McKinley had surveyed one hundred miles of unmapped coast line and the newly discovered mountains in a few hours— a job that would have taken many months by dog team or any other method.

The *City* meanwhile had groped a way through tattered patches of sea smoke caused by the colder air from the Barrier striking the warmer water, and stood out to sea. We rounded East Cape, which is the eastern portal of the Bay of Whales, and steered for Cape Colbeck.

3 A.M.
Tuesday
February 19th
At Sea

For cutting out for oneself the most miserable evening this

THE AVIATION MECHANICS.

Left to right:—E. J. Demas, Kennard Bubier, Benjamin Roth.

THE FORD HANGAR, WITH MULROY AND PARKER IN THE BACKGROUND.

(Courtesy Paramount.)

THE *City* AND THE *Bolling* UNLOADING ON THE BARRIER IN THE BAY OF WHALES.

Iceberg in Background.

earth offers, I most heartily recommend a night in an old sailing ship in Antarctic waters during a severe storm. There is nothing like it—at least nothing within my experience.

The weather is so thick one might cut it with a knife, or, better still, hack it apart with a hatchet. The wind is so strong that, even with a full head of steam and steering a course a few degrees off its eye, the old tub can hardly make its way against it.

We crest a wave and the propeller races with an abandon that threatens to tear it apart. I stood near the helmsman a while ago and the lash of spray and drift on the face was positively blinding. We could barely see beyond the waist of the ship. The wind twangs and plays on the rigging an unearthly tune.

We are constantly menaced by bergs which we cannot see until they evolve out of the mist, and they come gliding distressingly close alongside. More than once, I thought the *City* must give up the ghost.

Down below, in the engine room, it is frightful. The din is maddening, and the unrestrained pitching and tossing swiftly upsets the firmest footing. I take off my hat to Mulroy, Teddy Bayer, O'Brien and Sutton. They have kept us afloat this night.

It is bitterly cold. The spray falls on the deck as ice, and the air is choked with spindrift which cuts the face.

We have surrendered all hope of getting to the east by ship, and are struggling to return to the Bay of Whales. With bad luck, we lost sight of the Barrier, and no doubt have been blown somewhat off our course. Melville, Adams, Strom and Erickson have had a very tough time. And have done well. Melville was up nearly all night.

I'd give much for a sight of the sun.

> *7:30 o'clock*
> *Same day*
> *Bay of Whales*

We're back at the berth again, and I have no taste, at least for the moment, for further eastern excursions in the *City*. She's a fine old ship, the toughest of them all, as she proved last night, but she is no pleasure craft.

To continue the earlier entry: as I feared, we were well off our course. Blind as bats, we were heading merrily, under a full head of steam, sails set and a strong wind behind, when the sun suddenly appeared over the low mist in time for us to get a line on it with the sun compass.

This gave us our true direction and we found that we were headed straight for the cliffs of the west Barrier and we changed course, rather hastily, I confess. The old ship came about in one of the fastest maneuvers she ever made.

We then steamed slowly into the wind, and in an hour sighted the Barrier.

About seven o'clock we reached our berth. The sun was shining dully and dissipating the mist.

The *City* has become a bejewelled ship. Every spar and every line glitters with a solid casing of ice.

A stiff easterly wind is blowing, and our perch is none too secure. But now that we are here, we shall try to stay awhile. Every one is in need of rest.

The thermometer is tumbling. Winter cannot be far away. The sun is curving lower at the horizon.

We must get the *City* away.

In the scattered moments of calm that were allowed us during Wednesday and Thursday, we finished putting ashore the last of the supplies. Great masses of floe and bergs drifted down on us constantly, forcing us to shift our berth several times. Thursday morning, we were alarmed to discover that pancake ice had frozen about the ship while she lay, and the bay had frozen over near the east Barrier. All information I had been able to gather previously indicated that the ship would not be in danger of "freezing in" before March 1st. But all signs pointed to an early winter, and I was determined to send the *City* north before she became a permanent resident. With the small reserve of coal left in her bunkers, she could not long struggle against heavy ice.

So, on Thursday, we made for the east Barrier, to lay down several bases in the bays for later airplane flights from Little America, and to make a last few soundings near the Barrier. Toward evening, we ran into heavy fields of thick slush ice, with perhaps a hundred yards of open water between fields. Progress became increasingly difficult, and the wind, after we rounded East Cape, freshened to gale force, blowing snow in great sheets from the Barrier. Oddly enough, Little America reported at the same time a perfect calm. Gradually the fields of slush widened until their edges touched, and before long we were completely surrounded by heavy, congealing mush. Our situation was undeniably hazardous. A cessation in the wind must cause this mass to freeze instantly into solid ice, for the night before the thermometer recorded a new low of 19° below zero.

At ten o'clock, Captain Melville gave orders to come about, but when we tried to tack ship, she refused to reply. Ice, we found, had frozen about the rudder, and the combined strength of half a dozen men brought no response. Axes and saws fixed to long poles were brought into play, and after considerable hacking, which was not easy work in the gale, we managed to wear around. We made for the Bay of Whales, and five hours later were again tied up to the bay ice. The trip, though unsuccessful from one point of view, was significant from another. It proved, more vividly than theory could, that the *City* could not risk her presence in the Bay of Whales another day.

Accordingly I gave orders to Captain Melville to cast off at once. I know I shall never forget the moments that followed. Once more it was necessary to split the expedition into two divisions, and this time they could not be brought together before the following December. There was not a man among the 83 who left New Zealand who did not harbor in his heart the ambition of becoming a member of the Winter Party. But not all could join that group, which we had previously limited to 40, and for which number we had provided. More, it was obviously necessary to keep both vessels staffed with trained crews, and their work, in the larger purposes of the expedition, was not one whit less important than that of the winter party. But making that clear was not easy, for men whose minds have set up one ideal are reluctant to concede suddenly the equal worth of another. In the end, we increased the winter party by two—Quin Blackburn and Jim Feury, because we found we needed them. The hardest job I ever faced was when I told "Kid" Berlin, a fireman on the *City,* that Chief Engineer McPherson absolutely needed him on the voyage back, and we could not therefore let him remain. Tears streamed down his face, but he smiled at the same time, and without a word carried out his orders. He had worked like a fiend during unloading operations, and if ever a man deserved reward, Berlin deserved it. There were several equally bitter things I had to do before the *City* went. Teddy Bayer, an engineer on the *City,* had been equally helpful and I would have asked him to join the winter party had Chief Engineer Esmond O'Brien been able to spare him from the *City's* engine room.

I tried to tell them all, just before the *City* left, how greatly we appreciated their help and sportsmanship; and it was a strange thing to talk to a score of men, with bay ice as a platform and the listeners crowded about the rail of an old sailing ship, and a subsiding storm hurling spindrift across the Bay. Civilization was 2,300 miles away, and somehow words did not seem to matter. It is a feeling we came to know better in the Antarctic. An understanding wordlessness comes to take the place of language. And I feel that we reached it then.

We watched them weigh anchor, and move away with a flutter of canvas. Soon only the *City's* masts and spars stood out above the writhing sea smoke, and presently these were gone. The 42 of us were left alone to our problems.

It was almost impossible to believe that the most important preliminary operation of the expedition—the unloading of the ships—was actually accomplished; that 225 tons of supplies from the *City* and 440 tons from the *Bolling* had been unloaded and carried to the base, under really dangerous conditions, without the loss of a man and only the loss of one or two sacks of coal. Some statistician had already figured out that the sledges had travelled a total of 12,500 miles in the shuttle operation between the ships and Little America. To realize, as I did then, that this trying and undeniably difficult piece of work had been accomplished by greenhorns for the most part, was to bring real satisfaction. What had once been regarded as almost impossible was now done well and behind us.

It was too cold to stand for long on the bay ice, with the temperature at 29° below zero; our parka hoods were covered

Sea Smoke.

UNLOADING THE "FLOYD BENNETT" FROM THE *Bolling* TO THE BARRIER.

Several hours after this photograph was taken the Barrier collapsed and menaced the vessel as well as the lives of a

with frost. So we got aboard the dog teams which had been sent down to meet us, and journeyed to the base.

It was a journey which I had made several times before, but now my senses were more alert to the surroundings, and I would be remiss not to describe the trail, or rather the approach, to Little America. To the southeast the Barrier rose in the form of a cape, the walls of which glittered with blue diamonds and curved, higher up, into an overhang modelled perhaps by the wind. Behind this cape, the trail bore sharply to the east, and as Goodale raced his team around the curve the narrow corridor of Ver-sur-Mer Inlet opened before us. The ice floor of the inlet was now entirely covered in snow, which in turn was littered with crystals as large as marbles. In the sun these shone like jewels, and the whole inlet sparkled with thousands of pin points of radiance. The sledge runners grated against and sometimes crushed these crystals as they struck, and then whirred on the smooth, hard snow.

The old pressure ridges still lifted their shattered structures in the air, and we sighted several seal holes. The scene was in truth alive with colors, the blue in the ice cliffs to the North fading imperceptibly into the roseate hues of the Barrier. After we traversed the bay, the trail rose gradually, then with increasing steepness. The dogs had to dig in, bellies flat against the snow, to gain leverage, and their breaths discharged like jets of vapor from a valve.

A last pull, and we topped the rise. Little America lay before us. And we saw the three houses, with only a few feet of orange sides showing above the snow, the black hulks of the airplanes, the three spidery wireless masts spreading filaments of wire 65 feet above them, and underneath groups of beetle-like figures moved busily about.

Some distance behind the houses scores of crates and boxes lay in a shapeless pile, with the yellow heads of gasoline drums showing here and there above the snow. Stretches of tarpaulin showed where other caches lay protected from the elements. A line of brown tents and white ran through the center of the settlement, and nearby were the dog crates. From the mess hall, perhaps I should call it the kitchen, came the sounds of considerable activity and a welcome column of smoke. Tennant was preparing supper.

Behind the colony to the eastward, the Barrier curved around to form the basin. This basin was about a mile in diameter. The rim was formed by a series of little hills of snow except at the entrance to the west where it descended into Ver-sur-Mer Inlet. Here the houses were grouped. On the eastern rim ran a line of haycocks and crevasses. Far away, the valley disappeared into the flank of vaguely seen hillocks. East, north and south was the eternal Barrier, rolling and indefinite, glowing with strange, swiftly changing warm colors.

This was our home, and, now that the *City* was gone, we pitched in to make it firm and snug against approaching winter.

During the next few days, the battle shifted to the north, while the *Bolling* raced south with her second load, and the *City* strove to push north. And all the while the pack threatened to erect an impenetrable barrier between them. The issue remained in doubt for days, and during that period there was little rest for the radiomen or me.

The radios, I think, tell the story.

Feb. 23

COMDR. BYRD:

Ice seems thicker continually and is in pans of several acres. A few minutes ago struck a big area and broke ice about four or five inches thick for more than a mile. Making only about one knot. Freezing seems to be going on continually and in a few hours the *City* would have made headway only with greatest difficulty. The ice is also freezing in our wake as we pass.

BERKNER.

Later

Feb. 23

COMDR. BYRD:

We have wind SSW force 4. Under steam and sail pushing our way through new ice as far as the eye can see. The thickness of this new ice is from six to twelve inches and appears to be forming between the widely separated ice packs, which are small, but can be seen in every direction. Thus far we have had no great difficulty but it appears that the ice is getting thicker as we go along to the Northwest. Johansen continuously aloft looking for leads. We will keep you constantly advised as we progress.

MELVILLE.

Later

Feb. 23

CAPTAIN MELVILLE:

Suggest that you use kerosene lamps and hold down heating of quarters as much as possible in order to conserve coal. Good luck in your battle. I believe you probably have pack to the North and open water to the West around the 180th Meridian.

BYRD.

Later

Feb. 23

COMDR. BYRD:

Barometer 29.32. Wind SSE, force 5. Temperature of air 14, water 29. Making good time now through scattered ice pack under steam and sail. Occasional snow flurries but visibility good. Due to the fact that water temperature is rising and the new ice seems to be getting thinner. Both Johansen and I deem it advisable to proceed towards the *Larsen.* Agree that may be lighter pack westward, and have been setting more towards the 180th with seemingly improved conditions. Regards.

MELVILLE.

Next day conditions were worse, and the *City* ran her nose against very thick pack. By radio I asked the *Larsen,* which was then making ready to start north, to stand by and await the *City's* arrival. An emergency existed, for the *City's* supply of coal, sadly depleted as a result of constant steaming during the stormy weather at the Bay of Whales, was not sufficient to sustain her through a long struggle with heavy ice. If she failed in that struggle, she would in all likelihood become imprisoned in the ice for the winter, with attendant danger to her hull and crew. To discover such heavy pack so early in the season was a blow. It had developed many days in advance of its seasonal appearance, and when the *City* started north I was quite sure that she had a sufficient safety factor of coal to see her through. These facts I laid before Captain Nilsen of the *Larsen,* in the following message:

New York has not enough coal to keep her going if she meets further serious resistance from the ice. Needless to say, I did not anticipate the *New York* would have difficulty in keeping rendezvous with *Bolling* at position of *Larsen* to supply the *City* with coal and food.

I am sure you can understand the great apprehension I have for my comrades on the *New York*. As I consider the status of the *New York* perilous, there is nothing I can do but ask your help again.

The *New York* is now 270 miles from you, making 7 or 8 knots under sail and steam. She should be only 111 miles from you by noon tomorrow. I am hoping that you can delay long enough to give her fresh whale meat and coal enough to get her through the pack and to New Zealand. I can have the *Bolling* meet you and repay coal. Best of wishes.

I am reluctant to let the *Bolling* come through the pack as she has developed a leak in after hold.

                                                              BYRD.

Later

                                                       Feb. 24
COMDR. BYRD:

Lat. 76.52 S. Long. 171.50 W. Water temperature 28, air 21. Wind SSE, force 6. Sea moderate, sky overcast. Visibility good. Widely scattered pack during last four hours. Making good time under sail and steam. Bar. 29.22 falling slowly. After leaving Bay of Whales encountered new ice for at least 80 miles which appeared to close in quickly and freeze behind us. This ice increased in thickness to from eight to ten inches. At 11:30 we were stuck. It was possible to move forward again only by the use of additional sail and steam. Since that time conditions have improved up to the present.

                                                          MELVILLE.

Several days before I had accepted the inevitable, and instructed Captain Brown to give up his attempts to force the pack with the *Bolling*. No real emergency existed at the base, thanks to the careful planning and foresight which had governed the selection of material taken on the *Bolling's* first voyage. Naturally, we might have used the additional houses, the small airplane, and the 14 dogs which Brown had aboard, but we could manage without these. We had already decided to build snow houses to take the place of the wooden structures. Certainly our needs were not dire enough to risk the presence of the *Bolling,* as well as the lives of her crew, in the pack. It was an unpleasant task to deflect the officers and crew from a job they were determined to accomplish, but it had to be done. I instructed Captain Brown to stand by, outside the pack, pending the outcome of the *City's* battle. He radioed me as follows:

Feb. 25

Comdr. Byrd:

Your sad message received. Sorry not to be able to go through. All hands are raring to go. We have seen no ice thus far, so why don't you let me try? You know that experts said before it would be impossible to get into Bay of Whales. Would a depot at Scott's last winter quarters in McMurdo Sound do any good? My gang and I will go to Hell for you. Please answer, as we are still hoping.

Later

Byrd,

Barrier Station WFA:

This to inform you that we are now ready for departure. At present strong weather with heavy sea and we are trying to get out into clear water. We will ascertain from *City* her position and will endeavor to locate her. In my opinion it will be impossible to bunker her in this kind of weather and as far as I can see at present the only way will be to take crew on board and abandon *City.* Will keep you informed on progress if anything should turn up to the better.

Nilsen.

Later

Comdr. Byrd:

Our 8 p.m. position dead reckoning Latitude 74.20 S. Long. by observation 179.30 E. Crossed date line 5 p.m. and steering more west again to find clear water as we have again encountered a heavy pack of decayed bergs and old ice which is probably that reported south of *Larsen.* Heavy SW swell. Barometer 29.20. Wind SSE. Overcast. Obtaining frequent bearings on *Larsen* who also reports he is moving westward.

Melville.

The distressing fact in this episode that made me reluctant to press Captain Nilsen more than necessary was that we were asking him to risk the lives of 230 men for those of a score. He had informed me in an earlier message, that heavy pack enfolded his ship, and "it looks as if the packs have spread all over the Ross Sea from east to west." Nevertheless, he met the issue squarely with the promise, "If there is any real peril to *City* or any other ship, I will proceed at once with the *C. A. Larsen* and do our best." That he did. The *Larsen* was north of the pack that lay between two ships, and Captain Nilsen therefore dispatched several of his small fast chasers to the *City's* aid. A subsequent message reported that they had found passage to the westward.

The affair soon drew to a satisfactory conclusion.

Feb. 26

COMDR. BYRD:

We have direction finder on *City New York* and two of the chasers racing towards her. We following her. Slight NW wind, Temp. 2 centigrade minus, pancake ice.

NILSEN.

Feb. 27

COMDR. BYRD:

So far we have not picked up chasers but think we should see them nearly any time now.

MELVILLE.

Feb. 28

COMDR. BYRD:

Arrived at *Larsen* 11 P.M. last night. Went alongside 12:35 P.M. this morning. Took on board approximately 90 tons of coal and some provisions. Finished 3:30 A.M. and all sailed at 4 A.M. Now going through pack to Northward. All well. Regards.

MELVILLE.

And in this manner a potentially dangerous situation came to an end. Brown, on the *Bolling*, hove to outside the pack, awaiting the *City*, sent this message on March 1 :

Comdr. Byrd:

Noon position Lat. 56.47 S Long. 172.01 E. Strong NW gale, heavy, tremendous sea washing all over ship. Have been hove to since 2 A.M. Am going North. Barometer 29. Air 45°. One of the dogs got six pups during storm. All going well. Regards.

Brown.

It is, indeed, an ill wind that blows no good. We had hopes of using those pups very nicely in the following spring.

The building and organization of Little America was a fine piece of work. It was accomplished mainly under the direction of Dr. Gould and Captain McKinley, and the hammer of Chips Gould, the carpenter. The houses and the plan of locating them had been worked out in New York before our departure by my friend, Edgar Barratt, an architect, and his son, Roswell Barratt. This plan called for the erection of five main buildings, but as three of them were in the *Bolling's* hold when she turned back, we fell somewhat short of the blue print requirements. In fact, we would be confronted with considerable congestion in our quarters unless we made use of every plank and box we could lay our hands on. Here the ingenuity and economy of "Chips" Gould came into natural play, and I dare say there was not much more than a sliver of wood that he did not bend and nail to his shrewd designs.

From one of the airplane crates he built a machine shop and storehouse for the aviation mechanics, which was located about forty yards northwest of the mess hall. Parts of another airplane crate served as the walls and structure of a radio storeroom, which was located about half-way between the mess house and the administration building.

For Davies, the physicist, a non-magnetic house was evolved out of odds and ends of lumber. Braathen and Walden, the recluses of the expedition, were at work on a little house; and by quietly, in fact furtively, saving every scrap of wood that escaped Gould (and some that did not escape him), they soon had enough material to build a separate residence for themselves. This they put up about 75 feet south of the mess hall.

All kinds of construction were under way when the *City* sailed, and Little America was as busy as a boom town. George Black, the supply officer, was at work on his store house. This he created by digging a large hole in the snow just off the main trail between the mess hall and the administration building, about twenty yards from the latter. He caused the boxes to serve as their own protecting walls, and by covering the hole with a tarpaulin had a very snug shelter which was of course soon snowed over.

Several other additions were planned to the growing number of buildings radiating about the mess hall. One of these was the third bunk house, which was to adjoin Czegka's machine shop and open on a vestibule cut into the snow. On the other end of the mess hall we proposed to build a dark room and photographic laboratory for McKinley, Rucker and Van der Veer.

Hanson and his men were already at work on their radio laboratory, which was no more than a corner of the administration building. Into this limited space they must crowd their cumbersome and complicated apparatus. For power they depended upon the Kohler plant in the machine shop, the juice being carried overland by wires. This same plant also fed the lighting system, such as it was. We had even then begun to conserve gasoline, which this plant normally consumed, and June and Czegka had ingeniously arranged so that it used kerosene instead. It was essential that we save gasoline for aviation operations in the spring. Because the radio department would demand most of the power, the number of electric lights in the camp was limited—one for the cook in the mess hall, one for the radio generator, one for the Norwegian house, and two for the photographic laboratory. Another large bulb was used as a safety beacon on one of the radio towers. Gasoline pressure lamps and kerosene lamps provided the illumination for the other buildings and houses.

The principal structures in the colony were the administration building, the mess hall and the Norwegian House. The first of these was named the Edgar Barratt House; the second, the Roswell Barratt House, after the two men, my friends, who designed them, and the third was named the Biltmore. The first two were portable houses, designed and built in New

THE MESS HALL, WITH THE NORWEGIAN HOUSE IN THE REAR, UNDER CONSTRUCTION.

These houses were soon completely covered by snow.

"So Long, Good Luck." The Winter Party Bids Crew of the *City of New York* Farewell.

York to serve a particular purpose. They were divided, for example, into sections of 3 x 8 feet, each section weighing about 106 pounds, so that two men could handle them with ease. In a test in New York, before we left, it was found that either house could be assembled in five hours.

They were designed, naturally, less for elegance than for strength and resistance to cold. The walls were four inches thick. Outside was a layer of stiff building board, one-half an inch thick. Next were two layers of paper, a layer of building board, then one and one-half inches of insulating material, and then more fibrous building board. The outside was sealed with three coats of orange paint. The walls and roof were bolted to a frame of yellow pine. Not a nail was used in the structure, and the bolts with which it was tied together were not allowed to end on the outside. Transmission of cold was thus reduced to a minimum.

The foundation of the houses were set deep in the snow, and then, when the roofs were put on, snow was packed tightly and smoothly about them. In this way they were protected from the wind and snow, and only the fiercest kind of blizzard could injure them.

As ours was the largest expedition to winter in the Antarctic, we had our own peculiar problems. The fire hazard was an ever-present worry, for the loss of home by fire during the winter night could have but one ending on this inhospitable continent. We therefore set up the two main buildings 200 yards apart, knowing that if one burned, the other would escape. The supplies and other vital equipment were scattered about for the same reason.

There was still another reason recommending such distribution. The most persistent and insinuating foe to explorers who endure the winter night is monotony. It is a thing, of course, many of us know and for that matter endure even in the center of civilization; but nowhere else can it be experienced to such a degree as in the polar night. For there can be few ways in which to escape monotony. Bitter cold and incessant storms keep all but the hardiest men indoors a greater part of the time; and even they do not care to venture very far. Consequently, men are thrown into the utmost intimacy for months on end, within the narrow, restricting walls of their shacks; and the time inevitably comes when all the topics in the world have been sucked dry of interest; when one man's voice becomes irritating to the ears of another; when the most trivial points of disagreement become fraught with impassioned meaning. When that point is reached, there comes trouble.

By scattering houses and work places, we hoped to give greater scope to the physical activities of the men. It would not be necessary to remain cooped up in one place. And to assist communication, we ultimately created a fascinating system of tunnels connecting the various units of the colony. The first tunnel was dug between the administration building and the mess hall, a very laborious undertaking. It was six feet deep. Food boxes were laid along the sides. The corridor, then, was little more than the width of a man's shoulders; and the bigger men such as Clark, Strom and Smith had to go through it somewhat sidewise. Over the boxes we laid a strip of canvas. As the tunnel progressed, passages were opened into the store rooms and workshops so that, when we finished, we had a comprehensive system of subterranean communication which brought all the scattered units of the colony within reach of a traveller who need never once venture above the surface. Both Mawson and Amundsen had built short tunnels about their shacks, but never in the history of exploration was there a system as elaborate as ours. In them we dwelt what Mawson has aptly called a "troglodytic existence," a reduced and undeniably limited one, but on the whole a more active and diversified existence, perhaps, than most other expeditions were able to contrive.

Space does not permit of a full description of the multiple phases of our operations. The erection of the radio towers, for example, was a romantic accomplishment of itself. Two men who had never engaged in iron work before, Jim Feury and Teddy Bayer, assembled these towers, and the thoroughness with which they did it may be judged from the fact that the structures outlived the worst blizzards.

What busy days they were! And yet not a few of us found them to be happy ones. We met the advancing winter with a great show of industry and the satisfaction that well-ordered and effective labor brings.

CHAPTER VIII

INCIDENT ON THE ROCKEFELLER MOUNTAINS

THE winter night was in reality close at hand. Deepening shadows on the horizon at the midnight hour heralded its approach, and we now increased our efforts to have all external tasks completed before really cold weather set in. We were most anxious to have the cache on the Barrier transferred to the base; for successive snow storms and high winds had repeatedly covered it with drift and the supplies were buried half the time. After each storm it was necessary for all hands to join the snow shovel squad and retrieve them. Half a dozen dog teams and the snowmobile were assigned to this work, and the supplies poured in at a marvellous rate. The journey to the cache was hardly what one would call a hazardous one: the distance was only 4 miles, the trail was well marked out with flags, and the drivers had by this time become accustomed to the surroundings. But the swiftness with which storms fell and smothered visibility imparted an element of danger even to this short journey, and I repeatedly instructed the drivers to observe caution. In the event of a severe blizzard, I recommended that they try to wait it out, rather than run the risk of becoming lost and perhaps falling off the edge of the Barrier. For this reason, sleeping bags were considered compulsory equipment on all sledges.

In spite of these precautions, we did not escape a very serious "scare".

On the morning of March 4, Blackburn, Siple and Thorne set out with their teams for the cache. Siple had his double freight sledge, and Blackburn a small basket sledge. Conditions when they started were not bad, the wind was light and the temperature about zero. However, they changed very quickly, and within an hour the wind was blowing hard, and visibility was choked off by thick drift. In fact, Balchen and Strom, who came in from a trip to the Bay, reported that the drift was so dense it was impossible to see beyond the end of the skis.

Thorne and Siple presently came in with their loads, but Blackburn was not with them. A mile north of Little America they had turned off the trail to drop part of the loads. Blackburn's dogs, however, had refused to turn, and Thorne and Siple saw him disappear into the drift, vainly trying to halt the dogs. The two men managed to reach the base after some difficulties, and were somewhat surprised not to find Blackburn already there.

By this time the wind had risen to 40 miles per hour, and the drift was dense. It was snug enough in the houses, where the stoves threw off enervating warmth, and for a time we saw no reason to become alarmed over Blackburn's absence.

But when I learned he had failed to take his sleeping bag, then I did have fears for his safety. I took Gould and Thorne with me, and started down the trail. Outside was uproar, with the sharp edge of driving drift. We carried a compass. Every few feet we put down a flag, not only to guide ourselves back, but also Blackburn if by chance he was still stumbling about in the confusion of snow and wind. Some distance out we came across a new crevasse which had opened across the old trail, and in the storm it looked ominous. Reaching the cache, we investigated the small valley into which Thorne had seen Blackburn disappear, and finally made our way back to the base, without having come across his trail. However, we realized it was very possible that we passed within a few feet of him, with neither party aware of it, for the drift most of the time shut down visibility almost to the tip of one's nose, and the wind swiftly extinguished the loudest shout.

Without pausing we sallied forth, this time more to the west, and still failed to find him. I was then convinced that he was either lost to the east of the trail or still in the vicinity of the cache. I was reluctant to believe he had fallen off the Barrier, an idea that had taken hold of several imaginations.

A more efficient drag-net was set in operation. Gould, O'Brien and Feury went out to conduct a search along

Men at Work During Blizzard Building Tunnel to Prevent the Loss of Food Boxes Under Snow Drifts.

THE WINTER PARTY

the northern edge of the Barrier. They carried a goodly amount of alpine rope, and were tied together, lest one of them venture out too far. Then parties of dog teams were dispatched to the cache, whence they were to work, fan-wise, to the east and north.

The whole camp, by this time, was alarmed.

However, the incident closed on a happy note when a team under Vaughan, with Bursey, de Ganahl and Thorne in company, came upon several dark lumps in the snow, and found them to be Blackburn's dogs. Curled in a hole in the snow, with gasoline cans piled up to provide shelter, was Blackburn. He lay in the lee of his sledge, with the dogs dug in beside him. He was unharmed by exposure, although he had been out for eight hours, and I was pleased that he had had the good sense not to continue travelling when he realized he was lost.

One may judge his astonishment when he learned he was less than half a mile from the base, and the flags we had so painfully put down to guide him passed within 20 yards of his hole.

Wednesday
March 5

Still busy.

Brophy is no longer connected with the expedition. I have accepted his resignation. He is in a very nervous condition and it is impossible for him to continue to handle the details of the expedition.

I have urged him to take a long rest and hope he has the wisdom to do it. I have done everything within my power to make it easy for him. Heaven knows, there is still a great deal of work to be done in New Zealand, with units based there, and for weeks now we have had to handle no end of intricate details by radio from here, trying to straighten things out. His breakdown seems complete, and it is a great pity all around.

Mr. Tapley will be in charge of expedition affairs in New Zealand.

Several new projects are in the air.

Tomorrow, weather permitting, the dog teams will be sent out to establish three preliminary depots on the Barrier. These will be laid down in preparation for the spring journeys. With good luck, there is no reason why they should not be able to carry their loads at least 40 miles south.

None of the men, it is true, has had previous experience in Antarctic sledging, but the experiences of Vaughan and Goodale with Grenfell in Labrador and with Walden in New Hampshire, as well as the experience they have acquired during unloading operations, should stand them in good stead. Vaughan will be in charge of the first sledge, Bursey of the second, then Goodale and Crockett.

De Ganahl will be navigator and Petersen will go along as radio operator.

There have been many conferences, and I think the men now understand their problems. Apart from the necessity of getting the bases down, the trip will be beneficial from other considerations. There are many things to learn about the protection of hands and feet from cold and moisture, and how best to make use of the clothing which has been made for use on the tramp. Frozen feet and hands, uncomfortable nights, and real suffering inevitably follow failure to acquire proper protection. There are tricks in using a sleeping bag and in keeping it dry, in the preservation of mukluks, socks, mittens and the rest. Moisture collects in them, freezes, and causes all kinds of trouble. It is one thing to be told about precautions, but effective knowledge can be gained only by experience on the trail. There is also the problem of pitching camp and getting an early start in the morning—both very important points. We shall learn something as a result of this trip, and during the winter all hands can work up the best methods of "beating" these problems.

Gould is very anxious to make a flight to the Rockefellers, for a geological survey. Poor Larry, he has been compelled to dull his geological hammer on the ends of boxes while the rocks in the Rockefellers fairly cried out for investigation. Such a journey would be very important, but, frankly, I am not eager to see him undertake it at this advanced period with winter so near. The weather has been stormy and cold, and I am not sure the flight can be made without considerable risk.

We shall see what comes of the weather. If Haines provides clear skies, he may go, if he still wishes. If we can squeeze in this investigation now, we shall undeniably have that much more time for other work next spring.

Hanson and his men have been working steadily on the main radio set, and today they finished. Heretofore, we have cleared our traffic through the small sets on the *Bolling* and the *City,* with surprisingly good results.

The main station is a most prepossessing looking affair. Hanson has displayed real ingenuity in making the most of his limited space, and the corner of the administration building which we now call the Ochs Radio Station, in honor of the friend who has done so much for me. The Station is an anomalous blend of the primitive and the highly modern. On a bleak and roughly hewn table the various dials and bulbs rise in tiers of subtly organized combinations. It gives one a strange sense of power to realize that within these bare walls, hung with cumbersome winter clothing, is a force that puts us within one-eighth of a second of New York City.

And that outside, in the aircraft, is a second power that can carry us easily and at great speed over this formidable Continent.

How few of us realize that it is only during the past century that man has been able to travel rapidly, and to impose his will directly and instantly beyond the range of his voice. The mere extension of these abilities has ceased to surprise us in civilization; and no doubt because they are become commonplace conveniences, we are more sensitive to the nuisances they often do involve.

But down here on this dead ice cap, where what a man could do has heretofore been limited to the power of his legs and heart and the blind courage of his dogs and ponies, the possession of them is a wonderful gift. Even the ring of the telephone in the administration building strikes a note of cheerful competence. Or so it seems now. I suppose it will become a bother soon enough.

Thursday, March 7th, both units—the Fokker and the dog teams—took their departure from camp. Just before the departure of the teams, I dispatched Balchen and Braathen on a mission to mark a path through or around the pressure ridges and cracks in the bay ice, as well as the crevasses to the south-west of the camp. They were to mark this trail with flags, and thus save the base-laying party the inconvenience as well as danger of searching for a route. Some of these crevasses were open and others were closed over by shallow and insubstantial bridges, which might let through a heavily loaded sledge. Balchen and Braathen carefully identified a safe passage, and from that point on the drivers could expect smooth Barrier until they reached the place which Amundsen called The Trap.

Each team carried a load of 800 pounds, and the party was given the following designations:

TEAM No. 1—VAUGHAN

NON-MAGNETIC TEAM

Compass (requiring non-magnetic sledge)
Sleeping bag and gear
De Ganahl's bag and gear
50 flags
Alpine rope
2 pair of skis and bamboo poles
Navigating instruments
Amundsen's sledge meter [1]

TEAM No. 2—GOODALE

CAMPING TEAM

Sleeping bag and gear
1 pair of skis
1 axe
1 shovel
3 tents
4 ice picks
Man food

---

[1] This sledge meter, which Amundsen carried on the polar journey, was a personal gift to Admiral Byrd.

Team No. 3—Bursey

DEPOT-LAYING TEAM

Sleeping bag and gear
Depot supplies
1 hatchet
4 tents
Snow knife
1 pair of skis
Depot bamboo flagpoles
1 shovel
Emergency clothing

Team No. 4—*Crockett*

RADIO TEAM

Sleeping bags and gear
Petersen's bag and gear
Extra wood runner and bolts
Drill
1 axe
Six pair of snowshoes
2 skis and poles
150 flags
Extra compass
Sledge meter
Alpine rope
Emergency food
Radio set with mast [1]

In addition, the teams carried 1,700 pounds of dog pemmican, which was divided among the sledges in amounts that brought up the total loads of each to about 800 pounds.

Of the load, approximately 1350 pounds were to be distributed among three depots. The first, 20 miles south, the second 40, and the third 44. Vaughan was requested to use great care in marking the depots, lest the winter blizzards ob-

---

[1] This set is known as a portable transmitter, using two radio tubes of a type used almost universally in storage battery receivers. Power, 7.5 watts. Antennæ, a single wire held aloft on two bamboo poles sunk in the snow.

literate all traces of the trail. Hence the large supply of flags. Twenty flags were to be placed about each base, to the west, at intervals of a quarter of a mile, and an equal number to the east. The most precious thing in sledging on fixed rations is time, and the hours lost in searching for poorly marked depots have brought great suffering, if not ruin, to many exploring parties. Of course we could not hope to make these depots as conspicuous as a red traffic light on Fifth Avenue; but on a rolling plain of snow conspicuous for its lack of landmarks these little orange-red flags could be picked up by a sledge party even if slightly off its course. More, I saw in them the possibility of a considerable aid to navigation in the southern flights planned for the following spring, for they would provide control points for the checking of compasses in flight and as a check against local error.

The rest of the flags were to be used in marking the southern route, to facilitate the return journey. Because this was primarily a test trip, they were instructed to make liberal use of the flags, rather than run the risk of becoming lost. Storms of considerable force were to be expected almost any time, and it behooved a party on the trail to execute its mission as quickly as possible and return. This meant travelling even in the face of storm and semi-darkness: and under such conditions a string of closely placed flags, leading directly to the base, would be a life line.

The men were liberally provided with cold weather clothing. Lower temperatures than prevailed in the protection of our basin might be expected on the Barrier: in his first season's marches during March, Amundsen experienced temperatures as low as 45.4° below zero, [1] which he described as "rather fresh." [2]

The start of the trip was full of excitement. The clear, cold air was as heady as a draught of fine wine, which suffused a sensation of well-being in every one, dogs as well as men. The dogs were like coiled springs, waiting the signal to start. They filled the basin with the sound of barking. Some lay in the snow, munching it placidly. But others, impatient for action, quarrelled constantly, with a great show of force, but withal an

[1] Amundsen, "The South Pole," i, p. 232, 246.
[2] *Ibid.*, i, 246.

amiable intent. There were some excellent dogs among them: Bursey's leader, St. Lunaire, a brown Labrador husky, one of the hardest workers I ever saw, and possessing an uncanny sense of direction; Crockett's leader, Quimbo, a son of Chinook, eighty pounds of belligerency and competent leadership; Goodale's leader, Blizzard, a fine Labrador husky, of the same breed as St. Lunaire, with a splendid dark gray coat, and Vaughan's leader, Dinny, a black malamute with soulful eyes and the disposition of Puck. And there were, of course, in Vaughan's and Goodale's teams, those inseparable companions, Moody and Watch, Targish and Dingo.

When the signal to start was given, the teams went off with a rush, Vaughan's leading, with the drivers fighting to keep the sledges upright as they tore down the slope into the inlet and the dogs throwing up clouds of snow. They rounded the bend on single runners, and I thought: well, that's very fine now, but I dare say you will settle down to a less lively pace before long.

We turned to help the geological mission on its way. It was then 3 o'clock.

A short time later, the Fokker shook its skis clear of the Barrier, and headed east. Balchen piloted, June served as radio man and Dr. Gould, of course, was in charge. They carried provisions for several months, the usual emergency equipment and Larry's precious theodolite. I watched them start with some misgivings. With winter so near, any failure of this operation must result, I felt, in danger. Soon I received a message from the Fokker in flight:

Everything fine with plane about 40 miles from base headed towards Mts.

LARRY.

About two hours later a second message announced the Fokker's safe arrival at the foot of Chips Gould Mountain. Gould reported: "Sky overcast and no hope of getting position tonight. Very warm and calm. All hands eager to be in the hills tomorrow."

In Little America we turned to the task of getting rid of the snow that covered everything, and the snow shovel became the most prominent and hated thing in the camp. The Barrier cache was again obliterated by the blizzard, and a crew of men was sent out to locate and retrieve the remaining supplies. Another group was engaged in killing seals out on the bay ice. Killing Weddell seals is not exactly a sport. Even when the amateur hunters made loud noises in an attempt to arouse the beasts into some semblance of activity, they promptly returned to their snoring as soon as the racket subsided. Braathen protested that the only way he could escape a charge of murder was by first giving the seals a hearty dig in the ribs, which awakened them, and then rushing off to a sporting distance before he fired a shot: we really hated to kill these poor creatures, but necessity knows no law; we needed fresh meat in quantities, both the men and dogs, and had to overlook the niceties. Fortunately, by then, we had about 250 carcasses, and soon could call a halt to the unpleasant business.

Friday
March 8th

Weather continues good. Every man in the camp going full speed ahead. Gould, the carpenter, Mulroy, Parker, Rucker and McKinley are putting the finishing touches to the dark room, and Owen is assembling a library in my office. He has been appointed librarian. As we have about 3,000 volumes in the collection,[1] he has his hands full assorting them.

Both the Geological unit and the Trail Party report everything O. K.

Saturday
March 9th

A terrific blizzard has been raging all day, compelling us to shut down on all outside jobs. The wind at times reached a velocity of 60 miles per hour. A message from Gould says that everything is fine. There has been no word today from the Trail Party. No doubt Petersen has been unable to get up his radio pole in this strong wind.

[1] This library was named the David Lyman Library.

Sunday
March 10th

It was 19° below zero last night. The wind blew quite hard during the day, but it has fallen off, and we have dispatched four men and dog teams to the Barrier cache, under the leadership of McKinley. It is time we had all supplies in camp.

Both field units report all well.

The dogs here did not fare very well last night. They howled all night long. Possibly the sound of the wind awakened some strange emotion in them. Then, too, we found their crates packed full of snow.

Several of the dogs broke loose this morning, and engaged in a terrible brawl. They performed a great deal of extemporaneous surgery on one another, and two appear to be quite badly torn. Of course there was a lady at the bottom of the affair. There usually is. We all feel quite badly to have the dogs torn up in their own brawls, for they are great pets. Dr. Coman is busy taking stitches in the wounds.

Josephine I is having a hard time. Last night, when every one was asleep, save the watchman, she stole into the administration building and tried to make off with one of the rugs. The noise she made soon awakened every one, and there were loud protests. We were puzzled as to why she wanted the rug until we discovered that her crate was nearly full of snow, and her litter of puppies were shivering in the cold. I fancy she was doing her best to save them. As the snow accumulated, she and the puppies had retreated to the very end of the box, then, in desperation, the mother came out seeking help. She had to cut through six feet of tightly packed snow with her paws and teeth.

The puppies were in a bad way. This morning, we dug a hole in one side of the tunnel, and moved the crate there. It is much warmer in the tunnel, and perhaps we shall be able to save them.

Poor Josephine II was not as fortunate. Her six pups froze to death. She made a pathetic effort to carry them into the lee of the airplane machine shop, but they perished before she could move them.   We found her this morning trying to make the poor dead things suckle.   She was quite distraught.

We then moved her into the big box that Josephine I had occupied, and gave her two of the latter's puppies.   Josephine II growled horridly at them at first, but finally allowed them to suckle.   However, when we moved her and the puppies back to her own box, her attitude changed swiftly, and when our backs were turned she bit them, not severely, but just enough to show she was not taken in by this deception.

But after we had cleaned out her crate, freshened it and moved it to a new place, she appeared to be reconciled to the loss of her own puppies, and pleased with the new ones.

Owen finished the library this morning, and it is fine.

Monday
March 11th
Little America

The Trail Party has weathered the storm and cold, though with considerable discomfort.   Vaughan reports that he has run out of flags, and asks that the Fairchild be sent out to drop more, as well as candles and alpine rope.   If weather permits, we shall do it.   Haines, however, thinks it will be impossible.   The barometer is falling rapidly.

Vaughan asked for instructions.   I suggested that he use his own judgment.   I have great faith in the good sense and discretion of these fellows, and believe that if allowed to work out their own solutions to their particular problems, they will be much better off.

Gould radioed that he wanted to return today.   Conditions here were favorable, but changed suddenly in the mountains. Before they could start, a snow storm came up and they were forced to postpone the start.

The weather is up to all kinds of peculiar tricks.   Haines told me that he had never seen such rapid changes in the wind's direction as preceded the last storm.   The barometer during the storm had the worst drop I have ever seen; Haines, himself, confessed he had never seen it so low.   The graph of it looks like several steep hills.

I have had a conference with Rucker and Van der Veer

relative to the taking of motion pictures. They have again requested more freedom in the taking of pictures. They claimed that I kept them so busy with work about the camp that they have had little or no time for their photographic duties. God knows, we can ill spare extra hands now, but I assured them I would try to give them more freedom.

There is an old proverb to the effect that one picture is worth 10,000 words; I suppose that one good picture of the Antarctic is worth at least a dozen snow houses. Van der Veer and Rucker are craftsmen in their line, but unfortunately we have a greater need of snow houses than of pictures at this time.

We are having an interesting time with the two Josephines. Josephine I missed her two puppies today, and sallied forth to claim them. She retreated, however, when Josephine II showed fight, and fell back on strategy. She waited until her rival left the crate to get meat, then cautiously entered the box and tried to coax her puppies back. Josephine II happened to return in the midst of the affair, and at once drove off the distracted mother. I think we shall have peace now.

The recent storm created sastrugi all over the nearby Barrier, depriving us of every safe landing place within miles. At first we were greatly exercised by this, fearing that conditions would not improve and that the landing of the Fokker would therefore be attended by considerable risk. However, heavy snow fell last night and smoothed out the disturbances. Our landing fields are not at all permanent; they are good one day and bad the next. I have asked Gould not to attempt to return, however, until we notify him a safe landing area has been marked by flag.

Tuesday
March 12th
Little America

Another blizzard is on. I cannot understand why we should be having such a spell of bad weather. We have already had as many blizzards as Amundsen had during the whole year he was here.

All well with the field parties, but the good old *City* is

apparently taking punishment again. The following radio was received today from Captain Melville:

Comdr. Byrd:

Our dead reckoning Noon position was Lat. 49° 49′ S., Long. 168° 12′ E. Weather overcast, northwesterly gales, rough confused sea. Ship rolling and laboring under sail and steam. Bar. 30. Temperature of air, 47, water, 54. Distance from Tairoa Head, 263 miles. All well. Regards. 4 P.M.

Later:

Hove to in the throes of the heaviest gale of the passage. Wind 70 to 80 miles per hour with a terrific sea.

MELVILLE.

Vaughan reports that the Barrier continues smooth, and that a depot was laid 20 miles out. He believes he and the men can easily make 60 miles on this journey, but I told him that a depot at 40 miles would be quite enough. They are handicapped by a shortage of flags. I suggested that they build snow beacons, made of blocks of snow. It will be a bother cutting out the blocks, and setting them up every two or three miles, but the added safety makes the extra effort very worth while.

The storm that lashed the *City* very nearly ended her gallant career. From Berkner, on the 14th, there came the following message:

COMDR. BYRD:

We nearly didn't have any *City of New York* after yesterday. Wind blew continuously at 70 and 80 miles per hour for the 24 hours, and toward evening waves were running as high as the lower topsail. None of the men had ever seen anything like it. Ship rolled terribly and did two rolls of 60 degrees or more. As a result, all batteries were dumped bottom side up in battery room, and broke all big tubes but three. All floor plates in engine room shifted. One wave broke over boat and caused some damage. The starboard life boat tried to come through my port hole and smashed. Both rails were under water at the same time, and the wind was so strong you couldn't stand on deck. Wheelsman was lashed to the wheel after Percy Wallis was thrown clear over the spanker boom. He was slightly injured. The boiler was shifted a bit. Had bad time with salt water and battery acid in the battery room, but Shropshire and I went down promptly, rescued the batteries and lashed them to the floor. My lungs still sore. We had bad time and a lot of damage was caused to deck works. My shack shifted so had to take a quarter of an inch from door to get it cleared.

The *City* rode it out, however, in her indomitable and stubborn way, and reached port several days later.

Our concern now shifted to the Rockefellers, where Gould and his companions awaited favorable weather. As the days slipped by, without favoring them, our apprehensions mounted. When we had good weather at Little America, they had storm. And on the few occasions when it was clear at the mountains, we had blizzards. It began to appear that good conditions would never be had at both places at the same time; and with winter steadily approaching, this probability verged on being a certainty. The circumstances seemed to suggest a desperate action—a flight in the face of unfavorable conditions. We were not yet ready to attempt that. It would be a last resort.

The dog teams came in during the night of March 13. The men were tired and hungry, having made a day's run of 50 miles, but otherwise were in splendid condition. They had endured a week of constant storm and cold without a single case of frost bite. This augured well for the more prolonged journeys during the following spring.

Vaughan reported that the teams made their way across the crevasses south of the Bay of Whales with the men roped together. The first night they made camp a few miles to the south. The next day a 60-mile blizzard struck at them out of a dead calm, forcing them to remain in their tents all day. They waited a day and a half in the hope the plane would be able to bring them needed supplies, then pressed on, most of the time in blinding drift.

"It was very confusing," Vaughan said. "At times we could not see more than 20 yards in any direction. We had several days of low temperatures, 20° below in fact, but by moving fast we managed to keep quite warm. The dogs stood up very well, and gave no trouble. They were in such fine condition that, after laying the last base, we decided to make a go of the whole return journey, with only quick stops for meals."

The following depots were made and the following supplies cached:

20 mile depot, 180 pounds dog food, 50 pounds man food, 8 pounds clothing, and one lobster pot tent.

40 mile depot, 300 pounds dog food, 100 pounds man food, 8 pounds clothing, one lobster pot tent, and one primus stove.

44 mile depot, 300 pounds dog food, 371 pounds man food, 8 pounds clothing, two lobster pot tents, one primus stove, two pairs snowshoes, two ice hatchets, one hatchet and one sledge runner.

The greater part of these supplies were to be picked up and carried forward during the prolonged journeys planned for the following spring.

There was no word from Gould on the 15th. Nor the 16th. Nor the 17th. And on the 17th, which was a Saturday, I became genuinely alarmed. The absence of radio communication was peculiarly confusing. June had two complete radio sets—the standard set on the plane, and an emergency set. How both of them could be out of commission, unless the plane had crashed, was difficult to understand. But how they could have crashed was no less perplexing. It had been definitely agreed that the Fokker would not start until we radioed a favorable weather report, which we had not been able to do. It was impossible to believe, then, that a start had been made. But there, on the other hand, was the silence. How could it be explained?

We cudgeled heads over it night and day, and though our reasoning pointed directly to the cause of the silence, we never once suspected it. Only a crash could have disabled both sets beyond repair. We could safely suppose Gould had not started. We could assume he and his party were in distress. But not once did we have the wits to see what lay crystal clear in the logic. We beat around the Antarctic bush and stirred up nothing but reckless theories.

Thursday, I began to prepare for a flight of investigation.

The Fairchild was made ready for flight. The sun shone sullenly through thickish clouds, and there was a chance the weather would improve. But it became worse instead. Friday and Saturday were unfit for flying. There was still no word from Gould. Sunday I came to the conclusion every resource must be brought into action. The winter night was dangerously near. Every day was growing shorter and colder. I called the dog drivers into conference, and ordered them to make ready at once for a trip to the mountains. Thus, if conditions failed to improve for flying (and there was every reason to believe they would grow steadily worse) the responsibility of finding the Mountain Party must rest with the dog teams. Rather than defer their start in the hope of getting better weather, I decided to send them off as soon as the teams could be made ready. It would be well, too, I thought, to have them in the field in case anything happened to the relief plane.

Walden was put in charge of this party. De Ganahl, navigator, Vaughan, Crockett, Bursey and Siple volunteered to go with him. They were to carry enough rations for three months.

The mystery that held Gould's party was further confused by lack of information bearing upon its position. In his first message, Gould said they had landed at the base of Chips Gould Mountain, which would place them at the northernmost peak. But a subsequent position indicated very definitely that they were at the foot of one of the southernmost peaks. As the latter position was most likely the true one, I decided to set our course for it, when and if we started.

Meanwhile, the radio men continued to keep an emergency schedule with the party, sending frequent weather reports. Every hour we repeated a message that the Fairchild would fly at the first break in the weather, on the theory that June's equipment might be able to pick up messages even if it could not send. This vigil in the radio shack was unbroken. But the ether yielded not a trace of the beleaguered party.

Late Monday the weather appeared to grow better, and I gave orders to have the engine started. For the first time, it failed to turn over. The fault lay, we learned, in the primer. We hastened to remedy it. Just as the mechanics finished, the sky clouded over, the wind rose and the horizon filled with dense clouds. This was a bitter disappointment. One was helpless in the face of such misfortune.

The long-awaited "break" came in the afternoon of Monday, March 19. A small hole opened up in the cloud banks to the east, and widened gradually. A patch of blue sky showed through. A 22 mile wind stirred up some drift, but we could not expect everything. I conferred with Haines in the library. He was not very encouraging. He said: "Frankly, I consider a take-off dangerous. But it may be the best chance you will have this season. About one chance in three, I should say, that you will find good weather all the way. Damn it, you can't tell what this weather will do, anyway."

As long as the chance was there, we took it.

The Fairchild was on the line, and the mechanics were heating the engine with a torch when I came out to the field. Flame hissed and roared up the throat of the canvas funnel. which carried the blast of hot air into the hood which covered the entire block. Then hot oil was poured into the engine, the mechanics stepped outside, the inertia starter began its mounting, high-pitched whine, and in a moment the engine turned over musically.

The plane was moved into position with some difficulty, having become frozen to the snow in which it laid so long. The Barrier was far from smooth when we faced the plane's nose into the wind. Smith studied it with a practiced eye. "We ought to be able to get off," he said. "It all depends upon the strength of the skis." He smiled slowly. "Let's try it, anyway."

We took Hanson along as radio engineer.

Just about five o'clock, we started down the snow runway. The bumping was wicked, and the shock of the skis striking the sastrugi caused the whole plane to shiver. But we rose finally in a flurry of snow and headed straight for the mountains.

The hour was later than I had wanted: It was quite dark at night from 10 o'clock on. But beggars can't be choosers: we took what Providence offered, and were thankful.

It was a bit chilly in the plane, 10° below zero, and we were bundled up in heavy clothing.

The sun was behind us, and I could see it occasionally, a

THE FOKKER ON A FROZEN LAKE AT ITS BASE IN THE ROCKEFELLER MOUNTAINS.

VICTIM OF THE WIND'S FURY.

The Wreck of the Fokker.

LITTLE AMERICA.

The camp is entirely snowed under and only the radio towers, dog and sentinels show above the snow.

dull red disc surrounded by orange streaks. I laid a straight compass course for the southern end of the Rockefellers, to the position which Gould had radioed. The horizon was a blurred grayness, which presently gave way to masses of low clouds. It was one of the worst "flying" skies I had ever seen. The clouds were miles away, but seemed very near, and merged without a shadow to show where the horizon met the snow. The instinctive response of a pilot would be to fly lower and lower, trying to get underneath these clouds. Smith, however, kept his head and flew a straight, steady compass course. There was not enough sun to use the more dependable sun compass, and we had to place our reliance on the magnetic compass which was not particularly reliable.

The clouds soon closed in behind us, and we lost sight of the sun. Things became quite dim, a confused, dirty gray nothingness, through which we raced at a speed of 100 miles per hour.

We studied the surface constantly searching for the plane, in the belief that it might have actually started from the Rockefellers and been forced down. Once Smith pointed out a dark spot on the snow which, at a distance, bore some resemblance to a plane, but we saw presently that it was a yawning crevasse.

Shortly after 6 o'clock, we sighted, dead ahead, a mountain. Was it the one near which Gould was camped? The other peaks slowly lifted their heads, and in the murk they were no more than vague, pale gray mounds. We approached the first peak at an altitude of 2,000 feet.

It was now dim, but we could see sheets of drift weaving across the snow, which indicated a stiff wind. Smith stared down, and moved his hand around, to show the whirling character of the drift. "Pretty tough to land in that," he shouted. I thought so, too, but said nothing.

There was the more dreadful possibility we should not be able to see anything. A shattered plane and three men would not offer a very conspicuous landmark in a mass of dark ridges.

We flew over the mountain, circled it and then approached it again. We searched out the slopes, the valleys and the peak, but saw nothing. Could it be that Gould's position was inaccurate? If we failed to find them here, then we faced the heart-breaking task of combing 70 miles of mountain peaks. A more hopeless task I could not imagine.

A second survey gave up no traces of the party. I was about to order Smith to turn north to search the other peaks when suddenly he touched my arm, and pointed to the south. I saw a column of smoke bending indistinctly on the wind, then the flashing of a light. The first thought that came into my head was: Thank God, at least one of them is alive.

We swung over the light, and started to spiral down. Soon we could make out a landing "T" marked out with flags. We were apparently descending into a large basin at the foot of the mountain. In the dimness one had the sensation of dropping powerlessly into a porcelain bowl. The field, even from our altitude, appeared to be excessively rough. What seemed to be large lumps, two to four feet in diameter, spotted it. The pedestal of the landing "T" ran straight through them. But it looked bad, very bad.

"Shall I land?" asked Smith. One thing was certain, we could not fly another minute around that bowl. Visibility was much too bad. Another thing: Balchen and June would not have placed that landing "T" on dangerous ice.

I nodded my head.

He glanced again at the ugly surface, made a wry face and then throttled down cautiously for a landing.

I now caught sight of a small tent, and about three quarters of a mile away the outline of the plane. Its grotesque attitude showed quite plainly that it had crashed.

We came in with a thud, bouncing on a wretched surface, with Smith nursing his engine and solicitous for the limitations of his skis—an excellent and daring landing.

As the plane came to a halt in a smother of snow, I jumped out, with Hanson just behind. At first I saw no one, and my heart sank. Then a figure came racing toward the plane—that gait could belong only to a Navy man, June: then I saw a man of bristling red whiskers advancing in our direction. No other face on the planet supported such a growth. Balchen's, of course. But where was Larry? In a moment I saw him as well. He, too, was on his way to the place, but his progress was casual, and he was the academician to the very end—making the dignified entrance of a professor who happened, let us say, to breakfast late and found his class already in noisy session. It was so very much in character that I had to smile.

Even if I was capable of doing it adequately, which I am not, I would hesitate to describe my emotions at finding them safe and sound. However, the reunion appeared to bring joy to every one.

I asked Smith to keep the engine idling. With less than an hour and one-half before darkness, we could not afford to waste much time in conversation on the ice. Balchen and June were ordered to take Hanson's place and mine in the Fairchild, and return with Smith to the base. There was the inevitable dispute over who would stay behind, a gratifying demonstration of generosity on the part of every man, but I was fortunately able to enforce my decision.

We removed from the plane some food and a small sledge. Then Smith gave the Fairchild the gun, and it whirled off. Soon we lost sight of it in the gathering twilight.

March 19
Tuesday
Rockefeller Mountains

We have just finished an excellent supper which Larry cooked, and in a very few minutes I shall make use of June's sleeping bag. It is snug here in the tent, and I am peaceful in mind for the first time in many days. A few minutes ago we received word by radio of the safe arrival of the Fairchild at Little America. If weather permits, they will come out for us tomorrow.

We're none too optimistic about that. Tomorrow I shall discuss with Larry the idea of walking home. It will be a long and wretched walk, and I cannot say that I look forward to it.

The first thing I did after the plane took off was to find the reason for the rough appearance of the landing place. The spots turned out to be patches of solid green ice showing through the snow. The basin in which we lie is, in fact, a frozen lake—very different from anything we have seen around Little America.

I now have the story of this episode—part of it from Larry, part of it from June and Balchen, in the hurried talk before they left.

They reached here after two hours and ten minutes of flying. Like us, they were confused on landing by poor visibility. In their case, they tried to land downward on a steep slope, and when Balchen levelled off the plane was still in the air. Actually, he had to land at a gliding angle, and it was not a gentle one. I realize now what a perfectly fine job Dean Smith did.

They taxied up the slope, which leads up to a kind of terrace at the foot of the mountain, secured the plane with ice anchors, and made their camp. Gould dug a ski into the snow, and June used it as a radio pole.

March 8th, the next day, a stiff wind blew, and that, combined with the cold, prevented much work out of doors. On the following day, they laid a base line about a mile from the tent, and by triangulation Gould fixed the positions of the various peaks in the neighborhood. That done, they made a reconnaissance part way up the face of the nearest mountain, and gathered several fragments of rock for geological examination.

This, I judge, was about the end of good weather during their stay.

The wind thereafter blew constantly.

In a severe wind, the propeller revolved steadily, despite natural compression and the stiffness of frozen oil in the parts. As the wind strengthened, the wing lifted with it, and the lift was sufficient to raise the skis four or five inches from the snow.

Saturday, the 10th, brought snow and a stiff wind. Too bad to do any work, so they stayed in their sleeping bags until 11 o'clock. The wind rose steadily, and the breaking of the tent guys that had been secured to the airplane skis brought them tumbling out of the tent.

They found the ship banging up and down on the ski pedestals. Frantically, they began to pile snow blocks, which they cut out with knives from a nearby drift, on the skis, to keep them down.

The wind died down, and they were able to finish the

anchorage with some comfort. Then, without warning, the wind rose again, more fiercely than ever. The plane began to move once more, and they were hard put to it to keep it from carrying them away. The difficulty lay in the fact that the plane rested on firm ice, and it was hard to get a firm hold on it.

When they tried to anchor the left wing, the force of the wind fairly battered down their combined efforts. Several times, according to Gould, strong gusts lifted all three of them clear of the ground, while they held on to the wing, and swept their bodies almost parallel to the ground. It was numbing cold, and Gould said the driving snow hit the face with the bite of red-hot needles. Snow caught on their eyelids and froze.

"We could lean on the wind when we shovelled," June told me, "and if we didn't hurry, it whipped the blocks of snow from the shovel. We were constantly bombarded with lumps of snow carried down from the mountains, and believe me, they hurt."

How long did this keep up? "Hours and hours," Larry says, "we lost track of time."

The wind brought a rising temperature, the snow softened and to add to their misery, their clothing, their tent and their sleeping bags became soaking wet.

The barometer, Larry said, dropped more than an inch within four or five hours—incredible!

Toward midnight there was a lull, and they crept into their sleeping bags, to gain what little comfort and warmth there was in them. The wind rose again, and they returned to the battle, painfully cutting out lumps of snow and dumping them on the skis. They would creep out on their bellies, cut out a block, and then, when they stood up, the wind would hurl them back to the plane. Balchen worked like a madman, and his strength helped to stave off the final blow for hours.

Although the plane banged about, the guy wires held. Toward morning, Gould, Balchen and June crept back to the tent. They could do no more. The issue was in the laps of the gods. When they turned in, the wind was still on the make, and the din, Larry said, was awful.

Sunday morning the wind slackened, then freshened in

the afternoon, only to subside in the evening. They decided
to return to Little America as soon as the weather improved.

Monday, the 12th, more wind, and the situation was so
ominous Gould ordered them to remove the foodstuffs from
the plane. It snowed a bit, and the barometer registered
28.6. Tuesday was calm, but with an overcast sky. They
climbed the mountain, located all the peaks in the range by
triangulation, and from the summit glimpsed the new mountains we had discovered in the distance.

Wednesday, the 14th, wind averaged 35 miles per hour,
with gusts up to 60. Incidentally, these blows came mostly
from the north, and slightly west of north.

The next day was the worst of all. "Never saw anything
like it," June said. "When I got in the plane to keep the
radio schedule, the needle on the air speed indicator touched
88 m.p.h., and though she only banged up and down on the
snow, the ship was certainly going through all the motions
of flying. I looked out and saw Larry hanging on to a rope
attached to one of the wing tips. He was blown straight out,
like a flag. The prop was turning over very fast, and the
lines on the 'dead men' were so taut you could play a tune
on them. Mind you, the wind then was only working up to
bigger and better things. It blew so hard afterwards that
Larry refused to let me enter the plane, to keep the regular
10:30 o'clock schedule. We could hardly breathe."

The end came suddenly, while they were in the tent. A
gust, in contrast with which the others were breezes, carried
away all the lines. The plane burst clear, rose into flight and
flew backwards for half a mile, then crashed upon the ice, a
complete wreck. Balchen, a man who never gives up, battled
against the wind to reach it, and came back with the news they
had verified with their own eyes—the Fokker would never fly
again.

Gould believes the wind reached a velocity of 150 m.p.h.
(in gusts) and June said; "when it stopped it was so quiet that
it hurt."

The wind dropped off the following day, and they went
out to the Fokker. June reassembled the emergency radio
set, which was rather badly battered, and tried to raise the

base. He could hear the base operators sending, but apparently could not reach them.

The worst blow of all fell when the crankshaft on the generator broke. They could still hear with the set, but all hope of getting word of their predicament to the base was ended. It was the most depressing thing in the world, according to Larry, to sit in the shattered fuselage, and hear Little America discussing our absence with operators in New York, and not be able to send the explanation a mere 125 miles.

They were considering trying to walk back when June received the message saying that the Fairchild would be flown out with the first good weather. So they waited out the lonely days in their tent, never too confident that the weather could allow us to come.

Well, for all but Gould, the vigil is over. We shall now take up our own.

The next day, Wednesday, March 20th, I walked out to the plane, and saw how badly smashed it was. I was surprised to see that, save for the tips, the wing was undamaged. The plane had apparently landed on the skis. The ski pedestals, however, were split open, one ski lay clear of the plane, and the struts were bent and torn. The tail section was broken, the fuselage was ripped open and the cabin exposed. It seemed as if a great bird had come to grief, and this was its pathetic and broken carcass.

What interested me most was the propeller. All three blades were curled—unfailing evidence of a power crash. Beyond a doubt, the propeller was whirling when the Fokker made her uncanny flight. What a weird sight that must have been!

Little America reported bad weather, and when it showed no signs of improving I instructed McKinley, who was then in charge of operations there, to send out the dog teams. Gould and I decided to start walking until we met the dog teams. We piled a month's supply of food on the hand sledge, made a sledge sail out of canvas, which would help us along when the wind was right, and prepared to start within two days, if the plane was not already on its way.

Thursday
March 21

Weather continues bad at Little America, but it is fine here. The dog teams started yesterday, and are making excellent time. If the Fairchild is not able to start, they ought to reach here within ten days or so.

The teams are divided into two groups—a supporting party consisting of teams driven by Walden, Braathen and Siple, which is carrying supplies to 40-Mile Depot, and the regular relief group, consisting of four teams driven by Vaughan, Bursey, Goodale and Thorne, with Petersen as radioman and de Ganahl as navigator.

At 40-Mile Depot the supporting party will drop their loads and return to the base, but the relief group will strike due east for the mountains.

There is a great deal of melting in the immediate vicinity of these mountains during the summer months, and the basin in which we are camped consists of several hundred feet of solid ice. The terrific winds have blown some of the surface clear, and these patches are as smooth as glass. When the sun strikes this at a certain angle, the ice assumes a pale green color.

Larry is an excellent cook. His "hoosh" is fit for the gods. It is a mixture of pemmican, bacon and pea soup. As a steady diet, though, I imagine it would soon begin to pall.

This is a cold place. The temperature gets down to nearly 30° below at night, and about three o'clock in the morning the sleeping bags become chilly.

Later

Weather continues bad at the base.

We seem to be camped in an area of solid ice. Last night, when the temperature dropped, the air resounded with the sound of sharp reports, caused by the abrupt cracking of ice. Two bursts sounded loudly under the tent—under our sleeping bags, it seemed—and we all awakened with a start, wondering what new misfortune was in store for us. We shivered awhile in the cold, but the disturbances, which sounded like a sustained burst of rifle fire, moved farther away. We fell into fitful sleep.

Larry has done a very fine job here, and his report ought to bring out some important findings. He is convinced that Amundsen's "Carmen Land" does not extend this far north. If the snow were to disappear, he believes a shallow sea or basin would enfold the southern bases of the Rockefellers,[1] perhaps isolating several of the peaks.

I was astonished to learn he had been able to sight from the range the mountain peak we sighted to the eastward on our last flight. According to his rough measurements, the nearest peaks are over 50 miles away. The taller peaks, he believes, are about 5,000 feet high. He could make out the peak very distinctly. It was his first thought that these peaks are landmarks of a far more extensive glaciation than now prevails, which would forge another link in the chain of evidence proving the waning character of the ice age. If Carmen Land does exist, and if it does have a counterpart, then it is very possible that these mountains to the East are its limits.

However, we shall be able to determine these things with some preciseness next summer.

Today we went out to the small crevasses which surround this basin to the west and marked a trail through them with flags for the dog teams if they ever arrive. We also found a much better flying field to the west, and marked it with a landing "T."

I find myself in a most extraordinary position. Although beyond the reach of immediate assistance, I am able to direct my affairs with some flexibility, thanks to the radio. Since stuck on this lake, I have been in touch with the ships in Dunedin, my office in New York, the base and the dog teams on the trail. Matters are progressing smoothly.

Haines reported tonight the weather is clearing, and the plane may be able to start tomorrow. It cannot come too quickly to please us. I have asked Smith to bring June with him. It would be murderous to ask a pilot to fly a single-engined plane alone over this wilderness. A speck of dirt in the carburetor would mean his death. He could not

[1]McKinley's photographs using Gould's fixes of position definitely located the Rockefeller Mts. as a group of more or less isolated peaks and ridges beginning roughly in Lat. 78° 14' S., Long. 155° 15' W. and extending in crescentic shape to Lat. 77° 35' S., and Long. 153° 5' W., with the crescent opening to the west. There are at least 40 peaks in the group.

possibly make his way home alone after a forced landing. Now the question arises: Can the Fairchild hold five men? Even with three it is crowded. This problem we can meet when it arises.

About 5 o'clock in the morning of the 22nd, Hanson was informed by Little America that the Fairchild was on its way and an hour and a half later we sighted it. Smith landed it neatly. But joy over its arrival was soon forgotten in the larger question: How many could return? Who would remain behind until yet another flight could be made?

"Hop in," Smith shouted, "Room for every one. Next train leaves in six months."

The door slammed open, but neither Hanson or Gould moved. The same doubt was in the mind of both of them, and each was unwilling that he should not be the last to enter.

But as we had to learn, first of all, whether it would be necessary for any one to be left behind, I prevailed upon them to enter. The cabin, already crowded with equipment, appeared to be jammed. But at last I squeezed in, burrowing over furs and food, June slammed tight the door, Smith taxied into the wind, and lifted the ship in a climbing turn.

It was truly good to see the Barrier moving under us.

We sighted the dog teams 55 miles east of Little America, travelling fast. About 5 miles astern we could see the depot, marked by flags, which they had laid in accordance with instructions. Smith brought the plane down over the drivers, porpoised to show that he had the mountain party in the plane and that the teams were to return, a signal previously agreed upon, and then we raced for home.

Even from an altitude of 2,000 feet, the trail stood out clear and distinct on the Barrier, and we could follow it with ease.

We reached Little America at about an hour and 15 minutes later, and so far as we were concerned, the incident of the Rockefeller Mountains was over. Sunday morning, the dog teams came in, having marched all night and made a record march in the Antarctic of 63 miles [1] in temperature

[1] The longest previous march in the Antarctic was made by Amundsen when they covered 62 miles. "The South Pole," i, 222.

which dropped as low as 40° below zero. Balchen made a flight to the Ross Sea and reported it frozen over as far as the eye could see. The aviation season was over.

We were truly fortunate to escape the Ides of March as easily as we did. March was the worst month on Haines' calendar. Eight severe blizzards [1] marked it, more than occurred in any other month during our stay, and the snowfall was almost twice as heavy as in the nearest period, June, which was the middle of the Antarctic winter. Nor is that all. March was the cloudiest of all months. Haines' charts show that during its 31 days, there was only one clear day. Eight were partly cloudy and twenty-two very cloudy, which, in view of the awful conditions of visibility the slightest cloudiness brings, may indicate how very closely we pressed our good luck in bringing the incident to its end.

[1] The meteorological staff identified a storm as a blizzard only when severe enough to reduce visibility to a few yards.

CHAPTER IX

WINTER—BIRTH OF A CITY

WITH the units of the expedition together once more, we were willing to relinquish the entire Antarctic Continent to winter, save for the few yards that we had laboriously converted to our devices. Even the surface above these we were willing to give up, in favor of the more protected, warmer catacombs we had hewn underneath. We burrowed deeper. Everything that was movable was sunk into deep holes, and blizzards swiftly covered these. A hangar made of snow blocks was built about the Fairchild, and it disappeared with its wings folded back as if in resignation and its engine shrouded in a bulky canvas jacket. It would lie there, with a tarpaulin for its roof, until spring.

We then set about making a home for the Ford. An immense hole was dug, with a steep decline approaching it. With sixty dogs pulling at once, we dragged the fuselage into the center of the colony. The mechanics, Bubier, Roth and Demas, worked like fiends to finish the job.

Now all that remained was to get this huge bird into its nest.

First, we hitched a line to the snowmobile, which had shown a remarkable aptitude for hauling. Then half the camp was mustered into service and distributed at the ends of other lines. We heaved, we pulled, we dug in until the pressure of the lines cut in through heavy jackets. The monster followed grudgingly, then at last it plunged head foremost into its hangar—the coldest hangar[1] in the world. The tail was packed in snow, but about the nose we built a capacious chamber out

[1] Those two hangars were named the Guggenheim Hangars, after my friend, Mr. Harry Guggenheim.

of snow blocks so that the mechanics might continue to work on the engines.

Only two major tasks remained undone out of doors.

Part of the supplies were still in the Barrier cache. But these were soon brought in by men working under the direction of Captain McKinley. March blizzards made a hard task harder. Dense drift and snow repeatedly covered the cache, so that it was necessary for the men to spend half the day shovelling before they could even begin to move the stuff. After one heavy storm, I became worried that part of the buried supplies might never be found, and insisted that the entire area be carefully excavated. Here was carrying coals to Newcastle with a vengeance. There was much good-natured grousing over the order, enlivened by a steady stream of raillery from Taffy Davies and Cyclone Haines. Taffy had been digging for some time, without once uncovering anything, which Haines intimated was due largely to the fact he was simply letting the wind blow the snow off his shovel; so he regarded it as a vindication when his shovel struck something hard. Taffy whooped, and yelled for assistance. Snow flew merrily for a few minutes. Then Taffy dragged out the prize. The most unpopular device this side of the equator lay exposed.

"And I had to do it—snow shovels," he groaned. He let the bundle drop into the pit and covered his eyes.

The second task involved the acquisition of a last 50 tons of seal meat. Strom and Braathen were sent down to the Bay, and finally secured 32 seals. These were discovered far out on the edge of the newly-formed bay ice. All the other seal holes were empty, their inhabitants having retreated before winter. In fact, nearly all wild life had departed. Only a lone Emperor penguin and two skua gulls on the quest for garbage were seen. We should therefore have to get along with the meat we had.

We could then begin to see the end of work about the camp. All the huts were up, and the men were excavating a series of tunnels for the dogs. Our own tunnel system promised to be so effective that we decided to give the same protection to the dogs. The main tunnels ran west of the mess hall, and consisted of three long corridors in the snow radiating from the main chamber called the chopping house. The chopping house had an entrance to the seal pile, which was then covered with snow. Fortunately, refrigeration is not a problem in the Antarctic. The carcasses became as stiff as steel plate as soon as they were hauled there. One of the tunnels opened into a small chamber which was called the maternity ward. With six females in camp, a number of blessed events were a reasonable certainty. Siple also made use of another tunnel as an approach to his taxidermy station. He dug a deep hole nearby, roofed it with an over-turned life boat and connected it to the tunnel with a narrow corridor. This area was given the name of Dog Town, and it was the noisiest township on the whole southern hemi-sphere.

A second set of tunnels extended prong-like from Braathen's and Walden's house, which was fast becoming a celebrated residential quarter. They made their own chopping house, which they merged with a repair shop for skis and sledges, and presently had several leading industries housed under one roof. These tunnels were eight feet deep, and about six feet wide, and at intervals of six feet or more little alcoves were let into the sides to receive the crates. Digging these tunnels was a back-breaking order. For the housing of 80 primitive dogs involves its own problems. Unlike brow-beaten humans, who can be herded into groups without grievous friction, Eskimo dogs remain individualists to the last. They may dwell in the peaceful affinity of brothers for days on end; but for the favor of a lady or a hunk of frozen seal meat they will enthusiastically rend one another limb from limb. We had had half a dozen bloody brawls, due to the fact that some dogs were allowed to roam loose, partly because of carelessness or inexperience on the part of the drivers; and during this period two splendid dogs, Shackleton and Muskeg, were killed in a pitched battle over a female.

The crates, then, had to be sufficiently spaced apart to allow the dogs to move freely on a chain, and not near enough to permit them to come within fighting distance. We there-fore staggered them on opposite sides of the tunnels.

It would be well to tell here the story of Spy. Spy was one of Vaughan's dogs. Toward the end of March I found him in his crate, in a pitiful condition. He had pulled his heart out during the unloading, and now was so lame he could hardly walk. For some strange reason his coat failed to grow in thick, as with the other dogs, so his resistance to cold was low. Vaughan, who loved him as a brother, was of the opinion he should be shot: it would put him out of his misery. But it was decided to bring him into the house, where it was warm, and put him on a special diet.

We gave him canvas to sleep on. The only available space in the camp at the time was in my room, and old Spy lay there for two days, very much to the disgust of Igloo who attacked him whenever my back was turned. His joints were so crippled by cold that he could not stir, but he was on the mend. Saturday, March 30th, we took him out for a bit of exercise. It happened that his old team went by, with black Dinty in the lead, and his boon companions, Watch and Moody, in the traces. Spy watched them go rollicking past, and a spirit like that of the Old Guard must have taken possession of his pain-stiffened limbs, for he went out in a gallant spurt, overtook the team and with a final summoning up of strength forced his way to his place in the team.

It was one of the most beautiful things I have ever seen: and for a penny I would pluck a moral from it. The whole camp stopped working at the sight, and watched with wonder how Moody and Watch muzzled the veteran, and laid their paws on him in a most extraordinary gesture. That these wild and untrammeled animals should be capable of harboring so deep and lasting a sentiment was beyond understanding.

Spy gradually grew better and soon was sufficiently recovered to return to his crate. This splendid old veteran lived long enough to do fine work in the spring.

Tuesday
April 1st

We are getting a taste of Antarctic weather. Last night the temperature dipped to 47° below zero and today it is not much higher. Still digging tunnels. It is chilling work. There have been a number of cases of frost-bite, and we have been compelled to warn several of the men to be careful. The distressing thing about this painful affliction is that it generally finds its victims in an innocent frame of mind, blissfully unconscious of the harm done. We watch one another for the tell-tale patch of yellow-white on the cheeks and nose, and detecting them has become as insidious a game as beaver. "Beg your pardon, Mr. Haines, but I observe you have a frost-bite on your cheek." "Thanks very much, Mr. Harrison," with a tender rubbing on the spot, "but you might look to your own with advantage."

There's an art in defeating frost-bite. If rubbed too vigorously, the tissue is injured. A gentle, delicate pressure —or rather working of the flesh that is attacked—is quite efficacious. This must be done with the bare hand, which adds a zestful element of hazard to the operation. Some of the boys consoled their faces so long that they soon nipped their fingers, and were jumping up and down like lunatics.

The sun is still above the horizon, but sinking perceptibly every day. Its shadow effects are really marvellous. The slightest outcropping in the Barrier has a lengthening cone of violet and purple silhouette, and a man moving about is pursued by a shadow so immense and grotesque as to be positively embarrassing.

The sunsets are beautiful. They bedevil my mind struggling for adequate expression with so overpowering a sense of helplessness as to cause the best words to end in muddled indecision.

I must bring up a subject that has been troubling me. Some time ago I decided to withhold Owen's dispatches from the men. I had a definite reason for this. Publicity is the worst disease that a weak man can get. It nourishes dissatisfaction, even jealousy. It can rend the most compactly organized group of men. Down here I had hoped to get away from that evil. If it were possible, I wanted to create a single attitude—a single state of mind—unfettered by the trivial considerations of civilization. That is, I wanted—and, in fact, shall persist in wanting—the task to be more important than the personal contribution to it.

If I could have had my way, few names or all names would be mentioned in Owen's stories. Every effort would be a collective undertaking. But of course such a thing cannot

COMMANDER BYRD AT THE ENTRANCE OF THE HOLE LEADING TO THE
ADMINISTRATION BUILDING.

And Igloo, of course.

A FROZEN INFERNO.

Masses of ice thrown into a jumble of the pressure ridges in the vicinity of Little America.

be. Owen's job is difficult enough as it is, without encumbering him with limitations. No reporter who takes his art seriously, and Owen does, should be hampered in any way whatsoever, if it can possibly be avoided. News should be held inviolate.

Then, too, the men must be considered. I suppose that of all the men here I have the least right to talk depreciatively of the value of getting one's name in the newspapers; but I am certainly in a position to tell them that the privilege soon responds to the law of diminishing returns. With these men, however, the usual conditions are altered. Owen's stories are an indirect connection with their families and friends. Naturally, this is an important consideration.

What I do fear is the fact that the nature of the work the men must do, and are fitted to do, must of necessity give greater prominence to some than to others. There will be some who will receive scant mention, if any at all, in spite of the fact their work may be just as important to the expedition as that of the others. It is no fault of Owen's, but it is a pity it has to be. For I have striven to reduce all values to a common level, in which no job is meaner or more meritorious than the rest. If distinctions are drawn in the record, the whole plan must collapse.

In a word, we are trying to get away from the false standards by which men live under more civilized conditions. The Antarctic is a new world for all of us which requires its own standards, and these are materially different from those set up in civilization, whereby we venerate prestige, influence and associated characteristics and ignore the inconspicuous, but equally valid properties. Now that vital operations have ceased for the winter, the hand is quite as important as the brain, and the digging out of house entrances and windows after a storm, the care of fires, etc., are prime factors in keeping alive. *They* are the essential things. This fact I have tried to drive home, not always with success.

The men are, for the most part, of the volunteer type, proud, independent and ambitious. Every one of them is eager to participate in the scientific labors of the expedition, no matter how arduous they may be. Such work is obviously important; it provides its own incentive and fits into the standards that are venerated. The less conspicuous tasks they are inclined to swallow hard, and regard them as chores, I think, which might well be performed by professionals. But alas! if there was such a thing as a professional snow shoveller, fire tender, etc., they would have no place on an expedition. Moreover, the crux of the matter is that these presumably onerous tasks have become the vital things. I know, too, from experience that the volunteer type (I do not mean that all the men are volunteers, but with most of them the pay certainly must be one of the last considerations) does not always bear up well when praise, prestige and rank are rammed down their throats. Their spirit is bound to be affected. Gould, McKinley, Balchen and Haines stand squarely with me on this point.

However, now that there is more time for leisure it would be contrary to the principles of the expedition and high-handed of me to oppose the posting of the stories on the bulletin board. I am not at all sure that it will satisfy every one, but at any rate I shall do it. Merely seeing in black and white an account of what they have accomplished that day with their own hands and brains may convince them that it is not lost labor after all.

But I shall quietly try to spread the word, as I have done before, that the Antarctic is no place for the spotlight. It casts only a faint glow 10,000 miles away.

From time to time we had attempted to locate Amundsen's old camp, but without success. We decided to try it again, and on March 11th, I went out with Davies, Strom, Balchen, Thorne, Van der Veer, Goodale, and Crockett to make a last search while the weather remained favorable. It was a cold day, 38° below zero and we were bundled up to twice natural size in furs, parkas and mittens. Only the nose and eyes were visible, and from the narrow opening in the hood one's breath came out in clouds of vapor. We puffed like steam engines.

To the best of our knowledge, Framheim was about three miles to the south of Little America. True, we should have great difficulty in trying to recognize anything, for the Antarctic is an area of eternal change; and in the 17 years that had intervened, Framheim must long since have disappeared under the snow. But we still had the idea that we might stumble on it, and I refreshed my mind with Amundsen's description of the place, and, in fact, carried with me maps and the chapter in his book describing its location.

There were two ways to reach the basin he described. It was possible to go down over the bay ice, then up a long slope to the Barrier. But the ice was so broken up with pressure to the west of Framheim that the trip was almost a hardship. The second lay over the Barrier. We chose the second. Walking briskly, we pursued a course that brought us up a rolling rise in the Barrier, whence we descended into the valley of haycocks, from which tiny threads of vapor arose. We threaded these, ascended to the high rolling Barrier and then through a pass which brought us at last to the basin. As we stood on the rim of the basin, we had a perfect view of the Barrier, which was like a burnished shield, with glints hidden in its depths. We could trace the serrated edges of the Barrier, enfolding the Bay of Whales in a series of capes, and what we took to be Amundsen's Cape Man's Head was the southernmost of these. Even it had changed, and there was nothing in its profile to indicate the resemblance for which Amundsen had named it. Storms had worn it into a shapeless cliff. The bay ice stretched north in a plain of mottled gray, and beyond lay the Ross Sea, dark and immense under a brooding sky.

We trudged again up and down the basin, studying it from all angles, poring over maps, but with no more success than we had had before. A modest lump in the snow we tried to expand in our imaginations as the snow-banked remnant of Mt. Nilsen, but of Mt. Ronniken not a trace remained, unless the tiny haycock we saw was all that had survived its former eminence. Poor old Ronne, we thought, this will be a dreadful blow. Imagine having the mountain that is named after you reverse the order and become a mole hill! Even the flag pole on Amundsen's hut had disappeared beneath the snow, and a sensitive magnetic instrument which Davies had brought along failed to show any metal underneath the crust, although we tried it out in many places.

We had already tarried there much too long, and with

twilight approaching hastened home. It became quite dark at an early hour, and we had no desire to stay out-of-doors any longer than was necessary. As it was, it was nip-and-tuck with frost-bite all the way back. The wind was blowing which made a tremendous difference. The deadly little yellow patches blossomed on noses and cheeks with the spontaneity of flowers in the spring. In the space of a few minutes, I warned Balchen, he warned Strom, Strom warned Davies, and Davies warned Crockett of danger. We came into the administration building on the run, and as we opened the door a torrent of fog, caused by the cold air striking the heated atmosphere of the room like steam. One could have had a Turkish bath as he stood. It was good to be back to the stove, and the tea that Tennant provided was like nectar.

Because the sun would disappear in eight days, we decided to conserve daylight as much as possible. So at taps that night we ordered the clocks set ahead one hour. We had been operating on 180th Meridian Time, and by this device gained another hour of daylight. It was no doubt the first experiment with daylight saving time in the Antarctic.

The days shortened perceptibly, in spite of artificial opposition, and the twilights lengthened. There followed perhaps the most beautiful days of our visit. For as the sun rolled lower and lower about the horizon, becoming a dull, red orb that gave off little heat, the hues in the sky deepened and became intensified, and a rain of radiant iridescence seemed to drop softly upon the chill gray of the Barrier, warming and nourishing it into flame. It was a frigid world aflame with frigid colors. The cliffs surrendered none of their color as twilight approached, the somber sweep of Ross Sea none of its darkness: and the effect of night marching over the scene was inexpressibly strange.

We last saw the sun on April 17th, but its beauty remained behind. Its official departure was not set until the 19th, but the following days were cloudy and we saw no more of it. This last time it rolled like a burning disc around the northern horizon, touching off in a final burst of radiance the scene it would quit for four months. It poised for a while on the western horizon, and a long, tantalizing twilight began to spread gray tendrils over the Barrier. Then it dipped suddenly below the horizon. An eruption of green, blue, red and yellow diffused the entire southern horizon, and stayed for a time the descent of night. But night advanced with deepening power, and soon was in full sway of his empire.

That night the zenith was aflame with the aurora australis, the temperature dropped to 40° below, and from the bay came muffled explosions as from pistol shots, the sound of ice contracting in the intense cold. We began a new and mysterious life. Until August 22nd, a pale moon would be our intermittent companion.

We fell into our new existence with little change and with little sense of change. We attained it imperceptibly. For many the gradually deepening cold and twilight slowly cut off all outside venture. Lights burned all day. The windows, indeed the roofs, were covered with snow and the twilight that persisted for some days after the disappearance of the sun gave little light. Now that work had slackened, we slipped into old habits and imposed them on the others. We evolved a routine.

For months and months we had planned how we should be prepared to endure the winter. It can be a dangerous thing to throw a number of men into an Antarctic winter, and let them work out their own salvation. They may work together with perfect equanimity in the bright sun, when labor absorbs their energies and conditions allow them to withdraw to one side if some momentary incident happens to irritate or discompose them. A wise man and a shrewd man can mask his real feelings, even his character, under such conditions. And he is assisted in the deception by the fact that his fellows have neither the time nor the desire to penetrate the superficial. But the winter night will quickly expose all of us.

Escape, in the wider meaning of the word, is impossible. Except for a quick, freezing walk the four walls limit one's world; and everything that one does, or says, or even thinks, is of importance to one's fellows. They are measuring you constantly, some openly, others secretly—there is so little else to do!—and with, ten, twenty, thirty and, in our case, forty-two personalities of varying force in a state of flux, there must necessarily be impacts of a kind, not necessarily physical, but rather psychological. Deception, under these conditions, becomes impossible. Sooner or later the inner man comes into the open. He is the man that is important. It is he who is judged. It is this inescapable process that makes the winter night terrible for some men. For them it can be purgatory.

Still another insidious quality lurks in the winter night. The Antarctic is the last stronghold of inertness. And it is the almost irresistible tendency of inertness to draw all inorganic matter to itself. It is a phase of the whole cosmical process—the struggle between what is alive and what is dead, with life striving to extend itself into immortality, and inertness tending to pull all things unto itself. On this continent, whence all life has been driven, save for a few very primitive or microscopic forms, inertia governs a vast empire. It has the power to subjugate those who do not arise to resist it; and men who are limited and lazy, when denied free scope for the play of mind and body, find themselves slipping, as if drawn by centripetal action, into a dull, stupid, dispirited monotony.

Of course it is not a clear-cut thing. It is largely a condition of the mind. Certain men of a phlegmatic disposition can pass through such an experience with the facility of a duck shedding water: it leaves no mark. But other men find it real and powerful. Each day becomes a struggle for control. And finally each hour.

There are no doubt many ways in which the winter night may be opposed, but we seized upon the most obvious and practical one. Of course it was our inevitable associate— work. We gave him an ally, routine. These were our weapons, and I dare say we made effective use of them.

After all, it is not the Antarctic that is dangerous. It is the man, as nearly always, who makes it dangerous, through the natural expression of his vitality and his proneness to err. Impatience increases the destructive power of the Antarctic; patience draws its claws. The uncertainty here, as elsewhere, only here to a greater degree, comes largely from man himself. Because he is impatient and self-assured, he often steps beyond the limits suggested by prudence, and the blow falls.

At times it would seem that there is a malignant consciousness operating in that void, seeking man's undoing. But it is only that men have over-estimated their capacity.

On the temple of Apollo at Delphi there is written: "Avoid excess in all things." This we tried to impose as the guiding rule in everything. With that in mind, a definite routine was established, and it became impossible for a man to eat, sleep, dawdle or work too much.

Failure to observe a routine is, I think, the cause of much of the unhappiness that overtakes a wintering expedition. Without it the days and nights lose their lines of divisions, and the months prolong themselves into a monotonous, unending period.

Our days began promptly at 8 o'clock, once winter set in. At that hour Dr. Gould, with an unswerving fidelity to his office that was the despair of all, would lift a tousled head from his bunk, and boom in a voice that must have awakened the sleeping walls: "All hands out for breakfast." It was not compulsory that every one arise at that moment. The bitter cold that seized the first bit of exposed flesh (the doors had not been long shut by the night watchman) was enough to cause the hardiest man to withdraw hastily into the warmth of the sleeping bag again, to screw up courage for the final upheaval. But it behooved one to get up in a very few minutes, lest he give some malicious tormentor the opportunity of dumping him bodily from the sleeping bag. Except with the hardier spirits, the morning wash was a very casual affair.

Breakfast was served on the dot of 8:30 o'clock, and here there was no compromise. The long table in the Mess Hall accommodated only 21 men at a time. Late arrivals, after the second mess, in addition to being subjected to scalding "razzing," had to take their place at the end, and instead of being served, had to serve themselves. If they dared to ask for a glass of water, they were growled into subjection; and as the winter wore on, Cook Tennant and his aides developed the manner of a tyrant about to order the chopping off of a dozen heads when men made a habit of arriving late.

Breakfast consisted as a rule of canned fruit, prunes, mush or oatmeal cakes, molasses, syrup, and as a great treat we had ham and eggs. The eggs were unlike any eggs that I have ever seen. The yolks froze solid and no amount of frying could reduce them. Like baleful yellow eyes they reared above the white and stared you in the face. "Flat eggs" became a synonym of civilization.

When breakfast was finished, assigned duties were the order for the day. The specialists, such as the weather men, Haines and Harrison; the radio men, Hanson, Mason and Petersen; the physicist, Davies, had regular duties to perform. Czegka, the machinist, and Rucker and June, who had shown a remarkable aptitude for all kinds of mechanical jobs, generally went into the machine shop, to work on equipment. Tom Mulroy, the fuel engineer, distributed gasoline for the day's activity. It was his job to see that the expenditure was kept to a minimum, and he performed the job faithfully. But every one had something to do.

Scarcely before the last dish had been removed the mess table, which was the most ample one in the camp, was converted into a work bench. A stranger, coming upon us suddenly from the trackless void outside and stepping down the tunnel and peering inside, would have paused in astonishment at the sight of all this activity under the snow. He would have seen perhaps a dozen men clustered about the table, and the air would be reverberating with the clash of hammer on steel, and the screech of saws on spruce. The table would have been strewn with tools, parts of sledges under construction, radio gear, navigation instruments, dog harness, trail cookers, and heaven only remembers what else.

We were getting ready for the spring journeys and flights of exploration, and the manifold details involved in preparing for them gave all hands enough work to carry them steadily through each day. For while the experiences of the men who had preceded us in the Antarctic would largely govern procedure, nevertheless we hoped to be able to improve on them. Dr. Coman, for example, in addition to his work with specimens, was working out a daily ration for the sledge parties; June and Czegka had taken the celebrated Nansen Cooker apart and were trying to make it more efficient, for all the fact that it is one of the most efficient trail stoves in the world; the radio men were building a number of small sets so that every sledging group might be provided with one; Strom and Balchen, with an artistry and craftsmanship I had not suspected in them, began to build several sledges; and Rucker, Parker and George Black assisted Captain McKinley in developing the thousands of feet of film taken during the aerial surveys.

The photo lab, as Captain McKinley's shack was called, was truly a most wonderful creation, and there was scarcely a man in camp who was not called, at one time or another, to assist our aerial surveyor at his cabalistic rites. It was at all times an important center of industry, and it was much of the time a storm center of controversy, the issue being whether or not it should be condemned as a public nuisance. Poor Mac, he got it from every side. Developing aerial film is difficult enough even in a modern laboratory; but in the Antarctic it borders on necromancy. The film is hyper-sensitized and comes in rolls 75 feet long and 9 inches wide. It must be handled in absolute darkness. And to develop a single reel 200 gallons of water are required.

Now water, oddly enough, is a precious commodity in the Antarctic for the reason that it is produced by melting snow, and coal is the black diamond of the Antarctic. To bring Mac as near the water supply as possible, we jammed the shack next door to the kitchen stove in the mess hall. Chips Gould waved his wand and produced it out of scrap lumber. It was 15 feet by 15 feet, and built so low in the snow that the first blizzard covered it entirely.

There were actually two rooms—the dark room, which was shrewdly cut off from all light, and a space which served as office, drying and chemical room.

It took McKinley and his aides about two months to get everything in order; for everything that he does is dis-tinguished by meticulous care and precision; but at last he pronounced things ready, and plunged into the film "shot" over the Rockefellers, the coastline and the Bay of Whales— 8 rolls in all.

The 200-gallon tank was ready to receive the water, Tennant unhappily surrendered his stove for the morning, and McKinley hopefully lifted a bucket of snow on the red-hot lid. Half an hour's boiling produced but one-third of a

bucket of water—a very sad result. Another bucket was
hoisted on the stove, and the first carefully placed on the floor.
Before the second mass of snow was reduced to water, the
first bucket promptly froze. There was, as we found, a
difference of 50° in temperature between the air at one's
shoulders and the air at one's feet, owing to the loss of heat
in the natural circulation of the air.

We were in a stew then. For several days every available
man in the camp was busy making water for McKinley, and
every source that could produce enough heat units to reduce
snow was pressed into service. The entire camp was turned
topsy-turvy and Tennant roared vain protests over the desecra-
tion of his stove with unsightly pots and buckets. I dare
say there would have been revolution had not our mechanical
genius, Czegka, come forward with a most ingenious device.
His apparatus consisted of two 50-gallon gasoline drums connected together, with an opening in the top for snow. Under
each tank he rigged a large gasoline blow torch. The tanks
were set up on pedestals so that the water could be drained
off with ease. Thus, the water problem was "licked," and
McKinley returned into the good graces of the cook.

But fate was quietly doubling her fist for still other
blows. Getting rid of the water was an equally difficult job.
We could not merely let it drain off outside, as we fondly
hoped. The water froze as it fell, and within a few hours
a magnificent icicle had completely closed the outlet. So
a group of valiant men, who still had the courage to face a
snow shovel again, went out in the cold and dug a hole in the
Barrier, 25 feet deep and about 4 feet square. The first rush
of water hit the bottom with a crash and bore right down
through the snow. How far it fell, where it went, no one
could tell. We were never able to touch bottom there. But
that problem was ended.

There were others. Cold beset them at every turn. Each
morning all pipes and drains had to be thawed out before work
could be commenced. The developing film was kept warm with
heating pads, which were specially made to fit the developing
tanks. It was necessary to keep these tanks at a temperature
of 70° at all times. Freezing of the solutions at night was prevented by draining them off in a thermos jug. Then there

was the matter of drying the developed rolls of film, which must be kept intact. To this end Czegka, who was never at a loss for mechanical answer, contrived an 8-foot roll, the ends of which were buggy wheels—the first, and no doubt the last, parts of that honorable vehicle to find service in the Antarctic. The great difference in temperature that existed over a few feet of height was a problem here. After the reel was finished, McKinley discovered that it must be turned continually, else the film would dry on the top while it froze on the bottom. "I have it," said Czegka. "Just the thing—a small motor." It turned the trick for McKinley, but it played fast and loose with communication, and the radio men were on the verge of nervous prostration while it operated.

But the joyous part came when they started developing, and McKinley and his colleagues plunged into the stygian gloom of the dark room. For a time all would be quiet and serene, evidence that all was going well. It would end on a cry of pain—a collision in the darkness. Then muffled imprecations, rising steadily in grandeur and significance—McKinley had dropped something. Then a stamping of feet—their toes were getting chilly. For the difference in temperature was hard on the feet: it was not uncommon to see them working stripped to the waist, with a shoulder-high thermometer recording 70°, with fur pants and mukluks protecting the nether regions, and a layer of ice on the floor.

No, we never lacked for excitement when the photographic section was in operation.

Perhaps the most dramatic incident of the winter took place in the photographic laboratory. Davies was in there, one night, working. The small gasoline stove was burning. He began to feel strangely drowsy, but ascribed it more to weariness than to anything else. He noticed, suddenly, that one of the pups, which McKinley was accustomed to keep in the laboratory, was out, and was lying unconscious on the floor. Davies, who was mystified, picked up the pup and brought him into the mess room. Just as he crossed the threshold, he fainted. He had been poisoned, of course, by the fumes.

There was a cry for Dr. Coman, who came and in his calm way took command of the situation. Davies was as limp as a rag, completely out; and while Dr. Coman worked over

him on the mess table, I never saw the men so grave—for
everyone in Little America loved Taffy. Presently, however, Davies responded to Dr. Coman's ministrations, opened
his eyes weakly and asked, "What happened?" We hustled
him out into the open and walked him up and down. The
cold air brought him to, all right, but in our anxiety to get him
out we overlooked the fact that we had stripped off most of
his clothes, and he very nearly froze to death before we got him
back. He was soon none the worse for the experience, though.

From McKinley's laboratory came, perhaps, the most important geographical information of the expedition. When his
photographs were finally developed, I saw how faultlessly the
aerial camera had recorded all details within its range of vision.
During the flights in the fall, McKinley photographed about 80
miles of the coastline east of the Bay, the Rockefeller Mountains and the vicinity of the Bay of Whales. The overlapping
series of photographs not only provided a continuous record
of these areas, but also recorded all geographical details in
their intricate relationship. With these photographs and the
hasty notes taken on the flights before us, we saw how more
superior and less fallible was the camera than the eye. On a
pioneering flight, the eye is so burdened with details to watch
and study that it is, of necessity, attracted toward those things
which are most prominent; consequently, even with the most
studied attention, many things of importance are ignored. But
not so with the camera. For example, when the photographs
of the coastline were developed, a number of interesting pressure ridges, which perhaps indicated land, were discovered
some distance northeast of the Bay of Whales. These ran inland for several miles, with a central line of cleavage clearly
shown. Best of all, Gould's observations at the Rockefeller
Mountains had resulted in the establishment of a number of
control points from which, by a process of mathematics, it was
possible to determine the relative heights and distances of the
topographical features shown in the photographs.

Two types of aerial surveying were done. The first of
these is the vertical, which is taken with the lens of the camera
pointed down through the floor of the airplane. The oblique
is obtained by pointing the camera at a known angle through
an aperture in the side of the plane. Each has its distinguish-

ing characteristic. While the vertical gives greater accuracy, the oblique covers a larger area and includes the horizon in the picture. We decided to use the oblique in the Antarctic for two reasons: First, all area seen on a flight must be recorded. Secondly, accuracy in feet is not absolutely necessary in polar exploration. Although most of the photographs were oblique, about 60 square miles of the Bay of Whales were mapped by the vertical at an altitude of 7,800 feet. The beauty of McKinley's work lay in the fact that it was exact and faithful: whatever we saw, wherever we went was in black and white.

Luncheon could scarcely be called a formal affair—merely a break in the day's routine. About noon Tennant and his assistant, Arnold Clark, spread a buffet lunch on a small table near his stove. It was a case of helping yourself. A characteristic meal consisted of canned sardine and salmon sandwiches, and sometimes cheese. There was also tea and coffee and cocoa. This was the hour for general discussion, and it was a welcome break in work. It acquired the extraordinary name of "the ob". Its derivation is curious, and yet quite characteristic of such designations. On the trip down on the *City*, Bill Haines used to disappear occasionally with the casual, but perfectly credible, explanation that he was going out to "take an ob." We thought he meant an observation. But it was soon discovered that instead of devoting himself to meteorology, he steered straight for the galley, where he invariably wheedled a cup of coffee and an enormous sandwich from Tennant. So the phrase "to take an ob" was at first used derisively, in connection with any minor sophistry, and then was attached to this noon-day meal.

Work was resumed about 1 o'clock and continued until 4:30 o'clock.

Supper was the major event of the day. On that occasion the table was decorated with a table cloth—an oilcloth, to be correct—and simply by that distinction we are entitled to be classed among the more luxuriously appointed Antarctic expeditions. Supper was served promptly at 5 o'clock, but long before that time a group of men would be found gathered in the mess hall, waiting to pounce on a chair as soon as Tennant struck the bell which signalled the serving of the feast. The limited space on the plain pine benches made it necessary to serve nearly four sittings, and one's hunger was so ravenous, by 5 o'clock, that to sit by and wait was to suffer, especially when such eminent trenchermen as Strom and Crockett, who nearly always were first on hand, threatened to put away the entire meal.

Supper, like the other meals, was wholesome; but it could scarcely be called epicurean, even if we did confer fancy designations to our humble viands. There was always meat, dark mutton or roast beef, penguin, whale or seal meat. Meat is a preventative of scurvy, and for this reason it was emphasized in our bill of fare. There were several men who could not stomach these more pungent, gamier meats, and they went without meat most of the time. Soup was served first: it might be orthodox canned soup, but the time came, towards the end of winter, when we were beginning to economize, when no one dared to have it identified: better to eat and be ignorant than find out what the artful Tennant had used as condiments. I will say this, though; while some of my colleagues were of the opinion that either an old sail or sleeping bag had been used as a base for the brew, it always tasted good to me.

After the soup, we helped ourselves from large bowls, which were passed around. We had a large quantity of dehydrated and canned vegetables, such as potatoes, onions, spinach, beans, carrots and such, which Dr. Coman, with his eye on vitamins, selected in New York. There was always a dessert, perhaps custard, or pies, perhaps mince, apple or pumpkin. Then coffee.

Supper was an affair that never lagged. Breakfast was hurried, luncheon was a rest period, but supper was a social affair. Here the affairs of the day and the morrow were vivaciously discussed: here some special accomplishment of brilliance or dumbness always came in for approving or sarcastic review; and here the affairs of a remote and almost forgotten world were settled to a man's satisfaction.

CHAPTER X

CIVILIZATION DOES NOT MATTER

"WHATEVER merit there may be in going to the Antarctic," that excellent writer, Mr. Cherry-Garrard, has said, "once there you must not credit yourself for being there." To spend the winter at Cape Evans, Scott's old headquarters, or at little America "because you explore is no more laudable than to spend a month at Davos because you have consumption, or to spend an English winter at the Berkeley hotel. It is just the most comfortable and the easiest thing to do under the circumstances."[1]

I will go farther and say: once your ships have started north and the pack has closed behind them, there is nothing else you can do. You are there to stay, whether you like it or not, for eight months at least, and all the resources of the world, were they brought to play, could not liberate you sooner. If the climate is too cold and snowy; if you have a horror of bathing in public; if your stomach turns at the mention of fried penguin; if you detest sleeping in a reindeer bag which sheds hair in your eyes and nose—if these things bother you, there is precious little you can do about it. Having made your bed, you must lie in it and take what crumbs of comfort there are.

It is not a bed of roses, to be true. Neither is it the worst bed in the world. There were times when Little America seemed about one of the happiest and gayest spots some of us had ever known.

The period that followed supper was always—or nearly always—a delightful time. The dishes were pushed aside, pipes came forth, cigarettes were lighted, and men remained

[1] Cherry-Garrard "Worst Journey in the World," p. 178. Mr. Garrard was a member of the scientific staff of Scott's last expedition.

to chat or drifted off to join the groups in other buildings. There were some men who never seemed to rest. Ronne was one of these. His sewing machine in the corner of the administration building whirred during the day, and stopped only to allow his nimble fingers to fly, with a skill and sureness a woman might have envied, guiding a thread over his endless creations. Braathen, too, worked steadily on the model of the *City of New York,* which he started to build during the winter night, and on which he lavished the utmost care and attention. But for the rest of us this period was a time of relaxation, and we made most of the few hours according to our particular notions of what constituted leisure.

It was wonderful to observe how the characters of men and situations evolved. If one drew apart occasionally contrasts that would have passed unnoticed stood out sharply, and it was surprising to observe how certain men, normally ignored, had come into their own. There was a subtle reorganization of values. And yet, when one was immersed in it, there seemed to be little change, after all. What one saw depended on where one stood. For in a very short time the fact of living in crowded quarters, under the pall of the winter night, became the normal existence, and what had gone before a rather confused and unusual memory.

Here, as everywhere, men were clannish. Without conscious stimulation or organization, a number of groups, possessing a certain inherent solidarity, were slowly evolved. They created their own diversions, settled all things more or less to their own satisfaction, had their particular shining lights; and while all the men were, at one day or another, in each of these groups, there was nevertheless a definable kernel of organization that remained fairly constant. Still, there was less clannishness than one might have expected, for cliques were discouraged. And of course there was no actual separation. How could there be? We had the privacy of gold fish and elbow room of sardines. Nor was this the intention. It was more like groups of men in a club, separating and drawing together by the action of common interests, likes and dislikes. There was always a large group for, and often a small minority against, the policies of the camp. There was always a suggestion of internal politics in this minority

THE LONELIEST CITY IN THE WORLD.

Little America during the Winter Night by Light of its Beacon with the Radio Wires Sparkling with Hoar Frost.

CHARLES E. LOFGREN, Personnel Officer.

GEORGE W. TENNANT, Chief Cook.

Examining de-hydrated food with the Medical
Officer.

VICTOR H. CZEGKA, Machinist.

never too concealed,—just enough to make it interesting. And thus, in a rudimentary form, and without definite intention, we democratized the government of Little America, which was often satisfactory to all, and sometimes not, which is the unhappy destiny of all governments.

The outstanding institution was the gathering about Benny Roth's bunk which adjoined the radio shack in the Mess Hall. Here, every night, there was certain to be a crowd, and the congestion became so great, in fact, that it was called "Benny's Huddle." The "Huddle" was the hub of Little America, and if one stayed there long enough he was certain to know a little bit about everything that ever happened.

One might hear Chips Gould, perhaps, discoursing on maritime law and the merchant marine, facts pertaining to which flowed from him like a stream; or Balchen talking about prize fights and prize fighters; or Dean Smith, drawing on a mind that preserves detail as if etched in steel, discussing snakes, which seemed to exercise a powerful fascination on him, or telling stories about flying which were more vivid than fiction. Our reserved and almost reticent assistant meteorologist, Harrison, was often to be found there, willing to explain the caprices of the weather, but eager most of all to discuss baseball and baseball players, in which he had an absorbing interest. Dr. Coman, a man of many moods, brilliant, an academician, yet an adventurer at heart, was sometimes there, and when the talk veered around to travel, would occasionally tell, in hard, glittering anecdote an experience he had had during the four years he had fought in the French Army, although he seldom mentioned the war itself. The "Doc" knew many things thoroughly, his thoughts were often on a loftier plane, and he and Russell Owen became known as the "high-brows," the authorities on literature, world affairs, celebrities and the like. Prof. Gould stood apart in the nature of an institution by himself. If any man was liked by all, it was he. Larry was a blend of coolness and warmth. His friendly ways and his fairness endeared him to the Winter Party at Little America. Larry mingled, and yet was always respected. He was not above the telling of an occasional anecdote, distinguished for its dry and incisive wit. But most of all he was the oracle. When arguments waxed and flamed and drew to no conclusion, Larry was resorted to as the seat of judgment. His mind seemed to have held every fact that came into it. With him stood McKinley, third in command, the soul of tact and kindliness, with that peculiar, alert deference which slightly deaf persons often have, adding a mark of sympathetic attention to his bearing. We were fortunate to have such men as these two.

Arguments are at once the joy and affliction of the winter night. How many roared through Little America, like fire sweeping dry timber, I should hesitate to say. But offhand, well, one or two too many. Let the temperature drop to 70° below zero outside, we never lacked for burning issues inside. Was Bryan a fraud or a great and intellectually honest man? Is Babe Ruth a greater player than Ty Cobb ever was in his prime? Is the Bay of Whales really permanent, or might it not disintegrate some fine day and launch us all out to sea? Was Wilson garroted at Paris, or did he curl the rest of the Big Four around his little finger? Is the English Channel easier to swim than the Hellespont? Where can you buy the best steak in New York? Is the Thibetan plateau higher than the Polar plateau? What will you do first when (a) you reach New Zealand, (b) Broadway and (c) home?

Like country cousins, argument clung to us always. They started innocently, gathered increasing strength and became so fraught with passion as to threaten to bring down the roof. They seemed to have no end. Pertinacious minds, reluctant to concede defeat, would trot them forth, like horses under raps, and start them off again. Then the air would clear, the issue be decently interred; but before its bones had ceased to rattle, a new one was in the travail of birth. Probably the wisest thing we did, when we went South, was to bring a set of the Encyclopædia Britannica, the World's Almanac and Who's Who. These repositories of essential information were a godsend. That these estimable works happen to have lacked some of the facts that were, for a time, like life and death in Little America is due less to neglect on the part of the editors, I imagine, than to discrimination and perhaps a sense of propriety.

To get the scene one should have the background. The mess hall was a rectangular affair, longer than it was wide.

On one side was Tennant's range and sink. Two tables ran the length of the room, and about the center one, the mess table, ran an unbacked bench. Set in the corner opposite Tennant's range was the radio room, separated by a partition. There was no door, and the operators, Mason and Petersen, could be seen at work inside. The two bunks of Roth and Arnold were built in alongside.

On the side opposite Tennant's galley were arranged two tiers of bunks, six up and six down, like Pullman berths, which, instead of running lengthwise with the car, stuck out into the aisle. Here the comparison ceases. For these bunks were the plainest kind of things, simply slatted structures nailed to the wall and supported by beams. A man's worldly possessions hung up beside him on nails, a mass of clothing, wrinkled and damp, a picture or two, oddly enough, a calendar here and there. There was barely room enough between the bunks for two men to pass abreast, and with clothing and gear choking up the corridor, the scene, to a fastidious eye, was one of unhealthy congestion and intimacy.

But not at all.

These bunks were occupied by the following men: Mason and Petersen, Bubier and June, de Ganahl and Smith, Czegka and Bursey, Chips Gould and Tennant, Strom and Black. During the discussions about Roth's bunk, one would find perhaps half a dozen of them lolling in their own cubicles, those in the upper tier gazing down from an Olympian eminence and casting a phrase or two into the debate. Arnold Clark's bunk was really his castle and he had taken great pains to make it comfortable. He had made a very fine lamp from a glass jar and a chimney he had found somewhere. His bunk was over Roth's, and when the arguments were at their peak Clark might be seen curled in his sleeping bag, reading a book. He was a very quiet person—one of the quietest in the camp—but I am sure he took secret joy in listening to the mad discussions which raged beneath him. He was the soul of hospitality, and to visit his altitudinous retreat was like visiting the estate of a country gentleman; for Clark would welcome you with real old-fashioned hospitality and insist upon your having the most comfortable place in the bunk. Even when cigarettes were worth their weight in gold, Clark would always have one to offer. Bubier's bunk had something of the same mark of popularity. Bubier was the diplomat in the camp. It was his ambition to make things run smoothly at all times. He smoothed out the rough spots, and backed up the camp's orders with an aggressiveness which, nevertheless, was so slickly applied that it almost seemed gentle. De Ganahl might be at work in his bunk, tapping on a typewriter which he had swung on a most ingenious contraption, or Dean Smith writing in his diary, which is, beyond all doubt, the most voluminous and intimate record since Peppys'.

In the Administration Building we had a group known as the "Rat's Nest," a most unflattering title, but one that stuck. This was made up of Bill Haines, Charlie Lofgren, Henry Harrison and our witty Welshman, Taffy Davies. They shared the four bunks at one end of the building. Here, with Taffy and Bill as ring leaders, was concocted much of the deviltry that delighted and enraged the camp, and the subdued chuckling that was frequently overheard from that corner soon came to mean that some new outrage was afoot. As our cameramen, Rucker and Van der Veer, both genial souls, occupied adjoining bunks, the plotting often took queer and devious turns.

Save for the arrangement of things, the appearance of the administration building did not differ greatly from that of the mess hall. My quarters, the library and the room turned over to the scientific staff, took up one whole end of the building. Bunks ran along both sides, six sets of two bunks on the left, and two sets of two on the right. Those on the left were occupied by Ronne and Dr. Coman, O'Brien and Balchen, McKinley and Gould, Van der Veer and Rucker, and the others by the aforesaid conspirators. On the opposite side, Parker and Owen, Hanson and Mulroy. Beyond Hanson's and Mulroy's bunks were Dr. Coman's dispensary, a boarded partition, and the radio laboratory.

There was the same confusion of clothes and gear, the same congestion. Only the spoken words were different. The wind howled and sobbed eerily in the ventilators, and the cold draught from which one could never escape was on the nape of the neck and the feet.

But let us retrace our steps and seek out the third group in this colony. We step past the scientific room, cluttered with intricate gear, push open a door and enter a boarded vestibule. On the right is the Balloon Station, whence Haines and Harrison send up their inflated globes to test upper air circulation. There is a panel in the roof which can be moved back when the balloons are released and their progress through night air followed by a theodolite. Next to the Balloon Station is a door which opens on a tunnel leading to the Barrier surface; but we shall go instead through the tunnel to the mess hall.

A second door opens on the main tunnel, and as our flashlight bores a hole through the frosty darkness, its gleams bring to life the most wonderful colors. Pendant ice crystals on the ceiling and the walls glow in and refract the light with the brilliance of gems. It is a crystal palace hung with jewels. The feet crunch noisily upon the snow, and one's breath discharges in great clouds. This night it is chilly, 38° below zero in the tunnels, and on the surface it is much colder. We pass a series of side tunnels cut into the main tunnel. On the right are the tunnels leading to the medical storeroom and the main storeroom over which Supply Officer Black presides. On the left are tunnels opening separately on the Gymnasium and to Davies' Non-Magnetic House. Beyond these, is still another tunnel leading to the pit where Mulroy has stored the gasoline and the kerosene. As we round the bend in the tunnel, a beam of light creeps down our way—it is George Black, the supply officer, out to do some marketing. The light lifts suddenly, searching out a place in the wall. One sees Black's face suddenly illuminated as he stares, brushes the rime from the wall and extracts the contents of a box. So we shall have beans tomorrow!

We slide past him, with a quick word of greeting, for it is too chilly to linger. The tunnel opens abruptly on a vaulted chamber, roofed with canvas and full of boxes. It is still another storeroom. On the left is the coal pile, and to the right, under the overhang of the roof, is Tennant's meat supply storeroom. We traverse the space with a few steps, push open a door and are in the Norwegian House. Truth to tell, I had faithfully named it The Biltmore, as a tribute to the hostelry which had so generously housed the expedition at

New York; but Norwegian House it remained, not because any Norwegians lived there—none did—but because we had purchased it in Norway.

It is a cramped place about 12 feet by 16 feet. There is a kerosene stove under the only window, which faces south, and bunks take up nearly all the room that is left. There is a sledge on the floor, and the "Three Musketeers", Vaughan, Goodale and Crockett, are working over it, experimenting with a new kind of lashing. Siple is curled up in his bunk, reading, and Thorne is studying charts. Jim Feury is in a characteristic Antarctic attitude—prone, dreaming no doubt of the snowmobile with which he got such good results. The other occupants, Alexander and Demas, are not about. Probably they are in Benny's huddle.

Returning, we regain the corridor and at the end open a door into Czegka's machine shop, with its mass of tools and equipment, the Kohler humming with the peculiar rhythm of a well-kept engine. We push open another door into the mess hall. At the other end, another door, and the light searches out a path up a rudely cut staircase in the snow. Instantly the air strikes the face with the cut of a knife; it may not seem likely, but the difference between 30° and 50° below zero is real and biting. Groping up the stairs is undignified and acrobatic, for the risers have been worn down by constant use, and the passage, which is solidly filled after every blizzard, seems to grow narrower and more tortuous after every digging. We crawl and walk half-erect, and finally gain the entrance.

A cold, gray night, a dull, grotesque moon hangs on a Barrier ridge, and the snow exudes a pale distilled luminosity which is almost a half-light.

We make a break for it, hurrying as fast as our cumbersome clothes will permit. For there is a wind stirring, and its touch on the face is not exactly a kiss. We follow a well-worn path in the snow, which ends abruptly before a gaping hole, down which we dive, literally, and come up hard, after an abrupt descent, at the end of a chamber. It is divided into two rather large rooms, with a partition made of snow blocks. The first of these is the ski repair shop, a tangle of gear, sledges, harnesses and skis. The next is the chopping room, where the seal carcasses are hacked into pieces for the dogs.

A spattering of dark blotches standing out with horrid prominence on the white floor tell of a recent feeding. On the right a hole leads into the dog tunnels, from which come throaty growlings. If we peer in, we may see several pairs of eyes burning with hypnotic incandescence, which seem to say: "Be a good fellow, will you, come in and give us something to eat."

A strip of light is painted on a slit in the door, and in a moment we are face to face with an Antarctic phenomenon— the only two-man house in the history of Antarctic exploration. It is the shack that Walden and Braathen built out of odds and ends. They call it Luckheim—because, they said, they were lucky to get it. If we are lucky, we may find the tall and handsome Strom, with the body of a Greek athlete, the hands of a lumberjack, and the spirit of an artist, filling the place with the sounds of his accordion, singing haunting Norwegian folk songs.

But such is not our fortune. Strom's Muse has deserted him tonight, and he sits chatting with Balchen. Braathen is bending over the stove, the open door of which shows a fiery square, and tosses in a hunk of blubber. The frozen oil hisses and flames, and he hastily slams tight the door. The air is full of assailing odor of burning blubber, which offends the nose, causes the eyes to water and the everlasting soot quickly paints the cleanest face with an oily and well-nigh permanent scum. The stove is Braathen's pride and joy; he made it, with less elegance than profanity, out of a steel gasoline drum, and though it smokes fearfully, I dare say Chris would not exchange it for the finest oil-burner ever made. The square-built and taciturn Walden is hunched over a half-made dog harness, tugging at a pipe. What queer bedfellows, these two men. They have nothing in common save a love of dogs. Walden, the son of a minister, veteran sledge-driver of the Alaskan Gold Rush, a man whose dogs are his life; he loathes the Antarctic, hates it for its sameness, its lack of hills and game. Braathen, a foot-loose sailor, but a graduate of an evangelical college, as much at home here as anywhere, saying little but thinking much; before he came south dogs were unknown to him, but down here he treats them like children. He has taken the cast-off dogs, the lame and the weak, and built them into a wonderful team. Whether it was this interest or another that has drawn them together, here is the most impregnable kind of friendship. It gives them a life apart.

We had one other separate institution—Quin Blackburn, the tall, broad-shouldered surveyor from state of Washington. Behind the radio shack, he built for himself a snow house, braced with food boxes, and in the center of it he set up a tent. It was connected to the main tunnel by means of a narrow corridor— its only egress. "But suppose you have a fire. How will you get out?" we asked. Blackburn answered. "I shall depend upon the resources of Dr. Coman," who was, incidentally, the fire marshal of the camp. So he slept in the tent during most of the winter, with a primus stove and sleeping bag providing the only heat, a well-chilled disciple to the gospel of sleeping out-of-doors. As a consequence, he was nursing blisters of frost-bite on his feet and face most of the time.

Such, in brief, were a few of the personalities and characteristics of Little America.

No picture of Little America would be complete without mention of the dogs. Dog Town was a fascinating place. There the most tranquil peace and the most savage ferocity went hand in hand. The will of the stronger ruled it with iron discipline. It existed for work and chunks of frozen seal meat, the scent of which plunged it into ecstatic bedlam. Nights, when a solid stillness fell over the Barrier, the strangest chorus ever sung came up from the labyrinths. It was an uncanny experience to hear half a hundred dogs lift their voices in an ascending scale, reach a quavering high note, dwell on it a moment, then cease abruptly, as if at a signal. Quiet would fall, then the chant would begin anew.

It was the wolf in them, working off some dim emotion in melancholy song.

No matter how often the stakes and chains were inspected, there were always a few dogs that managed to break away. Then there was war, fresh blood on the snow, and the drivers would come charging from the shacks, slashing right and left with the heavy butts of whips. It was bedlam while it lasted.

The Eskimo dog has at times the ruthless self-will of a despot, and neither whip nor iron can prevail against it. I saw one of them, who refused to be broken to harness, face with snarling mouth the club of one of the drivers; in the end it was the driver who threw down his whip and confessed defeat. It was not a pretty sight, even if it is the law of the trail. One could not help admiring the proud, indestructible spirit of the beast.

These dogs can also be the friendliest and most playful fellows one could ask for. As a matter of fact, their natures have been much maligned as far as their relationship with human beings is concerned. They responded wonderfully to kind and thoughtful handling. The drivers on the whole had very little trouble with them, and inevitably became very keen about their dogs. Most of them were as gentle with us as the most innocuous house pet. Braathen had a small dirty white Eskimo, blind in one eye, which had been discarded by the other drivers as useless. He named it "Moose-Moss-Mouse", and by gentle, patient training turned him into one of the best leaders of all.

A number of the men, however, at first had scant liking for them, thinking them to be treacherous. One dog, Oulie, who was more than half wolf, had a terrible reputation, which the drivers wilfully blackened for the benefit of the more timorous members of the camp. He was a splendid dog in the harness, but absolutely untamable. One night, during the winter, Chips Gould went down the tunnel to repair the gate in the maternity ward, to keep the young pups from over-running the camp. He carried a kerosene lantern, which he put down on the floor and started work. In the midst of his hammering, he heard a noise and turned, just in time to see one of the pups making off with the lantern.

"Hey, drop that," Gould yelled. The puppy dropped it and fled, but in doing so overturned the lantern, plunging the tunnel into darkness. At once the other dogs, aroused by the shout, began to howl and the tunnel reverberated with the racket. The carpenter's wits quitted him; he lost his bearings, collided with one wall after another in a frenzied effort to escape from Oulie, who, he thought, was prowling about in the darkness, waiting to seize him.

He became hopelessly lost.

As he stood for a moment, dazed and bewildered, a soft,

moist muzzle, which he recognized, pressed against his hand.

"Birch," Gould whispered, his legs knocking.

Birch was one of the pets of the camp, one of the gentlest dogs of all.

The carpenter timidly ran his hand down her back, half expecting it would be torn from him. It was Birch, over-joyed to see him. "Thank God," Gould said. He fumbled about in the darkness, to disconnect the chain from the stake; then, firmly holding on to the end of the chain, he yelled: "Let's go, Birch." And she raced, just as he had hoped she would, for the mess hall. Nor did Gould surrender his hold on the chain until the door had slammed behind him, shut-ting out the tumult in the tunnels. He led her over to the galley. "Tennant," he said, "this dog has saved my life. I want to give her a whole leg of lamb."

The pups were the despair of the camp. There were at least a score of them, the sons and daughters of Lady, a small, nondescript Eskimo; Josephine 1, and Holly, a very beautiful full-blooded Eskimo.

Literally, they ran wild. They could not be cap-tured, but prowled about the camp, feeding on scraps of food that were put out for them, enduring the lowest temperatures without visible discomfort. In mid-winter, when the ther-mometer was down to 65°, Amy, one of Goodale's team, gave birth to five pups in the maternity ward. To make them as comfortable as possible, Goodale laid a bedding of straw on the floor of her crate. This was constantly damp, owing to the condensation of the mother's breath, and being afraid that they might die, he moved them inside his shack. But the un-happy mother took them back, at the first chance, to the tun-nel. Later, he tried to wean them on such delicate foods as cereal and oatmeal, which they spurned in favor of frozen seal meat. And within a few weeks they joined the wild band in-habiting the tunnel, becoming the biggest and the strongest of the lot. For all their rapacious manners, these outlaws were amiable creatures; and whenever I went walking they would come rushing forth in answer to the call, "halloa, halloa, halloa, halloa," and escort me down to the bay.

In the presence of these creatures Igloo was as cocky and fierce as ever. Familiarity breeds contempt, and he had long since got over the shock they first gave him during the trip South on the *City of New York*. He feared not even the biggest dog among them; no doubt, he believed he was a great fighter because we saved his life so often. He was even condescending in his attitude, especially toward the pups, although his life was really in great danger. We had to watch him carefully, because when he was allowed to run loose he invariably made for Dog Town. Almost always he returned in need of medical attention, which Dr. Coman never failed to give him. He accompanied me on my walks. As Nature had not provided him with a heavy coat, Ronne made him one of camel's hair, which covered his body and legs. This jacket was a source of undiminishing curiosity to the wild pups, and at every opportunity during the jaunt they would steal up from behind and nip at it, no doubt with the intention of finding out what this queer bundle was. These assaults so humiliated Igloo that he could scarcely contain himself; he would bide his time, however, and when one of the tormentors was off his guard, Igloo was on him in a flash. How he managed to escape his amiable assassins for more than a year is a miracle. On at least two occasions a slashing stroke missed his jugular by a hair's breadth.

But I have digressed:

There were ways other than work with which to make time fly. Games were popular. The ancient American institution of poker became an Antarctic pastime. The mere fact that money no longer had significance did not diminish the action of the game. No one ever thought of playing for money. A far more precious currency—cigarettes—was played for; and toward the end of the winter, when the supply ran low, the faces of the players were set with a grimness as if the Morgan millions were at stake. Eventually, those who won redistributed the gains, in order to keep the game going.

Bridge was a game favored by a few, particularly Dean Smith, McKinley, Harrison, Rucker, Czegka and myself. An old Navy game, "Acey Deucey," was also popular.

The Gymnasium was a very popular place. It was nothing more than a room built into the snow, perhaps 25 feet square and 15 feet deep, with a tarpaulin for a roof, which of course was covered with snow. Here, Balchen, Thorne, Dean Smith, Siple, Bursey, Strom, Black and Blackburn took regular work outs, even though the temperature in the room got as low as 50° below zero. A boxing match between Strom and Balchen was an almost weekly feature.

There really was no lack of entertainment. Toward the end of the winter, when radio reception was good, Petersen and Mason picked up the broadcasting stations at Wellington, which we overheard via the loud speaker in the houses. Every Saturday afternoon, at 4 o'clock, we listened in on the regular programmes broadcast by KDKA, at Pittsburg, and WGY, at Schenectady, which were sent directly to us. Most of the time these broadcasts came in perfectly, but at other times were hopelessly confused by abnormal atmospheric conditions. It was good to hear the voices of our friends speaking, but there were moments when we stirred uneasily. The last place in the world to which one should send a mushy message is the Antarctic; whatever note it may strike in the heart of the intrepid explorer to which it is addressed, it brings only pain—severe pain—to his fellows.

On Sunday, which was officially a day of rest, we had a regular motion picture show. A curtain was lowered at one end of the mess hall, chairs were grouped in front, the lights were extinguished and Rucker and Van der Veer began the show. I recall these affairs with mingled emotion. The pictures were presented to us by the National Board of Review, which seemed to have been consistently guided in its selection by a reverent feeling for antiquity. However, they did give us Charlie Chaplin in some of his old thrillers, which were run over again and again, to the great delight of every one; and if, as it frequently happened, the most exciting part of the film was missing, our movie experts immediately grafted on a fragment of another, which often led to wonderful things. I would hesitate to describe the actions of the audience; for the emotions which a respect for law and order compelled them to suppress in the more pretentious motion picture palaces at home, were allowed to run riot here, being stimulated by scandalous comments from our distinguished surgeon.

Twice a week during the winter the dons and pundits of

Antarctic University gave lectures on the various subjects associated with the research purposes of the expedition. Dr. Gould gave the course on geology which he taught at the University of Michigan and which nearly every one attended. Mason and Hanson lectured on radio science, June conducted a ground school on aviation to which Balchen and Smith contributed, and McKinley talked on aerial surveying. These studies were a welcome interlude, and recommended themselves on the ground that they would give the men a proper appreciation of the real objectives of the expedition. A number of men gained a great deal from them.

There was a victrola in the library in the Administration Building, which ground perpetually. The records were of jazz and classical music, and both, I think, were played to equally appreciative audiences. Every two or three days, either Chips Gould or Jack Bursey would come into the library and pick up their favorite records to play them over and over again. "The Bells of St. Mary" is a tune I am not likely to forget. I was working on my polar reports nearby, and had all the feelings of a distracted fugitive fleeing from a mad minstrel.

Civilization was never too far from us to bridge the southern oceans and the pack. Few of us will ever forget the night when Vaughan, who was in the group before the loud-speaker, was told of the death of his brother. Some one, who realized what was coming, tried to turn off the radio; but was too late. Even the collapse of the stock market in the early (Antarctic) spring had its painful repercussions. Smith, who became known as the Dean of Antarctic financiers, watched Chrysler go down with the thermometer, while he unhappily directed his broker from the Bay of Whales. The nights when Petersen or Mason was unable to pick up the latest quotations were dull and gloomy ones, indeed.

The daily "Press" sent out each night by the New York *Times* was intercepted by our radio department, and "published" each night on the Bulletin Board. Thus, we kept more or less abreast of the world's affairs, and new fuel for discussion was rarely lacking.

When other entertainments lagged, the amateur talent

produced its own. We had our "Antarctic Follies," which made up in brawn what it lacked in pulchritude. Crockett, Goodale, Feury and Bubier were the chorus, and they made a dashing appearance in skirts made from dish towels and wigs made from rope, although a generous showing of none too clean woolen underwear was hardly calculated to appeal to an aesthete. The humor was, I fancy, rather practical, often broad and not infrequently Rabelasian. While it delighted us beyond measure, I doubt whether it would seem particularly amusing to any one else. Too often the humor turned on some peculiarity, some phrase or incident that belonged only to us. The practical jokes, which are enjoyed only by the perpetrators, were always with us. Not long after we took up the routine winter existence, a crevasse, which widened alarmingly, was discovered in the surface to the north not far from the houses. Presently a second crack appeared to the east, and then a third to the west. We were literally surrounded by cracks, and the men who still held to the theory of the impermanence of the Barrier, viewed them with misgivings. An ignoble conspiracy was hatched and executed. Very early one morning, at 4 A.M. to be exact, when the temperature was about 40° below, Demas aroused the administration building with a cry, into which he put the whole force of his lungs,—"The Barrier has broken." Men who were always the last out of their bunks in the morning were first out this time. Some paused, shrewdly, to snatch adequate clothing, but others paused for nothing. Hanson, ever resourceful, grabbed a handful of tools and radio equipment with the intention of making an emergency radio set to inform the world of our peril. The vestibule was clogged with hurrying figures. But outside nothing was changed, the Barrier was still intact and the shivering, half-clad men filed back again, vowing deadly things. Poor Demas confessed later that he did not close his eyes for three nights, lest his tormentors rend him limb from limb.

The night that Owen stood the watch was a gala occasion. When the fire in the galley went out, several conspirators from the Norwegian House stole out and tied a coal sack around the chimney flue. They were up early the next morning, hidden in the tunnel, when Russell came in, none too enthusiastically, to make the fire. It was bitter cold. Shivering and miserable, he chopped the kindling, packed it in the stove and applied a match. It blazed merrily for a few moments, then a torrent of smoke poured forth. It gathered in volume, spread across the ceiling, then whirled downward in a choking pall. The occupants in the upper bunks awakened first, sputtering, then those in the lower tier. Imprecations and unkindly advice were hurled at the watchman, who was frantically manipulating every gadget on the stove in a vain effort to promote a draft. Several sufferers, of a sterner mould, crept from their sleeping bags to help him. Meanwhile the residents of the Norwegian House were pressed against the door, enjoying the sounds with unholy glee.

Just at the moment when those inside were preparing to abandon the house, until the smoke cleared, a spark found its way through the bag, set it afire and created a draft. The incident closed on the note of threatened reprisals.

If any particular quality of the conversation stands out in memory, it is the power of ridicule. Ridicule is a crushing force anywhere; in a crowded existence, such as a polar shack, it carries a sting that penetrates and destroys. There were several tongues that turned most neatly the sarcastic phrase called "the wise-crack," and innocent phrases were twisted and distorted out of original meaning. It was de Ganahl's unfortunate habit, when he crawled down from his bunk, to bring his big boots down on Dean Smith's head. Joe, who is the soul of politeness, always said: "I'm sorry " In a short time, it was a courageous soul who dared to say, "I'm sorry." The phrase "shipmates" was tortured out of existence. Compliments were almost never spoken. Hanson, a very considerate man, used to speak enthusiastically of the work of his aides until a nihilist labelled it "apple-rubbing" and "flag-flying." After that, few dared to risk exposure to the phrase.

Perhaps I have dwelt overlong on this side of the picture, in an attempt to show what men do and think in the winter night. Really, this is but a small fragment of the whole—

" . . . full of sound and fury,
And signifying nothing."

The day ended promptly at 10 o'clock, and here strictest routine prevailed. On the dot, the main lights in the house were extinguished, the fires were allowed to die out and the door was opened. The poor physical conditions that lowered the vitality of several wintering parties in the Antarctic was partly due to the fact, we believed, that the majority of the men remained cooped up in their shacks, breathing stale and unrenewed air, while the fires roared all winter long, day and night. The men who wished to do so, could read in their bunks. There was a regular semi-monthly allotment of candles, and the more thrifty men saved the tallow as it dripped and put it into glass jars which they converted into lamps by inserting wicks; others made kerosene lamps from pickle jars, food tins and similar containers. But after the door was opened, and as the heat from the fire diminished, these flickering lights went out, one by one, first in the lower bunks, where the cold draught quickly settled, then in the upper bunks, as it mounted. In a very short time, the temperature fell to 35° below zero, during the more bitter spells, and the snug warmth of the sleeping bag was not resisted for long.

Soon only the night watchman remained awake.

Being night watchman was one of the routine jobs of the camp. It was a lonely and sometimes a cold job. At first, Dr. Gould assigned the job to any man who happened not to have a day duty, but later the assignment was made alphabetically, and every one, with the exception of the cook and his assistant, stood the watch.

The watchman had certain privileges, however. His post was in the library. He was allowed a candle and a kerosene lantern. More often than not, he induced the cook to provide him with hot coffee in a thermos jug, and sandwiches, to fortify himself against the rigor of the vigil. The duties were varied and interesting. Every half hour he was required to step outside and observe the auroral display [1] and record

[1] Although the aurora was first observed March 16–17, a regular watch was not established until April 3, owing to the necessity of using every man to put the camp in order. The watch continued uninterruptedly until

his report in a book that Davies had provided for that purpose. This watch, however, was later taken over by Demas, who stood it most of the winter, because he believed he could make use of the quiet to pursue his studies. Demas is one of the most studious young men I have ever known. The watchman also had to check up, at frequent intervals, the direction and velocity of the wind, which was accomplished by means of an ingenious, electrical recording device that Haines had rigged in the scientific room. At least once before 2 o'clock A.M. and once afterwards, he was obliged to make the rounds between the main houses, both via the tunnels and overland, if storm did not preclude the latter trip. This was a precaution against fire. At 6:30 o'clock in the morning, he kindled the fires in the galley and the stove in the administration building, called the cook, filled the bucket on the library stove with snow, so that the others might have warm water with which to wash, and so to bed.

The duty was not especially complicated, and the watch was popular with some men for the reason that it allowed them the solitude for reading and study. The walk overland between the houses was, for those who had the desire to find it so, a rich and stirring experience. On clear, calm nights, a silver moon was often visible, stars glittered with abnormal brilliance, and the trackless expanse of the Barrier was dominated by a silence so deep and profound that it seemed to be physical. At such a moment no place on earth could be more quiet. Then, from afar off, would come perhaps the distant rumble of the Barrier breaking, or from nearby the terrifying reports of contracting ice, like a burst of rifle fire. Once or twice I heard a snow quake—an extensive rumbling and shaking under foot as the crust of vast snow fields to the south settled to a more solid level. Then the silence would restore the equipoise.

Inside the huts, a silence of a different nature: the lulling whirr of the revolving cups of the anemometer overhead, not unlike the sound of an idling propeller slightly off center,

October, when the sun began to shine all 24 hours. The aurora was last seen September 26, 1929. A total number of 7,412 half hourly observations were made over this period. The method of classification used was that of Dr. H. U. Sverdrup.

and, when it was very cold, the thrumming of the taut wires supporting the anemometer pole, the fainter sound of men breathing, and sometimes an indiscreet phrase mumbled by a sleeper.

Despite the cold, there were some men who went out of doors every day, for exercise and fresh air. Save during the worst kind of weather, I made this my practice, and there were many others who did the same. Sometimes we walked in groups, but more often went alone, not because we did not want company, but because we wanted privacy more. A few minutes of reflective contemplation under the broad arch of sky were always good. We followed, as a rule, the trail to the westward, down Ver-sur-Mer Inlet to the Bay.

There was always something new to be found there. Pressure ridges changed their shape constantly. New ones appeared, rising, in some cases, to heights of 30 and 40 feet, taking on eerie forms in the half-light. Far off when the moon was out, the cliffs of the western Barrier were visible, their white walls merging dimly into the gray overtones of the night. In certain places voices carried marvellously. One could hear men talking as if they were nearby, although one or two miles away. The swish of skis on the snow carried on the crisp air very clearly.

Dr. Gould and Davies made studies of ice formations, particularly of the crevasses in the neighborhood. The ice pits to the north of the camp were fascinating, although they scarcely approached in magnitude the chaotic disturbances to the southwest, where the Barrier met the bay ice. I was determined to investigate these, and during the winter descended one of them. It was done on a very cold day. The temperature registered 50° below, and on the way to the crevasses Strom froze his toe so severely he had to run back to the camp, to thaw it. However, he returned quickly. Because the cold stopped the chemical action of dry batteries, we could not use flashlights. Hanson had rigged up a searchlight to a portable gasoline generator, which we trundled to the scene of operations. In the party were Strom, Siple, Vaughan, Feury, Dr. Coman and Thorne.

We came to a halt at the brink of one of the largest chasms. It was perhaps three feet across. The searchlight was pointed down, but it failed to show the bottom as the crevasse did not fall straight, but bent in at a sharp angle. Strom made a series of lines fast about my chest and, with the others holding, started to descend. Just as I reached the first curve in the wall, the line across my chest began to choke me. I yelled at the top of my lungs, but the sound from the gasoline engine was so loud that they did not hear me. With my legs spinning wildly over space and unable to gain a foothold on the smooth walls, I thought, for a moment, I might choke to death. But a few vigorous tugs on the line brought quick response from above. I was hauled out, and on the surface rearranged the lines, then went down again.

The beauty of that descent I could not hope to describe. The beam from the searchlight fell on immense ice crystals, some of which were from 5 to 8 inches long, which festooned the walls, and burned like myriads of gems. The walls themselves, when I glanced back, had in the light of the searchlight turned into emerald green and blue and purple and seemed transparent.

Preceded by a shower of crystals, I descended slowly. About 15 feet down, the crevasse turned sharply, and I carefully picked my way from projection to projection. About 40 feet down, I touched bottom, and found myself standing in a grotto, with the domed walls curving in above me, and the refracted illumination from the searchlight falling through the slit rose in a glorious rainbow. Here and there a few thin columns of vapor rose trembling from the floor. To the right and left the walls closed in narrowly, so that I was unable to go more than a few feet in either direction. The thermometer which I carried registered only 15° below zero.

In response to my signal, Strom lowered a crowbar, and I attacked the ice underfoot, to determine whether the ice on which I stood was solid or merely a bridge. In spite of diligent prodding, I penetrated no more than a foot, where I came to solid ice. I tasted a bit of the slush, and it was unmistakably salty. The sea water, then, filled the crevasses in the vicinity of Little America from sea level down. Of course, it is probably frozen all year round. What fascinated me most were the ice crystals, which littered the floor of the crevasse. They were extraordinarily large and perfect in structure. These Antarctic flowers are formed by the vapor from the warmer sea water rising, condensing and freezing, the successive droplets forming long, pendant crystals.

There is one point I should like to make clear. The notion that the winter night is pitch dark is an exaggeration. A completely dark night is the exception rather than the rule. On what was presumably the darkest night of all, June 21st, when the sun is at its greatest distance below the horizon, a narrow ribbon of pale red illuminated the northern horizon at noon. Often, after a stiff blow from the south, the darkness of a water sky, which indicated the Ross Sea was open, stood out sharply against the lighter hues of the night. Throughout July, save when the sky was overcast, a widening arch of light in the northern sky heralded the slow-returning day. The winter night is, as a rule, a dark somber gray rather than total darkness. And, besides, one does become accustomed to partial darkness.

The Aurora Australis, the Antarctic equivalent of the Aurora Borealis, which rarely failed to appear,[1] imparted a lovely illumination to the night. Most of these displays were seen shortly after midnight, although there was generally a second period of subsidiary maximum between 6 and 7 o'clock at night. They were but rarely seen at noon. By far the greatest number appeared in the east, and the fewest in the direction of the south magnetic Pole. The appearance of the aurora in the west came generally in the nature of an advance guard to the more brilliant display in the east.

The aurora is perhaps the most beautiful gift of the heavens. Its form changes constantly, and its coloring and intensity vary with a rapidity that baffles the eye. The fainter displays were usually white, with a greenish or yellow-white overtone, but with increasing intensity other colors—pink, red, violet, green and yellow—made their appearance. On May 4th, we saw a gorgeous display, in which every form of the aurora made its appearance—glows, curtains, arches, coronas, streamers. Shortly after 7 o'clock, a series of undulating curtains stretched across the sky, almost overhead, from

[1] Mr. Davies reports that the proportion of clear or only partly cloudy nights on which the aurora was observed between April 3 and Sept. 26 is more than 90 percent.

Russell Owen, of the *New York Times*.

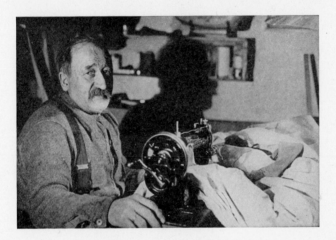

Martin Ronne, Tailor.

The Radio Department:

Left to right:—Howard Mason, Lloyd Berkner, Malcolm Hanson,
Carl Petersen, Lloyd Grenlie.

THE MAIN SNOW TUNNEL CONNECTING THE ADMINISTRATION BUILDING AND
THE MESS HALL.

Food boxes line the upper walls, and the entrances to several of the storerooms can be
seen. Most of the rooms were hewn in the snow.

east to west, with a band of pink and purple running along the edges, and rose and straw-yellow softly suffusing the interior. For a few moments these curtains rippled and shimmered, as if shaken by some Olympian hand. Then they parted, and a mass of colors, deep and intense, whirling and turbulent, came in, like actors taking the stage, and filled the Heavens with color. Once I had the unusual experience of seeing an aurora, a sunset glow and the moon at the same time. It occurred on May 19th. I had stepped out for a breath of fresh air. Far to the north the distant sun, shining on distant parts of the world, painted a thin line of yellow on the horizon. Due east, the moon, red and glowing, strove to push clear of fragments of cloud wrack that obscured its face; and from the north to the south the aurora weaved in pale and lovely curtains.

But the Antarctic night can be as black as the darkest pit, when the sky is overcast or stormy. On such occasions the daily walk had a spice of adventure. The beacon on the northeastern radio tower was always turned on when conditions were bad, but even its friendly and reassuring wink was obscured by light falling snow. On June 25th, during the severest blizzard we had theretofore experienced, Harrison insisted upon taking the overland trail between the houses. In the dense drift he lost his way, and if the wind had not shifted slightly, so that he caught sight of the beacon, in the brief time it was exposed, it might well have been the end of him. Our cook was nearly lost in the same way. Toward the end of the winter, we honored Tennant with a holiday, to give him an opportunity to study the Antarctic from a different position than the galley. He celebrated it promptly by getting lost between the main houses; and after vain feints through the murk stumbled at last upon the mess house. He was so chagrined that he would not venture out thereafter except when the sky was clear, for which we were properly grateful.

It was easy to become lost, even within a radius of fifty feet of the camp. After a blizzard, everything about Little America, save the radio towers, was buried in snow. The houses and the airplane hangars were obliterated, and it took a practiced eye to distinguish the identities of the shapeless

mounds that showed above the surface. In a storm, even
these few landmarks disappeared; and the walker thus over-
taken had to rely upon a sense of direction and a glimpse of
the beacon to guide him home.

However boring may be the subject of weather in civilization, it is ever a lively topic in the Antarctic. It is a vital
subject to the scientists, in the first place. And its vagaries
and excesses were interesting to all.

May began with a warm spell. On the 2nd the thermometer registered as high as 13 degrees above zero. But
on the 4th it plunged to 42° below. On the 26th, a wind
from the south-southeast drove it up to 5° above after an
uninterrupted spell of sub-zero weather, but the wind shifted
again to the east and before the day ended, the thermometer
read 38° below zero. The monthly average was 22.6° below.

June was rather a temperate month, with a mean temperature of 10.7° below. On one day, the 9th, it was actually
warm, the thermometer registering as high as 15° above zero.
This month was marked by two extraordinary phenomena.
On the 11th and on the 19th what was undeniably a misty rain
fell, which, as it clung to windward side of the radio towers
and other exposed surfaces, formed a rime which built up into
a beautiful fringe of ice crystals. From one end to the other
the camp was festooned with these ice flowers, some of which
were three to four inches in length, and the scene was in-
describably beautiful. There were a number of occasions
on which fog formed at temperatures as low as 40° below
zero, in quantities thick enough to obscure objects less than
1,000 feet away. That water vapor can exist in a sub-cooled
state in nature at such low temperatures was a great surprise
to many of us, and science has not yet evolved a satisfactory
theory for its presence.

Next to March, June was the snowiest month of our stay.
The snowfall for the month was 16.2 inches.

July came in frostily, with a temperature of 60° below
the first day. It went out with a roar. The wind reached
a velocity of 75 miles per hour for one minute on the 30th [1],
and on the 31st was still blowing hard. For 27 days the
temperature fluctuated between 2° above and 69° below. On

[1] This was the highest wind velocity recorded at Little America.

the 28th, it plunged to 72° below zero. [1] On the 31st, it recorded 11° above. The monthly average was 44.7° below. Five blizzards, three of great severity, distinguished July. Yet, from the point of view of clearness, it was the best month of all. There were 17 clear days.

August came in warm, with a temperature of 15° above, but it went out in a chill, the temperature for the 31st being 66° below. During a severe storm on the 16th, the barometer dropped to the lowest point ever recorded in the Antarctic, 27.82 inches. [2] Yet much worse storms were heralded with a less drastic fall. Over and over again, it was shown that the barometer was wholly unreliable in foreshadowing weather conditions in the Antarctic. On the 22nd, the winter was officially closed when the sun returned.

How cold was it, really, at Little America?

Well, let us look at Haines' charts. During 114 days the temperature reached 40° below zero; on 62 days, 50° below; on 33 days, 60° below, and on three days, 70° below. Yet it was subject to violent changes. During a blizzard on the 5th and 6th of June, the temperature rose from 49° below to 16° above in the space of 20 hours—a change of 65 degrees. A rise in temperature of from 30° to 40° within a few hours was not uncommon during a blizzard; in fact, was a characteristic resultant. So we came to welcome a blizzard as a mixed blessing: it was a nuisance by itself, but it generally lifted the siege of a protracted cold spell. However, when the wind shifted to the south, as it often did after a blizzard, the temperature retaliated by falling quite as rapidly as it rose. So we never had reason to complain of the heat.

These excessive temperatures had singular effects. One of the most fascinating manifestations to men who had never heard of the phenomenon was the freezing of the breath. When the temperature went under 60° below one's breath froze as it exhaled, with a sound like a wind rustling over snow. It is an uncanny thing, and the day when it first was observed, the incredulous members of the expedition insisted

---

[1] This was the lowest temperature of the year, comparing with Amundsen's lowest of 74.4° below zero.

[2] 27.85 inches reduced to sea level.

on going outside to test their own breaths, before they would
accept the fact.

When the temperature fell below 55°, kerosene lanterns
used in the tunnel would go out, though not a breath of air
was stirring. The fuel, of course, had frozen. The rubber
insulation on the telephone wires became brittle and broke
when handled. Rucker and Van der Veer had a horrible time
with their motion picture cameras. In severe cold, the moving
parts would bind, owing to unequal contraction. Under 25°
below, the film began to break, and the men had to rethread
them with bare hands, while their frozen fingers stuck painfully to metal parts. After such an operation, I have seen
them dancing about in the snow, hugging their hands under
their armpits, like men possessed. The slightest bit of moisture in the cameras froze the moment it was exposed. The
instruments were usually left outside, for on coming in contact with the warm air of the houses they immediately were
covered with frost. In cases where cameras were brought in,
before they could be used again, it was necessary to take them
apart, wipe them thoroughly and bake them for several hours
near the stove. If Rucker or Van der Veer breathed on the
lenses, however slightly, the vapor froze in irremovable frost
and went out of action. Yet these two men accepted this
inconvenience as part of the job: I have seen few men so
absorbed in their work as Van der Veer was absorbed in his
photography.

The light, drifting snow was no less a nuisance. It sifted
into everything, through the narrowest of openings; and
whether the ultimate place of lodgment was the surface of a
lens or the back of one's neck, it invariably found a way
through. Unless one took great precautions, a walk in these
lowest temperatures was likely to bring real suffering.

When winter came, we were well-clothed to meet it,
thanks to the labors of Ronne, who worked so hard making
and repairing clothes for the rest of us that he had no time
to attend to his own.

The fundamental unit of cold weather clothing is the
parka, which is the Eskimo's overcoat. It is a development
of ages of combat with the cold and is the most nearly
perfect thing of its kind. Mine was made of reindeer skin,

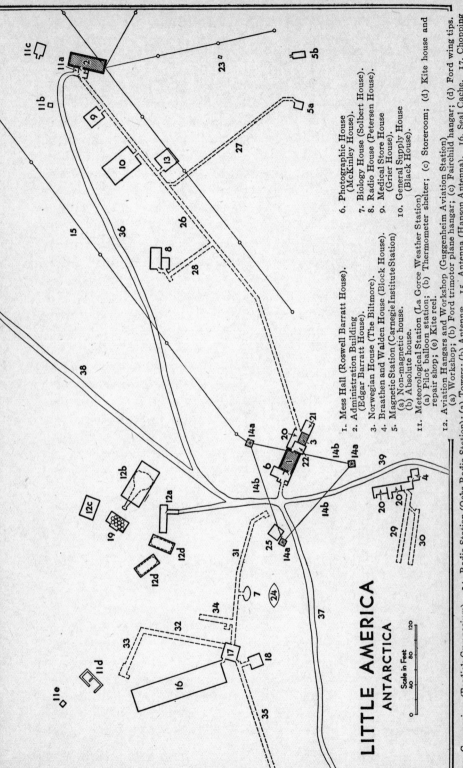

LITTLE AMERICA
ANTARCTICA

Scale in Feet
0 40 80 120

1. Mess Hall (Roswell Barratt House).
2. Administration Building (Edgar Barratt House).
3. Norwegian House (The Biltmore).
4. Braathen and Walden House (Block House).
5. Magnetic Station (Carnegie Institute Station)
   (a) Non-magnetic house.
   (b) Absolute house.
6. Photographic House (McKinley House).
7. Biology House (Solbert House).
8. Radio House (Petersen House).
9. Medical Store House (Grier House).
10. General Supply House (Black House).
11. Meteorological Station (La Gorce Weather Station)
    (a) Pilot balloon station; (b) Thermometer shelter; (c) Storeroom; (d) Kite house and repair shop; (e) Kite reel.
12. Aviation Hangars and Workshop (Guggenheim Aviation Station)
    (a) Workshop; (b) Ford trimotor plane hangar; (c) Fairchild hangar; (d) Ford wing tips.

13. Gymnasium (Fosdick Gymnasium). 14. Radio Station (Ochs Radio Station). 15. Antennæ; (a) Towers; (b) Antennæ. 16. Seal Cache. 17. Chopping House. 18. Maternity Ward. 19. Gasoline Cache. 20. Storerooms. 21. Coal Cache. 22. Machine Shop. 23. Radio Direction Finder. 24. Life Boat. 25. Snowmobile. 26. Main Tunnel (Lofgren Tunnel). 27. Magnetic Tunnel (Ronne Tunnel). 28. Fuel Tunnel (Bubier Tunnel). 29. Dog Tunnel (Walden Tunnel). 30. Dog Tunnel (Strom Tunnel). 31. Dog Tunnel (Parker Tunnel). 32. Dog Tunnel (Rucker Tunnel). 33. Dog Tunnel (June Tunnel). 34. Dog Tunnel (de Ganahl Tunnel). 35. Dog Tunnel (Van der Veer Tunnel). 36. Path between Administration Building and Mess Hall (Greason Street). 37. Trail to Bay (Finley Trail). 38. Trail to North (Carson Trail). 39. Trail to South (Grosvenor Trail).

with wolverine rimming the hood. It weighed about six pounds; yet even during walks when the thermometer registered as low as 60° below zero, it offered adequate warmth. It is my opinion that a reindeer skin parka, if properly made and worn, offers double the warmth of the wool parka at half the weight. During the coldest weather, I rarely wore more than twelve pounds of clothing. The cut of my parka I borrowed from the Eskimos at Etah, on the theory that, having lived for centuries in the polar regions, they surely must have developed an efficient cold weather garment. During my daily walks I often tested out new kinds of clothing.

The parka fitted the body snugly, especially about the hips, with a flap that went under the crotch and buttoned in front. It carried a hood, the edges of which projected beyond the face, so as to shield it from the wind. The armpits were made very large, so that the arms could be drawn inside for additional warmth. In a dead calm one can endure very low temperatures with slight discomfort. In fact, a walk at 50° below in still air is rather an exhilarating experience. It is the wind that is cruel. The faintest wind, moving supercooled air against the face, tortures the traveller to distraction. If the wind is not too strong, the projecting rim of the hood forms a cushion of air warmed by the face and offers some protection. But otherwise if the wind is dead ahead, it is better to turn the head sideways. Often, during walks in bitter cold, I came across my colleagues beating their way back to Little America stern first, rather than expose their faces to the knife-like edge of the wind. How great a difference the wind causes was proved by a series of experiments made by Dr. Coman and Mr. Davies on the cooling power of the air under different weather conditions. On July 28th, when the temperature was 70° below and the velocity of the wind about 2½ miles per hour, the skin lost 52 millicalories per square centimeter per second. On August 16th, when the temperature was 5.5° above, and therefore actually 75° warmer, the skin lost 95 millicalories per square centimeter per second. The difference lay in the wind which was then blowing at a velocity of 30 miles per hour.

During a walk, with the temperature in excess of 60° below, my eyelashes froze quite tight. It was so difficult trying to keep them open that I decided to make a face mask. The final product, which was made by June, resembled a baseball mask. It consisted of a wire structure which was covered with wind-proof material. A funnel-like arrangement led to the mouth. The air was drawn in through the nostrils, and it was expelled in turn through the mouth. As the exhalations condensed and collected in the funnel in the form of rime, it was brushed off with the hand. It was an inconvenient device, but it offered great protection. Rucker invented another type, which fitted over the eyes like goggles and had a wool curtain which draped over the jaw. This curtain was tucked around the neck of the parka, and could be fitted in whatever shape was desired. For example, if the wind was striking the left side of the face, a breathing hole could be made on the other side, and the mask immediately froze in whatever shape it was put.

I suppose we turned out a thousand different kinds of things to beat the cold, some of which were successful, some of which were not. The basis of most of them was reindeer skin, which I believe to be the lightest and the warmest fur that can be had. It is much warmer per unit of weight, than seal skin and, therefore, much more efficient. We had brought the skins of fifty young reindeer to the Antarctic, and these Ronne turned into sleeping bags, parkas, and pants, for the men who could not be properly equipped from the ready-made supplies brought from the United States. The pants were generally made of the softer portion of the hide and were not as thick as the parka, because the limbs are less susceptible to cold.

The feet are the most vulnerable point to frost, especially on the trail. Moisture forms as a result of the cold air coming in contact with the heat of the body and collects as rime, and frost bite, if precautions are not taken, is the result. The warmest boot that I know of is the finnesko. It is entirely covered with fur. Several layers of felt are padded on the bottom, and over them is laid a matting of saennegrass. This grass absorbs the perspiration, and so helps to keep the feet dry. When the shoe is removed, the saennegrass can be lifted out, the rime brushed off and the boot itself kept free of moisture. It may seem odd, but moisture is the curse of Antarctic travellers; it is an enemy no less malicious than wind.

The hours we spent in planning our cold weather clothes, both before we left New York and during our stay in the Antarctic, perhaps exceeded the time we devoted to any other single thing. We steeped ourselves in the lore evolved by such experienced polar travellers as Scott, Shackleton, Mawson, Amundsen and the others. When experience justified it, we added some new development of our own. Always, as we experimented with different kinds of clothing during the winter, we had in mind the proper equipment of the trail parties which we should leave in the spring and the airplane personnel who might have a forced landing far from base. Once the journeys began, proper clothing would be no less important than food.

Let us consider the boot. A simple thing: enough leather to encase the foot and protect it, thongs to bind it tight— what more is necessary? Much, much more. Some of the finest brains enlisted in geographical research have struggled futilely with the problem of what constitutes the most efficient boot for polar travelling. Failure in this respect can bring dire suffering. For every man who freezes his hands in the polar regions, there are 25 who freeze their feet. If Achilles was vulnerable in one heel, polar explorers are particularly so in both heels.

With ski boots, for example, the problem lies in inducing shoemakers to make them large enough to accommodate extra protection. Whether it is because they object to excessively large boots from the point of view of art, or simply think that you are wrong, I do not know. The fact is, in bitter cold weather adequate warmth can be secured only by the use of three or four pairs of stockings, plus a liberal quantity of felt and saennegrass on the bottom of the boot. If the throat of the boot is not large enough to admit the enlarged member, the traveller is out of luck. To guard against this contingency, I borrowed from Amundsen the largest boot used on his expedition, and had the boots that were made for us modelled on the same heroic mould. They were about size No. 14. How large they were may be judged from the fact that when I had my boots cut down for summer use, they were still large, even though diminished by three sizes.

No one on this expedition had reason to criticize the boots as not being large enough. The boots were ample enough for temperatures of 70° below zero. They were, of course, much too large for summer wear, and especially for use on a long sledging journey. It was, therefore, necessary to redesign later and make them smaller. Thorne, for example, designed and made an entirely new type of ski boot with material which he had brought to the Antarctic. Balchen and Strom also proved very skillful in cutting down the stock boots for summer use. These boots were made with a flexible leather top, with a leather sole half an inch thick, and were especially strengthened in the heel, where most of the wear comes in skiing. The beauty of these boots lay in a shrewd arrangement by means of which the size could be altered without the impairment of snugness. A pucker thong secured at the heel ran about the ankle, and this could be loosened or tightened, according to the number of stockings one decided to wear. We learned many new things during the winter. When subjected to excessive use, the uppers of these boots, which were fastened to the soles as with ordinary boots, had the tendency to pull loose, and were very difficult to repair. On Thorne's suggestion, we carried the fabric of the uppers outward instead of inward where they were seamed to the sole, and as a result were not troubled by the fault again.

Complementary to this supply of clothing we had windproof shirts, parkas, pants, mittens, socks and sleeve protectors. These were made of a fabric similar to that used in making airplane fuselages, which is so closely woven that the wind does not readily penetrate it. The windproof pants and parkas were worn over fur clothes, and were splendid for keeping drifting snow from seeping down one's neck and into one's boots. I rather believe that windproof material was used more extensively on our expedition than on any previous expedition to the Antarctic. How very effective this windproof material is can be appreciated only by a person who has faced a biting wind with and without it.

The sleeping bags were mostly made from reindeer skin,

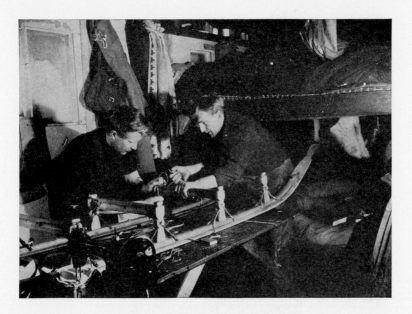

BALCHEN AND STROM BUILD A SLEDGE.

ROTH, RUCKER AND JUNE AT WORK.

Dr. Francis Dana Coman, Surgeon and Biologist.

William C. Haines, Meteorologist.

Frank T. Davies, Physicist.

and were covered with windproof material. Sleeping bags were at once the joy and the torment of the camp. I doubt whether there were any two that were alike. Each man modelled his according to his personal theories, with the result that some slept with untroubled serenity and warmth and others complained of cold all winter long. My bag had a cover which fitted snugly and had a zipper arrangement so that it could be drawn closely about the throat, thus preventing the warm air from escaping. Braathen, on the other hand, built his bag with a complicated arrangement of straps and flaps by means of which it could be altered at will. It was the most intricate thing of its kind that I have ever seen, and getting into it was like putting on a full dress uniform. But it worked.

Enough clothes to keep warm, enough food to eat, a few things to divert the mind occasionally—these are the only things that are required in the Antarctic. It is amazing what contentment can be had from them. "What do you miss most in the Antarctic, Taffy?" I asked our physicist. He replied, "Temptation."

CHAPTER XI

MORE PLANS AND PREPARATIONS

"But you will come away hating one another. The winter night will be a dreadful bore." Thus, our well-meaning friends as we started south. Now hate is an emotional state that may be acquired anywhere, in a Fifth Avenue drawing room as easily as in a Siberian garrison—more easily, I dare say. And boredom is a surfeited state of mind that has no connection with lines of longitude. Hate? No, we had little of that. There were passing irritations, of course—most of them mild, a few intense. Some, it is true, lasted a long time. One man may have talked too much, to the occasional distaste of several of his fellows. Another had an ungovernable tendency to lose everything he needed the next moment, and would turn the camp topsy-turvy until he recovered it. And still another insisted on telling long, elaborate and (to many) pointless yarns. One or two men were undeniably lazy and this was irritating to all hands.

The great balancing force was the strength of loyalty that infused the organization. Even the lazy man sincerely and keenly wished the expedition to succeed and I should prefer a laggard who sincerely liked his expedition to an energetic man who is unable to give loyalty to anything—not even himself. There are such men, but fortunately we had none of them. Otherwise, our government could not have lasted. But show me a group of men who have lived for a year in unbroken harmony, whose gorges have failed to rise ever so faintly at these very same nuisances or similar ones, and I shall have the doubtful privilege of seeing inhuman dolts.

Boredom? Certainly we were bored at times. There were for all of us periods toward the end of winter when it seemed that time stood still, and the spring and the sun would never come. But those were rare occasions. We were so taken up

238

with special tasks that had to be done that spring seemed to be rushing at us, and the night too short to allow us time for leisure, much less to be bored.

Bear in mind that the men who went south with me were unusual men, picked from thousands, and for the most part were keen men, with an interest in the unusual. A few were brilliant, most were above the average, and the rest were the type of men you can find anywhere and everywhere, doing the routine and the odd jobs of the world with steady sureness. Some were students, with a passionate love of knowledge for knowledge's sake, and some would not have given a pin for all the knowledge you could pack in the *City of New York*. Some could take a piece of wood, a bolt of cloth, or a fragment of metal and turn it into the neatest and most ingenious contrivance an exploring party might wish for, and there were others who could not keep a fire going if their lives depended upon it. Some were of the virile, out-of-doors type, to whom "roughing it" was a pleasure, and others hated it as a meager and limited existence, and refused to venture far from the stoves until spring came.

But every one of them had a special thing which I thought he did well, or he had an especially fine character that fitted well with our scheme of things. Otherwise he would not have been there. They were prepared to suffer hardships. Had they not, they certainly would not have come. They were willing to endure them without the reward of personal gain. Still they came. These men were not sentimentalists. They were men who had been around, and could penetrate to the true nature of things. And because of the common interest, the common objective and the common keenness, they were capable of a loyalty, tolerance and vivacity that are rarely found except under these circumstances. I had to smile when told that presumably sophisticated New York magazines were inclined to regard them as Rover Boys. Sophistication, I take it, consists of finding more and more fine things to hold up for ridicule by and before intelligences that are too lazy or dishonest to investigate the facts. Least of all they were that. They were as a group the most unafraid men I have ever met.

Some persons have a queer way of looking at things. Surprising as it may seem, we did not enter the Antarctic to create a newspaper story or to develop a motion picture.

Hardly. We were in search of information, information that had perhaps no immediate practical usefulness, but that was certainly of great value to science.

Now surely it was worth while to prepare extensively so as to bring pioneering, which is undeniably hazardous, to as low an order of risk and discomfort as is possible. Half the labor of mankind is directed toward finding a more efficient and less dangerous way of doing things. Yet the head of an immense corporation said on our return: "You did your job too easily. It lacked hardships and tragedy." Rubbish!

No Antarctic journey, whether by air or by surface, is easy. Too many fine men have died, too many more have suffered hardships beyond the ability of other men to describe, to permit that statement to stand. Of course aerial exploration of the polar regions is vastly less troublesome and very much faster than sledging. But each has its particular risks, which are obvious enough not to require definition here: enough to say that the gain in comfort and speed that the airplane provides is offset somewhat, at least at this period in its development, by the independence of ground travel from all but the worst kind of weather and its comparative security from all but the worst kinds of hazards.

So often we make the mistake of believing that because a mission is executed with sureness and without mishap it must have been easy. The history of polar exploration is full of contrasts. Witness the southern journeys of Scott and Amundsen. For years it was the practice of certain critics to minimize the risk and the difficulties in Amundsen's dash to the Pole. Even Scott, on being confronted by the Norwegians' tracks a few miles to the Pole, decided hastily they must have found an easier way.[1]

The two parties, Amundsen's returning north after reaching the Pole, Scott's still pressing desperately southward, passed each other unseen about 75 miles apart on the polar plateau; and what a picture that must have made, were there an eye to take in both. On the one hand a party moving rapidly and surely according to plan, always on schedule, always confident, light of heart and full in stomach. And on the other hand a party lifting itself from one superhuman

[1] "Scott's Last Journey," vol. i, p. 374.

effort into another, from one crisis to another, exhausted by attrition, hunger and storm, weakened by injuries, their endurance falling steadily behind their needs, until at last they perished, all of them, on the trail.

Amundsen's journey was perhaps the easier one. It was so for several reasons. He chose dogs for transport, whereas Scott, who had little faith in dogs, threw in his lot with Manchurian ponies. Amundsen also took his risks. He was the first man to dare to winter on the Barrier: and in doing so reduced his southern journey by 100 miles. This, was a bold stroke recommended by judgment. And, finally, he cut out for himself an entirely new route to the Pole, with all the risks involved in that choice, whereas Scott knew what he had to face, as he pursued the route by means of which Shackleton had come within 97 miles of the Pole in 1908.

This is no criticism of the gallant Scott. There were variables in his problem that no one, save the excellent men who lie with him in his whitened sepulchre, are qualified to determine. In dying, in failing, he gave the world something much more worth while than success. He gave it an intellectual experience worth the attainment of a dozen South Poles.

But let us bear with the living. There can be only one Scott, and martyrdom, whatever our distinguished critic might have thought, was not to be our destiny, if we could help it. We were humble workers, as afraid to fail as we were eager to succeed. "Victory awaits him who has everything in order— luck, people call it? Defeat is certain for him who has neglected to take the necessary precautions in time: this is called bad luck." [1] Even so, the caprices of the polar regions may upset the best laid plans.

The hours and hours we spent in working out every detail of the planning that preceded every journey can be taken as evidence of the care with which we approached these particular problems. Nothing was left to chance. Committees were appointed to investigate all propositions, and to work out the most feasible plan of operations and the most effective equipment with which to accomplish the job. We had with us one of the best polar libraries in the world, and this was used extensively, to supply information that we lacked in personal

[1] Amundsen, "The South Pole," i, 370.

experience. By the end of winter the volumes on the Antarctic had been worn shabby and were discolored from uninterrupted use.

There was, for example, the committee on the Polar Flight, consisting of Balchen, McKinley, June, Smith, Parker and myself; mechanics Bubier, Demas and Roth sat in on these conferences and gave us valuable advice. This committee had the task of working out the specific operation of getting the Ford to the Pole and back. This was no mere matter of gassing it up, and flying there and back. Apart from the difficulties of navigation, which must be anticipated and prepared for, there were scores of problems on the proper solution of which would rest the success of the flight. How much fuel and oil would be required to accomplish the flight? What constituted a safe reserve? What was the maximum weight that could be allowed for emergency food and sledge equipment in case of a forced landing? What was the minimum that could be taken, to insure the safe return of personnel? How much weight could be allowed for engine repair equipment in case a forced landing can be made without injury to the plane? What separate courses of procedure would be most effective for relief of the Polar Party in case of a forced landing some distance from the base: (a) for the Polar Flight group, (b) for the base party and (c) for the dog parties in the field?

These were but a few of the problems that bore on this single undertaking: and the pros and cons were argued and discussed all through the winter night, before the final plan was drafted.

Perhaps it would be interesting to sit in, for a few moments, on one of the sessions of this committee. It convened after supper generally in the library, which served also as my office. Three sides of the library were taken up by shelves, on which Owen had neatly stacked the books. The only picture on the wall was that of Floyd Bennett, for whom we named the Polar plane. It was draped with an American flag. Near the center was a small caboose stove which threw off a ruddy glow. In one corner was Lofgren's desk, and in another was Owen's with his portable typewriter on it. There were three different types of collapsible chairs. We were jammed rather closely together, as the library was only about twelve feet square. Often a blizzard, which raked the Barrier mercilessly, howled

and moaned in the ventilator, a sound like nothing else on
this earth.

Even intimate friends would scarcely have recognized in
the group the men who had started from the United States.
June's luxuriant black beard gave him such a convincing resemblance to General Grant that one looked quickly for the
loose-fitting campaign coat, and the right hand hanging limply
at the lapel. No less startling was Smith's resemblance to
Lincoln, for his beard was cut in the same way, and his tall,
loosely-hung body and high brow were more than a passing
parallel. Were it not for the heavy clothes which we all wear
this might have been a conference in a campaign shack on the
Potomac. In spite of the warmth of the stove, there was
always a cold draught circulating about one's back and feet
when the wind is blowing.

Byrd: "It would now appear definite that the Polar
flight cannot be made non-stop."

Balchen, with a smile at McKinley: "Not unless we make
McKinley walk. His weight and food and extra clothes and
the weight of the camera and film make the difference. If we
took gasoline instead we could do it." [1]

McKinley, with a broader smile: "If I wasn't partially
deaf, I would knock you down for that, Bernt."

Byrd: "Well, we can't get around that. McKinley and
his camera have to go. Mapping the area between the base
and the Pole is as important, to our purposes, as reaching the
Pole itself. Let's make this definite: hereafter, in all calculations the weight of McKinley and his camera are to be considered essential load."

Balchen: "Of course the limiting factor on the range of
the polar flight is the ceiling of the Ford. If we expect to
clear the 'Hump,' [2] we should have a minimum service ceil-

[1] I confess that this dialogue has been edited. No stenographic form
could hope to catch Balchen's charming accents and his experiments in
syntax, and none would dare repeat the emphatic expletives which sooner
or later become accepted words in the polar idiom.

[2] The "Hump" is the name we conferred upon that part of the Queen
Maud Range which we hoped to hurdle. In our calculations for the
flight, we decided to climb the Axel Heiberg Glacier, more or less following Amundsen's path, because it appeared to present, according to Amundsen's surveys, the lowest stairway to the plateau. The height of the pass
was estimated to be 10,500 feet. Surrounding it were the great peaks of

ing [1] of 11,000 feet. The maximum load that will give that service ceiling is, if I recall correctly, 12,500 pounds. If we take off with a load of say 14,500 pounds, we will use up the difference in fuel on the way to the Mountains. We have worked out the Ford's range both graphically and with Brequet's formula as modified by Diehl, and they check, giving a range, with the gasoline and the heavy load of equipment we must carry, of about 1700 miles. That's not enough to take us from Little America to the Pole and back. But if we plan to lay down a base in the vicinity of Queen Maud Mountains it would give us a fuel reserve of about 15 percent over needs from Little America to the Pole and back to the mountain base."

Smith: "I don't think it would be wise to attempt the flight, non-stop or with two stops, with less than a 20 percent factor of safety. If we meet head winds, we'll be out of luck. Winds are so changeable down here that we may have head winds both going in and coming out. What do you make the distance to the Pole?"

Balchen: "820 miles."

Byrd: "I make it 790. Well, we must get this more accurately, and run some careful fuel and altitude tests next spring. We may get an improved or lesser performance down here. So our figures now must be tentative. Taking everything into consideration—food, tools, sledges, medical supplies, tents, scientific gear, radio, etc.—what do you estimate to be the minimum take-off load from Little America?"

Balchen: "About 14,500 pounds, maybe a little more."

Byrd: "I've got it nearly to that figure."

June: "We have now figured out that a month's supply of food is enough, allowing 75 pounds of food per man."

Byrd: "Not enough. We would be foolish to start with less than two months' supply, and I prefer three. We cannot

---

Ole Engelstad, Don Pedro Cristopherson and Nansen, rising from 15,000 to 19,000 feet, according to Amundsen.

[1] By service ceiling is meant the altitude at which an airplane has still the capacity of a rate of climb of 100 feet per minute. Absolute ceiling is that altitude at which it can climb no farther. These quantities change, naturally, with a given plane according to load and horsepower. Owing to the great elevations with which we had to contend, we were reluctant to diminish the service ceiling below this point lest we meet strong winds in the pass or over the plateau, in which case we would require a generous reserve of horsepower to climb or maneuver out of danger.

afford to experiment with food. Man-hauling is the toughest kind of pulling. If we are forced down at the Pole, or near it, it will take us at least two months to walk back to the base of the mountains, and we might not be able to do it at all with any amount of food. If Amundsen were here he would say it couldn't be done. I have talked this over with him a number of times. He had no faith in men man-hauling long distances, specially without depots, and pulling on a plateau 10,000 feet high. Dean, will you please read Shackleton's, Scott's and Mawson's books, and draw up in table form the distances that have been travelled by man-hauling? We are probably over-estimating our abilities."

McKinley: "Personally, I'm in favor of two flights—a base-laying fight and the polar flight. It will give me two chances to photograph the Queen Maud Range. Visibility may be so poor on the polar flight, if it is tried non-stop, that we won't be able to get decent pictures. But from your point of view, two flights are not good. It will involve two landings away from base."

Byrd: "Well, the second is the lesser of two risks. Suppose we do put down a base at the foot of the Queen Maud Range, to be picked up on the return from the Pole. We ought to be able to cache enough gasoline to make a flight over Carmen Land before returning to Little America. That is, if weather permits. We could then make two flights in one. Besides, with a lessened load we ought to be able to improve performance on the plateau."

Parker: "Where do you believe the base ought to be put?"

Smith: "About 400 or 500 miles out, and I'm in favor of putting it right at the foot of Axel Heiberg Glacier, if we can find a smooth place. It will be easier to find and, on the flight back, we won't have to fly so far to reach it. The distance is about 350 miles, I think. Now the limiting factor on the base-laying flight is the amount of load we can land safely at this base. It would be hazardous, in my opinion, to try to land with a load of much over 13,000 pounds. To land with more would put a wicked strain on the ship."

Balchen: "We figured we could land with 13,000 pounds. We allowed a month's supply of food for four men for emergency on this flight, and considered 450 miles as the distance of the base from Little America. Weight of the plane, less gasoline and with all other essential load, in rough figures, is 8,490 pounds. Gasoline required for flying 800 miles, plus 20 percent safety factor, is 2,800 pounds, assuming consumption of 53 gallons per hour. Total, 11,290 pounds. If we take-off with a load of 14,500 pounds, that leaves us 3,210 pounds for gasoline and oil to be dropped at the depot, which is equivalent to 500 gallons of gasoline and 25 gallons of oil. We will use about 1,500 pounds of fuel flying to the base. Our landing load then will be about 13,000 pounds. We can get away with that."

Byrd: "I don't see how we can allow for less that 440 miles to the base. Here is my list of ideal equipment for the base-laying flight."

	Pounds
Weight of plane, with cranks, tools, etc.	6,710
Additional tools	18
2 blow torches	60
2 motor covers and funnels	34
Radio	109
Survey camera	100
Motion picture camera	40
Food, 4 men, two months, at 69.05 lbs. per man per month	552.40
Sledge equipment, plus clothes both reserve and worn	624
4 men, not including clothes	700
Plane navigation equipment	36.50
Miscellaneous equipment	50
25 gals. oil at 8 lbs. per gal.	200
Gas for 900 miles at 6 lbs. per gal., and consumption of 52 gals. per hour, with 20% safety factor	3,370
Total	12,603.90

"Even with a take-off load of 14,600 pounds, we then could only carry about 2,000 pounds of oil and gasoline to the base."

June: "The amount of gasoline you can cache also depends upon whether you carry it in cans alone, or in cans held in boxes. In 5 gallon cans, the gasoline averages 7 pounds per gallon; with the boxes, 9 pounds per gallon. If the field is bumpy, you ought to have boxes. The cans won't stand much pounding around."

Byrd: "We shall figure on that later. But first of all, let us figure out our needs for the polar flight, and from that work backward to the base-laying flight. Here's my list of ideal equipment for this flight:

	Pounds
Plane with skis, fire extinguishers, cranks, tools, etc.	6,728
3 blow torches	85
3 motor covers and oil funnels	50
Radio, not including sledge radio	109
Aerial survey camera	100
Motion picture camera	40
Food, 4 men, 3 months	828.60
4 men (not including clothes worn	700
Sledge equipment (includes clothes worn)	624
Gasoline for 1,200 miles, allowing 20% safety factor, 780 gallons	4,680
50 gallons of oil	400
Large and small chronometers	6
Operative and ship compass	14
Extra sun compass	1
30 smoke bombs	15
Miscellaneous (not anticipated)	50
Total take-off load	14,430.6

"We may assume an average speed of 100 m.p.h. The distance from Little America to the Pole is approximately 790 miles, and back to the mountain base 1135 miles. That means 11.35 hours flying time, if all goes well. If we take 780 gallons of gasoline from Little America, we shall have enough for 15 hours, or 3.65 hours above expected needs. That gives us a safety factor of 24%. We shall then have 190 gallons of gas in the tanks. If we carry out the schedule for the base-laying flight, there will be an additional 265 gallons which can be picked up there, or a total of 455 gallons, equivalent to 8.7 hours. With that amount, we could make a 100 mile flight to the East, to investigate Carmen Land, and return to Little America with a safety factor of 25%. That ought to be about what we want."

Parker: "I think that some of your weights are too high. The weight you give for sledging equipment can be reduced, and also the repair equipment."

Byrd: "We ought to get correct figures on these things immediately. Harold, you start the fellows moving on this. Hanson has promised to give me the exact weights on the radio equipment within the next few days. Blackie ought to be able to help you with the other things. Every item must be weighed carefully, even to the fractions. If it is possible, we ought to try to get away from here with a take-off load of less than 14,500 pounds for the base-laying flight.[1] By cutting down equipment to bare necessities, and reducing the rations to two months, we can reduce the weight to 13,800. But I am not sure that this skimping is wise."

Balchen: "Smith and I have worked up the performance tables, and they show that we can't expect very much in case of engine failure on the plateau. If one of the engines fail while we are over the plateau we shall have to come down. Whether we can bring down that heavy load safely on the rough surface is doubtful."

Parker: "A single-engined plane would be the most efficient plane for this hop. The fact that we have three engines will offer no protection on the plateau. If any one of the engines stops, we shall have to come down. As a matter of fact, the risk of a forced landing on the plateau is substantially increased with three engines over a single engine. There are three that might fail instead of one. And there is little gain in safety to compensate for it.

McKinley: "It's a pity we lost the Fokker."

Smith: "Well, we can still greater improve performance here by decreasing the pay load."

Byrd: "All right. Let's see what we need. Harold, what is the minimum weight you allow for tools?"

And so it went on, as Mr. Webster's comic strip says, long into the (winter) night, until reams of paper had been covered with scribbling and figures, and the library was blue with tobacco smoke.

Meanwhile, Professor Gould and his aides were working out the journey of the Southern Party, which became known as the Geological Party. The planning of this journey was no less complicated than that of the Polar flight. The pur-

---

[1] The reason for this is probably already clear. A lessened load meant less strain on the skis at the take-off, better performance in flight and an increased ceiling.

poses of this journey were several. Primarily, the party proposed to make extended glaciological and geological studies in the central area of Queen Maud Range, in Carmen Land and in the unnamed highlands which Amundsen had noted between Latitudes 81° and 82° S. [1] The Queen Maud Range was one of the most important places left in the world to investigate geologically. Then it would be a great help to have the party in the vicinity of our base at the foot of Queen Maud Range before the polar flight was attempted for two reasons: (1) to relay daily weather reports to Little America, so that Haines might be able to predict with greater certainty the weather conditions we were likely to meet in the flight: and (2) to stand by as a relief unit in the event of failure of the flight. Altogether the scope of the Southern Party was one of the most extensive and significant single efforts of the expedition.

The physical difficulties alone involved in the journey would be great. It called for 1,300 miles of sledging, and, if successful, would be one of the longest and most important sledge trips on record made in the interest of pure science.

The objects of this journey were considered so important that during the winter night the activities of the entire camp revolved about its preparation. It was planned that they should leave on the main advance about the middle of October. The Supporting Party, which would assist the Geological Party in advancing its loads out, was to start about two weeks earlier. Next to the routine scientific work, the preparations for this journey took precedence over everything else. Proper preparation was absolutely essential, for the reason that none of the men who would compose the two parties, with the exception of Mr. Walden, had had any previous experience in long-distance sledging. Walden was a veteran dog musher of the old school, and had had a great deal of experience hauling freight in Alaska. But this experience, of course,

[1] Amundsen, quoting from his diary of January 18, on the return from the Pole, described sighting again at Lat. 81° 20′ the pressure ridges he had seen on the way out, and behind them a great mass of ridges and peaks, running northeast and southwest, as far as the eye could see. "Great was our surprise when, a short time later, we made out high bare land in the same direction, and not long after that two lofty white summits to the southeast, probably in about (Lat.) 82° S". Amundsen, "The South Pole", ii, p. 170.

had nothing to do with the intricate planning of food, tents, cookers, distribution of loads, bases, et cetera, which are essential to a prolonged sledging trip in the Antarctic.

But these two parties were fortunate in having the two geniuses—the machinist Czegka, and the tailor Ronne—to help them. They worked at fever heat during the winter to turn out material for both the Supporting Party and the Geological Party. In fact, every man in the camp was behind these operations, and it was one of the most splendid co-operative efforts I have ever had the privilege of seeing. June, for example, placed his mechanical talents unreservedly at their disposal, and Demas slept out doors in a tent during some of the coldest nights in order to get information by means of which the troublesome accumulation of ice in reindeer sleeping bags might be defeated. From beginning to end, the project was a matter of infinite detail, the smallest unit of which could not be ignored.

Space does not permit of a full recital of the planning that went into the development of this unit. It is possible to do no more than hint at them. As we grappled with the intricacies of load on the polar and base-laying flights, so Gould and his men were at grips with the same enemy, but in a different dress. Food—just enough of it, no more, no less than was absolutely necessary—was their problem. They would be out nearly three months, and had to feed not only six men, but also 54 dogs. If we racked our brains on the problem of laying down a single base, they tortured theirs in the planning of eight. In planning the polar flight, we weighed time almost down to the seconds. They doled it out in days, then hours. Time is the universal measurement in the Antarctic. For us, hours spoke for gasoline, gasoline meant flight, and flight meant accomplishment and also safety. For them, days spoke for food, and food for everything.

Buried in the snow behind our colony we had a finished and excellent vehicle to carry us whither we planned: it needed only the application of mathematics, about eighteen hours of good weather and perhaps a bit of boldness and good fortune to see it through. They had to build their sledges, and if weather would inconvenience them only when excessively bad over long periods, certainly they had need of boldness—great

boldness, resourcefulness and unremitting physical effort—
to see them through. We were fortunate in knowing our
jobs more or less exactly: airplanes and flights were our
particular business, and the fundamentals had been drilled
into us. Long-distance sledging was a new thing to them.
However, they made it their business during the winter, poring over books until they knew them nearly by heart. And
if, when they started, their knowledge was partly the theoretical knowledge of the academician, at least they knew what
it was all about.

Sledges? They experimented with a dozen different
models and a hundred different lashings until they developed
the types they believed would best serve their needs. Many,
many intricate details had to be worked out. For example,
what shall be the height of the framework above the snow?
If too low, the framework may not clear a rough surface, and
if the snow is soft, the runners will sink, the framework
will drag and pulling will be beastly hard. Yet if too high,
a heavily-loaded sledge will capsize with exasperating per-
sistency. Well, shall the height be six inches, seven or eight?
What proportion of the surface shall come in contact with
the snow? If too much, pulling may be terribly hard,
especially in cold weather, for then the snow is like sand-
paper. If too little, then the sledges will sink in soft snow.
Very well, let us see what Nansen, Scott, Peary, Amundsen,
Rasmussen, Shackleton and the others have to say on the
subject? And what does Walden think? A good sledge is
a beautiful and efficient thing. It must be rigid in its framework, yet flexible enough to give when travelling over a
rough surface, so that the whole strain shall not come
on any single part of the sledge. This is vital. It is by no
means a simple vehicle. The efficiency of sledges varies
according to its number of factors: its length, weight
carried, surface conditions, workmanship, etc. All these
things must be estimated.

After a series of conferences with Dr. Gould, the following
memorandum was issued dividing into departments the research
which was necessary for this and allied problems, and the
work was assigned as follows:

Memorandum No. 36

The following are given duties as stated opposite their names:

Southern Party:

In command	Larry Gould
Dogs, dog food and man food	Dr. Coman
	O'Brien
	L. Gould
Detailed list, with weights of material to be taken on each sledge	Vaughan
	O'Brien
	L. Gould
Bases, safety precautions	L. Gould
	Vaughan
Skis	Thorne
Sledges	L. Gould
	Strom
	Balchen
Tents, whips, harnesses and gang lines	Goodale
Food cases, sleigh sheets	Crockett
Navigation and flags	L. Gould
	O'Brien
Radio	L. Gould
	Petersen
Sleeping bags	Thorne
	Crockett
	Goodale
Clothing (all but foot gear and gloves)	Vaughan
Devising methods of keeping clothing dry	Thorne
	Vaughan
	Goodale
	Crockett
Foot gear	Thorne
	Vaughan
Gloves	Goodale
	Crockett
Arrangement of tents	L. Gould
	Goodale
Trace Protection	Thorne
	de Ganahl

Problems of the same nature, if of lesser magnitude, faced the Supporting Party, whose job it was to precede the Geological Party in the field and lay down four bases, at intervals of about 50 miles, on a journey which would carry it 200 miles south, through the most dangerous crevasses met by Amundsen and his party on their entire Polar trip. In a sense, the success of the Supporting Party would largely influence the success of the Geological Party, for the latter would be dependent upon these depots. The duties were divided as follows: the assignments being worked out with de Ganahl and Walden.

Supply Officer (for both parties)	Black
Supporting party:	
Sledges	Walden
	Strom
	Bursey
Dogs	Bursey
Dog food, man food and navigation	de Ganahl
	Siple
Skis and harness	Braathen
Safety precautions	Strom
	de Ganahl
	Siple
Tents	Walden
	Strom
Radio	de Ganahl
Bases, sleeping bags, clothing, keeping clothing dry, etc. (will cooperate with and make use of data worked up by Southern Party)	de Ganahl
	Braathen
	Siple
Fuel and Cooker for both parties	Gould
	Czegka
	Mulroy
Medical kit, both parties	Dr. Coman

Each person charged with a duty such as safety precautions, methods of keeping clothing dry, arrangement of tents, sledges, etc., is requested to write out ideas in detail, for discussion with all members of the party. If agreement cannot be reached, the minority opinion will be included in the report. Lofgren will then compile a booklet.

R. E. BYRD.

The fruits of the many efforts were scores of conferences and, finally, a most comprehensive booklet prepared under Dr. Gould's direction, which described in detail the proposed operations of both parties, the procedure by which they were to be carried out, and the methods by which the expected difficulties of the trail might be solved. It was an excellent job, concise and compact, the product of great thought and planning.

Let us pause a moment to look into the plan.

The Supporting Party, which we planned would depart south about the second week in October, had several functions. The major task, of course, was to lay down a series of depots, from which the Geological Party might replenish its supplies both on the way out and back. It was essential that the Geological Party, which faced a much longer journey, should travel as light as possible. Its second responsibility was to make a trail, especially through the crevassed areas that Amundsen reported at Lat. 81° 7'.

These depots were to be placed as follows:

	Position	Miles from Little America[1]
Depot No. 1	Lat. 79° 21' S	44
Depot No. 2	Lat. 80° 10' S	93
Depot No. 3	Lat. 81° 00' S	143
Depot No. 4	Lat. 81° 45' S	188

After putting down Depot No. 4, the Supporting Party was then to turn back and return to the base. Then the Geological Party, which would meanwhile have started south, would press along the trail, picking up the man food and the dog food cached in the depots, to replace amounts used during the journey, and from Depot No. 4 on, it would lay its own bases. These depots were to be placed at:

	Position	Miles from Little America[1]
Depot No. 5	Lat. 82° 35' S	238
Depot No. 6	Lat. 83° 25' S	288
Depot No. 7	Lat. 84° 15' S	338
Depot No. 8	Lat. 85° 00' S	383

[1] These figures represent geological miles.

The need for the extension of the depot system is, perhaps, self-evident. A polar expedition, like an army travelling through a ravished country, must carry its own supplies. It cannot forage. It cannot even expect to meet an occasional animal, as in the Arctic. To attempt to carry its rations throughout the journey would be a herculean task, even if men and dogs could go through with it. So the depot system becomes the inescapable alternative for a long journey. As most trips of this kind are pursued more or less on a straight line to a definite objective, the problem of establishing depots is not particularly difficult. The needs of the party, both of men and dogs, are carefully computed, and definite amounts are cached at definite distances on the outward—or, in this case, southern—journey. These can be picked up on the return journey, so that the party, on its way back to the base, need be carrying only enough food, plus a determined amount for emergency, to see them from depot to depot. In short, if all went well, by the time of the polar flight we should have a well-marked line of communication to the Queen Maud Range, for the support not only of the Geological Party but of the Polar Flight Party as well, if it came to a cropper.

Of course, there must always be an element of risk in the most conservatively computed plan of this kind. A protracted blizzard, failure in dog or man power, the meeting of unexpected difficulties can play hob with the schedule, and the history on polar exploration is full of distressing incidents growing out of the "unexpected." Unless the schedule is sufficiently flexible to take up slack, the time may come, if hard luck befalls the party, when hunger, then suffering and even death exact the toll. As with the Polar Flight plan, the time schedule for the Geological Party was worked out with an allowance of 20 percent as a safety factor, for bad weather and other unavoidable delays. Amundsen, under similar conditions, allowed 18 percent and in spite of much bad weather found this to be more than adequate. However, Amundsen was one of the fastest and most resourceful of sledge travellers, and the Geological Party was inclined, quite wisely, to rate itself considerably below his par.

Again, we were fortunate in that we brought to the Antarctic our own rescue parties. If the dog teams failed, aviation was there to back them up: and vice versa. This, I believe, was one of the most effective weapons in our hands.

The schedule was as follows: (The time intervals indicate that which was allowed for travelling from depot to depot.)

	Southward	Northward [1]
Depot No. 1	3.5 days	1.5 days
Depot No. 2	3.5 "	1.5 "
Depot No. 3	3.5 "	2.0 "
Depot No. 4	3.5 "	2.0 "
Depot No. 5	3.5 "	10.0 " [2]
Depot No. 6	3.5 "	2.0 "
Depot No. 7	3.5 "	2.0 "
Depot No. 8	3.5 "	3.0 "
	28 days	24 days

Other time allowances:

To stand by at base for Polar Flight	7 days
For geological exploration	32 "
Return journey	23 "
Southern journey	28 "
Total	90 days

The expected consumption of man and dog food on the southern trip, together with reserves, cached for the return trip, were calculated as follows:

To Depot	Dog Food Consumption	Dog Food Cached	Man Food Consumption	Man Food Cached
No. 1	236 lbs.	45 lbs.	47.04 lbs.	100 lbs.
No. 2	236 "	45 "	47.04 "	50 "
No. 3	236 "	63 "	47.04 "	100 "
No. 4	236 "	63 "	47.04 "	
No. 5	236 "	315 "	47.04 "	189 "
No. 6	210 "	63 "	47.04 "	40 "
No. 7	210 "	63 "	47.04 "	40 "
No. 8	210 "	63 "	47.04 "	40 "
	1810 lbs.	720 lbs.	376.321 lbs.	559 lbs.

[1] The reason for the allowance of greater speed in the return journey was the expectancy they should be able to travel much faster with lighter loads.

[2] 10 days were allowed here for the side-trip to Amundsen's reported high land.

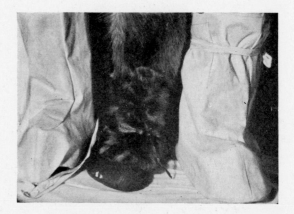

Dressed for 70° Below, showing
face mask.

Reindeer skin mukluk and canvas overboot.

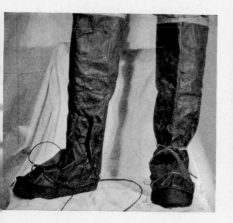

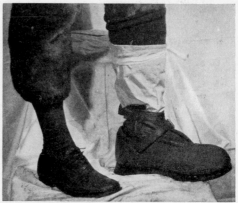

Waterproof summer mukluks made of seal skin.

Ski boot contrasted with ordinary shoe.

COLD WEATHER CLOTHING.

"It Isn't So Hot."

(Courtesy Paramount.)

The ration was worked out according to the recommendations of Dr. Coman, and represented a complete and well balanced diet. The total weight of man food requirements was computed at 1209.6 pounds. This was the weight of the food the Geological Party proposed to carry. Part of it, however, was to be relayed by the Supporting Party. In addition, there was a reserve of 250 pounds of man food which had been deposited in the first depots in 1928—a very generous reserve and emergency supply placed where they should be most likely to need it—near the end of the homeward trip.

Calculating the weight of the dog food was an equally difficult problem. The main ration we proposed to use was the dog pemmican compounded by Dr. Malcolm, which theoretically represented a balanced diet. It had never been tried before on long journeys in the Antarctic, but we were encouraged by the report of Taylor, who had 13 dogs steadily sledging on it on Mt. Cook, in New Zealand, that they were in excellent shape. During the winter this pemmican was put up in cakes of 1.5 pounds, representing a daily ration, so that it could be transported easily and distributed with less likelihood of error on the trail.

Dog food schedules were computed as follows:

Consumption on Southern Journey	1810 pounds	28 days
Stand by for Polar Flight	294	7
Geological Explorations	1008	32
Return and side trips	720	23
	3832 pounds	90 days

Amount of dog food to be taken from Little America by the Supporting Party	378 lbs.
To be distributed from caches laid in 1928	780 lbs.
Total carried by Geological Party	2674 lbs.
Total	3832 lbs.

The decrease in the consumption of dog food from Depot No. 5 on would proceed from the inescapable economy practiced on all long-distance sledging trips—namely, the disposition of the worn-out dogs. It is more merciful to put them to death than let them die of hunger, roaming the Barrier. It may seem cold-blooded—and I suppose it really is—but a table of expectancy is worked out, like the actuarial tables of the life insurance companies, and such a contingency must be provided for. It was proposed that the Geological Party should depart from Little America with five teams of 9 dogs each. The following schedule was drawn:

From Little America to—

Depot No. 5	5 teams (9 dogs each)	45 dogs	17.5 days
Depot No. 8	5 teams (8 dogs each)	40 dogs	10.5 "
For Polar Flight	4 teams (7 dogs each)	28 dogs	5 "
For Exploration	3 teams (7 dogs each)	21 dogs	32 "
For Return	3 teams (7 dogs each)	21 dogs	23 "

This was the stark necessity, laid bare of sentiment. But I shamelessly confess that we hoped to defeat it in a large measure. It is a dangerous and an unwise thing for explorers to allow their judgment to be swayed by love of these animals that serve them, yet we found ourselves in exactly that position. If it was at all possible, the Geological Party proposed to maintain four teams of nine dogs each from Depot No. 8 until the return to the base, and if conditions were favorable the aviation unit planned to drop a sufficient quantity of food at the mountain base to see most of the dogs through.

So much for the larger aspects of the journey.

There was the matter of equipment.

Camping equipment must be strong enough to withstand the hardest kind of handling, and yet light enough not to be cumbersome. There are as many different kinds of tents, I suppose, as there are explorers. There are two-men tents, three-men tents and four-men tents, and the shapes, sizes and weights vary according to the personal predilections of the particular school of thought to which an explorer happens to belong. We had about a dozen different models that we took down, products of my experience in the Arctic, and tents used by successful explorers.

Tents are vital. As with the sledges, we planned to make our own tents. We had brought the material south, and Goodale was appointed the research specialist on tents. He tried out many different types during the winter. The qualities which stamped a good tent for a sledging journey of this kind are: (1) that every square inch of space shall be economically employed, (2) that it shall be strong enough to withstand a high wind, (3) that it can be well ventilated, (4) that it can be put up and struck easily and quickly, (5) that it shall be strong enough to withstand the hardest kind of handling, and (6) that it should have a color that can be seen afar and will also absorb the heat of the sun.

In the end, we hit upon a design which was called the Woods tent, because it so nearly resembled the tent of that name which we had brought from the United States. The Geological Party actually decided on three types—two of the Woods pattern, and a pyramidal tent for cooking designed by Ronne. Ronne's tent was very similar to the tents which he had made for Amundsen. It was made of light wind-proof material over a framework of bamboo poles and stood about 6 feet high. It weighed only 25 pounds. The Woods tent was of the same material and approximately the same height and weight. Its shape, however, was quite different. It was more or less wedge-shaped with a ridge pole running its length at the top and bamboo poles in the four corners. Its value lay in the fact that it could be put up very quickly and though it had no center pole, thus saving space, it was very strong. Its entrance was like the sleeve of a coat, the opening of which could be tied together after one had crawled into the tent. It was, therefore, snow tight. Each tent was provided with anchor lines so that it could be tied securely to the snow.

From time immemorial, explorers have had difficulties with cookers. The perfect cooker—well, there is no such animal, nor can there ever be one. The problem is to get a stove that will melt snow in a comparatively short time and at the same time burn very little fuel; it should be light, strong and easy to start, for time is a most precious element on a long sledging trip. The most efficient cooker heretofore devised for the trail was the Nansen cooker, invented by the great explorer whose name it bears. This cooker is built around a two-burner primus, than which there is no more reliable burner for the polar regions. But this cooker could be improved slightly, we thought, and if a few minutes could be saved in the cooking of each meal on the trail, much of the hardships inherent in sledging might be reduced. Few things are more nerve-racking after a day's hard pulling than to sit, in damp clothing, with a bottomless stomach crying for something warm and nourishing, waiting for a pitifully weak flame to reduce snow to water, then bring water to the boiling point.

The cooker which Czegka devised, with the help of June, was, we believe, an improvement on Nansen's invention, if not a great departure from it. It utilized double walls, so built that all the heat generated by burners is put to useful work before it passes out of the cooker at atmospheric temperature. It has three pots—a center pot, holding four quarts, a ring pot holding nine and a top pot holding four—in which is placed the snow. Spigots are let in the sides, so that the water may be drained. The snow in the center pot is melted at the end of seven minutes, and begins to boil after twelve. About a third of a pot of water is produced. However, by this time enough hot water has accumulated in the ring and top pots to be drained off the center pot and used to fill the center pot. Soup is then cooked in the center pot, and, meanwhile, the ring and top pots yield enough water for the making of tea. So the soup is distributed, the water from the other two pots is transferred again to the center pot, and by the time the soup is consumed, a pot of boiling water for tea is at their service. In short, a full meal may be had in from 30 to 40 minutes.

It may sound complicated, but it really isn't.

Still another device was proposed for sledging. Any one familiar with polar literature will know that getting an early start in the morning is one of the most difficult tasks of the journey. It is hardship enough to quit warm sleeping bags. It is torture to wait in the usual huddle for warm food. Amundsen, Scott and Shackleton all have spoken, almost in despair, of the daily battle to get underway at a seasonable hour. Gould decided to have the Geological Party try oatmeal for breakfast, which was to be cooked the night before and sealed in vacuum buckets, thus insuring warm food immediately upon arising. I must confess that I was horrified at the idea of "puddling" around with oatmeal on a sledging trip. Pemmican, tea, biscuits, chocolate bars and erbswurst seemed to me to be enough, but Gould and his men were thoroughly determined that it could be done, and they were to prove that they were right.

There were many other things that had to be taken, and figured out with nice precision. Only a person who has taken a long sledging journey can appreciate the detail that must be worked out. Harnesses must be made strong, yet light, and a proper amount of reserve equipment taken to replace that which wears out. Ski poles and needles, theodolites and toilet paper, mitts and trail markers, whisk brooms to brush the rime from saennegrass and windproofs, navigation instruments and even strips of orange cloth to be spread on the snow according to the intricate patterns that were devised as a means of signalling to the plane in flight. And so on, *ad infinitum*.

In all, it was proposed to carry a grand total of 5,368 pounds and 14 ounces, distributed as follows:

Personal equipment	335	lbs.	2	ozs.
Man food	1221	"	10	"
Camp gear and fuel	331	"	5	"
Dog food	2674	"		
Dog gear	58	"		
Extra sledge equipment	12	"	4	"
Navigation, surveying and meteorological equipment	91	"		
Skis	27	"	12	"
Trail markers	173	"	8	"
Motion picture equipment	65	"	2	"
Still camera equipment	18	"	5	"
Radio gear complete	300	"		
Safety devices	40	"	9	"
Tools	20	"	5	"

A load, then, of 1,073 lbs., 12 ozs. per sledge

"But that's far too much," Mike Thorne protested. "If we have cold weather at the start, it will be very difficult to make good time with such heavy loads."

Most of the men were confident, and a few were dubious at first, and it was decided that the Geological Party should make a test trip in the spring before the main advance was started to determine whether or not the theories could stand up against the hard facts of experience. These preliminary spring journeys were to show that in the Antarctic the best laid plans are subject to change.

The planning of spring activities by no means monopolized the efforts of the expedition during the winter. The scientific staff was constantly at work, especially the magnetician, the meteorologists and the radiomen.

In addition to the ordinary surface observations of pressure, temperature, wind, etc., Haines and Harrison made pilot balloons every day, in a study of the upper circulation of the air. Some of these soundings were made to altitudes of 30,000 feet and more, and are significant in that the unbroken series of observations will throw considerable new light upon the atmospheric circulation in high southern latitudes, when they complete their reports. Curiously, the movements of the upper air were found to furnish the only reliable indications by which immediate changes in weather might be prophesied.

Our senior meteorologist had decided that there was no sense in being cold if one could avoid it; and when the thermometer tumbled into the forties, fifties and sixties below zero, the devices and schemes by which he enlisted assistants for the more disagreeable jobs are past recounting. He would cast a covetous eye on our bright young men, a number of whom thirsted for knowledge, and by shrewd argument which turned, generally, on how a knowledge of meteorology would help him get along in the world, would finally lead an unsuspecting youth into the cold.

Not long afterwards the assistant might be seen inflating balloons in the Balloon Station, and heating the candles which are attached to them so that the balloons can be followed through the darkness by theodolite. The candles had frozen so hard they had to be warmed before they would burn. All this while, our beloved chief meteorologist might be observed huddled in the shelter of the station, out of reach of the wind, generous to a fault with sound advice, but painfully short on assistance. His success in thus gaining cooperation was such as to cause Davies to define him as "the nominative of the verb to co-opt." I shall never forget how Taffy, after suffering for weeks under Haines' amiable tyranny, finally applied the same principle to his study of magnetism.

Taffy trained several young men to help him, then sat back, in the warmth of the stove to await results. To his horror he found them, when he went out to supervise the job, working heartily under Haines, who had recognized their possibilities and over-night proselyted them to meteorology. But, seriously, Haines is one of the most conscientious men I have ever known. I can say that because I know him as the result of having had him on two expeditions, and the dirtiest weather could not prevent him from accumulating an immense amount of data which he had set out to get.

Haines' and Harrison's job was full of minor difficulties, which sprung from the excessive cold. When the temperature reached 60° below, the supposedly non-freezing ink which was used in the pens of the self-recording instruments froze so hard they would not work. A bit of alcohol and a few drops of glycerine were added to the ink, and thereafter the instruments recorded beautifully during the coldest weather. Once a week the record sheets in the thermograph and the hydrograph had to be changed, which required bare hands and ruffled more than one disposition. Approaching 70° below zero the clocks of the recording instruments failed, even though nearly all traces of oil had been removed from the mechanisms; however, after a few adjustments, they worked perfectly. Rime and snow often collected in a hard, gritty layer on the anemometer cups, producing a slight error in the reading of wind velocities; it was necessary to clean them frequently. The powdery drift of the blizzard sifted through minute cracks in the instruments and not only impeded the movement of the pens, but often accumulated around the drums in quantities large enough to stop the clocks. During the worst blizzards of the winter, the meteorological department was in its stations most of the time, fussing with clocks and instruments, treating them with meticulous solicitude but deploring the urge that let them be led to the Antarctic.

Another source of worry was the formation of frost on the lenses of the theodolite. Harrison, following the tiny flame of the candle as the balloon mounted higher and higher in the night, had to scrape off the frost with a small stick every few minutes, lest he lose sight of the balloon. During the coldest weather, frost occasionally formed on the inside of the lens, and there was no remedy except to bring the instrument into the house, take it apart and bake it thoroughly.

In spite of these handicaps, the instruments functioned as well as could be expected under the severe conditions: in spite of its wilful perversion of surplus man-power, the meteorology department functioned with consistent excellence; and the records are extremely important and trustworthy.

The magnetic work was another branch of the scientific investigation which was prosecuted throughout the winter. This work was done under the direction of Physicist Davies and his assistant, Arnold Clark. The instruments were provided by the Department of Terrestrial Magnetism of the Carnegie Institution, of Washington, D. C.

The subject of terrestrial magnetism, which concerns the lines of force that make the earth one huge magnet, is a vastly important problem of research. About the earth there lies a field of magnetic forces the origin of which is still unsolved, and science stands doubtful at its boundaries. The problems of magnetism are closely tied to every-day affairs. Magnetic storms influence wire and radio communication and the exact relationship between magnetic storms and the electrical condition of the atmosphere is unknown and troublesome. Lack of data concerning magnetic variation and its progressive changes has impeded navigation; on approaching the Antarctic, we had seen for ourselves how unreliable the ship's compasses had become; in flight they were almost useless. Auroral displays still defy explanation, and scientists wonder what causes the regular appearance of certain types of aurora and their movements, why they occur more frequently at some places than at others, and what relation they bear to magnetic disturbances.

How complex and wide this field of research is may be judged from the fact that despite inquiries that have been made all over the earth, the data accumulated has not been sufficient to provide a complete explanation of magnetic phenomena. The most fruitful field for investigation is the polar regions, especially the Antarctic. Here magnetic storms are more intense than anywhere else, the transient magnetic and electric variations and storms are more pronounced because of the nearness to the magnetic Pole and the changes in the magnetic force of the earth are considerable over comparatively small distances. Moreover, because of the strides made in allied sciences, particularly relating to correlations between magnetism, polar lights, atmospheric electricity, radio reception, earth-currents and solar activity, the need of more data from the polar regions was pertinent and important.

This branch of the expedition was fortunate for several reasons. Little America was situated far enough from the South Magnetic Pole to allow accurate measurements of magnetic elements to be continuously recorded. It was well situated in the belt of the greatest auroral activity in the southern hemisphere. And the year 1929 was a particularly promising one for magnetic-electrical observations for the reason that it coincided more or less with a period of maximum sunspot activity. The previous magnetic and electrical observations which were made in the Antarctic, first by the German expedition, 1901-1903 and the British expeditions, 1901-1904 and 1910–1913, were done in a period of minimum sunspot activity.

The observations were made in two huts, one of which was for a continuous photographic record of the magnetic elements, the other for absolute observations made at intervals to fix the values on the photographic records. The first of these, which was called the non-magnetic hut, was built in the snow about 70 yards south of the main tunnel between the houses. Because iron could not be used in the structure, "Chips" Gould used only brass and copper nails when he made the frame. Then Ronne made a brown tent to fit it. The house was entirely buried in the snow for the sake of heat insulation, as all experiments with artificial heat proved to be more of a nuisance than a help. Nevertheless, the temperature in the hut on occasions fell as low as 35° below zero.

In this hut three elements were measured—the declination, horizontal intensity and vertical intensity of the earth's magnetic field. Because the instruments recorded photographically, it was necessary to keep the hut in darkness.

The second observatory, which was used for making measurements of absolute values, was nothing more than a house of snow blocks, with a canvas roof. As part of the observations were astronomical, the hut was above the surface. It was one of the coldest places in Little America. Each series of observations took from four to five hours, and between the cold and the wild puppies which repeatedly invaded the place, Davies had a dreadful time. Dr. Gould lessened the burden, however, by volunteering to assist him, and they took turns thereafter making observations while the other held the puppies at bay. The incautious visitor who did not announce his arrival by a shout was likely to be greeted with a shower of ice missiles.

The observatory functioned from May, 1929, to February, 1930, and more than 240 daily records were obtained. It is too early to generalize the results obtained. Magnetic conditions were, in general, highly disturbed. The declination or direction of the compass frequently varied as much as three degrees during a single day, and on one day oscillated through an arc of 4½°. Quiet conditions were the exception, and these occurred mostly during the winter and spring. The angle of dip at Little America in 1929 was 82⅓° (at the magnetic Pole it would be 90°), the declination averaged 107° east of north, i.e., the direction of the south magnetic Pole was 17° north of west.

In addition to the magnetic work, and auroral observations, Davies continued the experiments on the determination of condensation-nuclei which he had begun on the voyage across the Pacific. Nucleation determinations are of great importance in the study of the electrical condition of the atmosphere, and the studies carried out by Davies were the first ever made on the Pacific ocean or in the polar regions. With Dr. Coman, he measured the cooling power of the air under varying conditions of temperature and wind velocity; and as assistant to Dr. Gould he made a study of glaciological conditions at Little America, particularly with respect to the measurements of temperature gradients, density determinations and the effects of different temperature periods on the growth of crystals.

Our Welsh magnetician therefore was one of the busiest men in Little America. With a carefree impunity we had to admire, he scrambled in and out of some of the worst crevasses about the camp, during the winter, risking life and limb for the sake of getting a few temperature readings at varying depths, a cluster of ice crystals or a specimen of ice.

The Radio Department, which was under the direction of Mr. Malcolm Hanson, was one of the most effective and important activities of the expedition. Few men worked harder than Hanson, Petersen and Mason; and none did more to smooth its way. Much of the equipment necessary for communication had not been developed to a point where it was commercially available when the expedition left the United States, and a considerable part of it had to be especially designed and constructed for conditions in the Antarctic. The radio receivers carried in the three planes, for example, were literally built from the bottom up by Mr. Hanson and his staff, after preliminary flights in the United States. How important and intricate was the communications problem of the expedition may be judged from the fact that 24 transmitters and 31 receivers were used. There was sufficient equipment to supply the two ships, the main base, three airplanes, three dog team parties and two sub-bases. Of this a large part was redesigned and rebuilt during the winter.

As with the other phases of our multiple activities, radio was studied exhaustively. Constant and effective communication was essential to Little America, to the flight activities and to the trail parties. There were frequent conferences during the winter at which the details of all equipment were worked out. The measure of the thoroughness with which Hanson, Petersen and Mason worked lies in the fact that not once did their equipment fail us.

The emergency equipment developed for the planes was superb. The three planes were capable of operating on both high and intermediate frequencies, and therefore were virtually immune to all but excessive radio disturbances. In addition each plane was equipped with an emergency set, for use in case of a forced landing. There were also provided a radio compass and a directive radio transmitting beacon, both of which were effective, within certain limits, as a means of navigating the planes in the event of sudden fog or blizzard shutting down visibility while in flight. By means of the first, which would cooperate with intermediate frequency signals from the plane, a bearing could be transmitted to the plane from the base to indicate the proper steering direction.

The second sent out a distinct type of signal exactly to the north, south, east or west; and by following this path the radio man or the pilot on the flight could guide the plane back to the base. This type of beacon, which is called the crossed-coil, equi-signal beacon, has since been developed to a high state of perfection by the Army and the Department of Commerce and is now used extensively on commercial airways. But when we went south it was still largely experimental.

The same care and thoroughness went into the development of the radio equipment of the southern sledge parties. The problem here was a peculiar one, and yet not radically different from others that faced us. The equipment had to be sturdy enough to withstand the pounding of sledging, and yet light in weight. It had to be simple to operate, because most of the men who were to use it were comparatively inexperienced. The sets were built and redesigned during the winter, and use was to prove how shrewdly. At the same time, the men developed de Ganahl and Crockett into fairly good operators for the Geological and the Supporting Parties. Both Smith and June took an active part, when time allowed, in radio activities.

Apart from its practical assistance, which was immeasurable, the radio department conducted an unbroken series of research investigations of radio conditions in the Antarctic. With Davies, Hanson made a study of the relations between radio and magnetic conditions. He also made a study of the Kennelly-Heaviside Layer, a mysterious phenomenon which is described as a radio roof which surrounds the earth and is essential for all long-distance, short-wave communication. It is presumed to consist of electric charges or ions liberated by the sun's radiations in the upper levels of the atmosphere, where the air pressure is negligible. The position of the lower limit of the layer apparently varies according to the height of the sun, and hence upon the time of the day, the time of the year and geographical position. As an electrical conductor it has the property of reflecting, by progressive refraction, the radio waves which reach it from the earth, thus sending them back to a useful path, rather than permitting them to escape and become lost in space. For years this phenomenon had been studied by engineers, and a number of conflicting theories prevailed as to its nature and extent in the Antarctic, particularly with regards to the effects of the prolonged absence of the sun during the winter months and the proximity of the magnetic Pole.

Hanson developed a method of measuring the height and condition of the Heaviside Layer at various seasons, and he took to great pains to test it. During the coldest weather in July, when the temperature was close to 70° below zero, he, Vaughan and de Ganahl made several sledge trips ten miles out on the Barrier, to send groups of electrically timed, brief radio impulses to Petersen. The first time they were ready to start, the dogs froze their noses and paws, and the trip had to be postponed. Later Hanson went out with de Ganahl, Crockett and Bursey, and the four of them manhauled a sledge for five miles, in a temperature of 68° below zero. They planted flags every 100 yards to guide them through the darkness. When they pitched camp, it was so cold taking measurements that Hanson, who was sitting on a box, put a primus stove behind his legs, covered it with his parka and became his own furnace. But in the end he got the measurements he wanted.

The most fascinating place of all, however, was the main station in the Mess Hall, WFA. Here Petersen and Mason eavesdropped on the world. They chatted with the Graf Zeppelin on its flight around the world. They talked with the Russian Polar Expedition at Franz Joseph Land. They communicated with the University of Michigan's station at Greenland. An enormous amount of traffic flowed between them and the experts under Fred Meinholtz, who is the chief of the radio department of the New York *Times*. The handling of this traffic—in all, 2,000,000 words were transmitted from WFA—was possible only through the exercise of patience and resourcefulness. Time and time again, when important messages were awaiting delivery, the ether resisted the impulses, and Mason and Petersen spent hours in painstaking experiment, shifting from one frequency to another, until they found a "break" that would let them through. I think these men took particular pride in overcoming difficulties when they were at their worst. There were very few days when they were not able to maintain their regular two-way schedules with New York and the ships at New Zealand.

No picture of the expedition's operation during the winter would be complete without mention of the ships' party at Dunedin. Their job was a hard job, for waiting is always hard on energetic men. Nevertheless the crews under Captain Brown and Captain Melville never lost their sturdy independence and patience. For the expedition's treasury was running low, Commissary Officer Reichart was obliged to prune expenses to the bone, and the men lived under fairly straitened circumstances. Yet most of them asked for no more money than was absolutely necessary to support them and their families. Taylor, for example, took his dogs to Mt. Cook and used them as transport, causing them to earn part of their expenses.

Nor would it be complete without mention also of our New Zealand representative, Mr. Tapley, and his general manager, Mr. Duncan. No members of the expedition worked harder than they; and I confess frankly that without their efficient and delightful cooperation we might have found our task impossibly hard. The Dominion of New Zealand, from the Prime Minister down, was always kind and helpful; but the Tapleys and Mr. Duncan were generous to a fault.

CHAPTER XII

THE START OF THE SOUTHERN PARTIES

ALL during August, save when the sky was overcast, a steadily enlarging shimmer of gold and red burned and waned on the northern horizon. The hours of darkness grew shorter. Spring was in the air—but not the kind of spring of which poets sing in more temperate climes. From the 16th to the 18th raged a severe blizzard, turning the outside world into chaos. When it ceased, the temperature began to fall steadily. On the 19th the Antarctic equivalent of the robin—or shall we say the ground-hog?—a timorous Weddell seal—poked a brown head out of the thin ice over a blow hole, took one breath of the frigid air, and hastily drew it in again. He drew back none too soon, for a man hungry for the taste of fresh meat pounced at him with a pole.

On the 20th the radiance in the north grew and splashed the Barrier with a gold and yellow effulgence. The return of the sun was nigh. A few of us stole a march on it by climbing the radio towers, thus gaining a pre-view of its long-anticipated return. It was cold up there, and Rucker and Van der Veer suffered tortures to carry their heavy camera to the top for the sake of a novel "shot." The sun was a gorgeous sight from this precarious perch, half a hemisphere of warm splendor suspended beneath a strand of coral clouds. In the south a moon that was green cheese was set, wan, pale and ethereal, in a vaporous purple firmament.

That day Braathen and Bursey killed a seal on the bay ice, so we had fresh steak for supper. Balchen and Strom put on their skis and journeyed to Framheim, to report on the condition of the crevasses through which the Southern parties must defile. They returned over the bay ice, and saw that many changes had taken place. New upheavals had lifted new pressure ridges, deep crevasses had been formed and were partly drifted over and the surface was badly torn and broken. Winter had torn the place to pieces as if it was so much scrap paper.

We began to dig out now, with a vengeance.

Thursday, August 22d, the sun returned officially. A yellow immensity, distorted by refraction, it peeped over the horizon, past a gossamer veil of clouds, awakened the slumbering colors in the Barrier cliffs, rolled along the horizon a while and then, its job done, sank in a marvellous sunset. There was the same rush for grandstand seats on the radio towers, but not even the most devoted admirer of Apollo cared to remain long in his perch. The temperature was 40° below. Dean Smith dropped a glove, in his hurry to ascend, and though he came down like a circus acrobat he was not fast enough to escape a nasty frost bite. His hand was burned and seared when he grasped the iron.

The sun's return was celebrated appropriately.

The American flag was raised, to signal its return, and was left flying until the base was abandoned. Then Ronne, representing the Norwegians, and Davies, the British, raised the flags of their countries, in a ceremony which had for its purpose the honoring of the achievements of the British and Norwegians in the Antarctic.

A Victrola played the bugle call to arms, and all uncovered. The wind was blowing and it was chilly.

That night we celebrated joyfully. As the sun's return coincided with Dr. Gould's birthday, the two celebrations were merged. The best and worst features of each were preserved. Although I dare say it would be interesting, a description of the affair has no place in this volume: I can only submit the report which the meteorological department included in its monthly paper: "A mild tornado struck the mess hall on the night of August 22nd-23rd and left a trail of wreckage in its wake."

The sun rose a little higher every day, remained up a little longer, and slowly advanced his rise to the east. Spring was in its flowering, but it was a chilly spring. Snow covered the camp, and only the chimney pipes and the radio towers stood

THE AVIATION PILOTS IN CONFERENCE IN THE LIBRARY.

Left to right:—Dean C. Smith, Alton N. Parker, Commander Byrd, Bernt Balchen, and Harold June.

RETURN OF THE SUN.

Little America unfurls the American flag and beside it the British and Norwegian flags.

above the surface. In fact the weight of the snow on the houses was so great that the roofs of two of them were sagging. We began to dig out, timidly, lest a walloping snow storm nullify the work of the shovel squad.

August went out with a temperature reading 66° below zero and September came in with the same impressive low. September was the second coldest month of all. It was the one month during our sojourn in the Antarctic during which the temperature did not once rise above zero. The highest reading was 2° below on the 18th, the next highest was 11° below, on the 17th; for the most part, it fluctuated between 30° and 60° below. The mean temperature for the month was 44° below. September ended on the frosty low of 63° below, and we bade it farewell with shivering gladness.

Some of the men now began to suffer. Owing to extravagant use, the supply of cigarettes was nearly exhausted. The cry of pain that went up when Supply Officer Black announced the crisis must have been heard by the tobacco workers in Virginia. There was no recourse save to roll our own, with poor paper and pipe tobacco, which we did painfully and badly. Cigars were already more precious than—as a matter of fact, the cigar, at that period of Antarctic civilization, allowed of no comparison; it stood for absolute luxury and opulence. The man who owned a few was spoken to with deference by the rest, and the aroma that escaped from him was a tantalizing rebuke to the others who had not been so frugal. Our *Times* correspondent, with a self-denial which no one suspected in him, had carefully budgeted his supply and so had enough to eke out the winter. There were several others, too, who had put aside a few boxes of cigarettes and cigars against absolute need; and it was astonishing how they were brought forth on special occasions. "Have a smoke," some one would say, and lo! he would offer a real cigarette. Henry Harrison told me that the most precious gift he ever received was when good old Ronne gave him a box of cigarettes.

The month raced past, for all the cold, on the wings of expectancy. We were eager, all of us, to be off on our various missions: the Supporting Party to its depots, the Geological Party to the Mountains, the Polar Flight Group to the Pole.

Monday
September 9

Shovels to the fore again.

Today the Aviation Unit began to dig out the Fairchild. Just a mass of snow marks its hangar. Haines tells me that 93.8 inches of snow have fallen since the first of the year, according to his calculations. Of course much of this has been lost through ablation. The surface about the mounds, however, seems to have been built up at least five feet higher than before. There is a most marvellous streamlining of snow about every raised place.

Wednesday
September 11

The houses are as busy as factories. The southern parties are making final preparations for the trail. Every one is at work at something—sewing parkas and socks, repairing harness, testing tents, relashing sledges.

The quietest place in camp is Braathen's House, and Owen, seeking quiet for his literary productions, has fled there for sanctuary.

More seals have been seen in the bay, big, fat fellows.

Temperature today 68° below. Can spring be far behind?

Tuesday
September 17

The shovellers have burrowed into the Fairchild hangar. The plane has come through the winter better than I had dared hope. No snow was found in the cabin—just a trace of ice crystals. The mechanics are getting ready to take down the engine. If the weather is good, we ought to have both planes in the air early in November.

After a week of dazzlingly clear atmosphere, the sky clouded and remains generally overcast. Today, there is a ten-knot wind, and with the temperature down to 43° below it has an edge like a razor blade. There were a number of frost bites today, none serious.

Friday
Sept. 20th

We have had a wild time with the dogs. They are so over-joyed to be above ground once more that they have forgotten all manners and training, and run about the camp like lunatics.

It is simply impossible to get them into harness. After a patient hour's work to get his team in line, Crockett finally gave up an unruly pair and started off with six dogs. Instant-ly they dashed around in a mad circle, slamming the sledge around as if it weighed nothing at all, while Freddy yelled and cursed and tried to hold on to the careening sledge. In the midst of these revolutions, the dogs suddenly sighted the en-trance to their tunnel, and with impish perversity raced right down, carrying sledge, Crockett and all. It was a frightful tangle.

Bursey and Vaughan had no better luck. Vaughan's big black leader, Dinty, from whom we had been led to expect things, was as wild as a stallion, and sooner than it takes to tell it his sledge was upside down in the snow and everything a noisy confusion. Braathen's team made a racing swing about the camp, but came to grief when the dogs ran head-on into one of the guy wires supporting the radio towers. The impact cut the harnesses, and poor Braathen had to chase two of the dogs down into the Ver-sur-Mer. It is a wonder they did not break their necks.

I wish we had more dogs. The dogs that Taylor has at Mt. Cook would certainly come in handy now. Beyond a doubt we shall have to train some of the wild pups that have been running about the camp. It will be hard enough to catch them, let alone train them. They are wilder and fleeter than March hares. Their size and strength speak well for their future usefulness. Actually, they appear to be in better condi-tion than the dogs that were pampered throughout the winter.

Wednesday
September 25

We put the new airplane sledge that Balchen and Strom made on the scales this morning and found it weighed only 20½ pounds. It is a beauty. This is to be our transport in case of a forced landing on the polar flight. I have decided to take it on my daily walks to practice man-hauling.

The chimney in the administration building, which lasted through all the worst storms of the winter, collapsed in a 15-knot wind, and fell through its hole, choking the place with soot. We had a devil of a job getting it back—the temperature was 50° below, and many hands were nipped before it was done. Our quarters are filled with greasy soot. It will be days before we can scrape things clean.

Thursday
Sept. 26th

Still driving ahead on preparations for the southern journeys.

Thorne put on skis today and made a trip to the old Barrier cache. In spite of the heavy fall of snow, the trail still visible, although only a furrow in the surface, and most of the flags were still up.

Siple and Bursey have just returned from a trip to East Cape by dog team.

Saturday
September 28

Temp. 60° below at its lowest today.

Our dog power is dwindling much too fast. Spee, one of the best dogs in Goodale's team, was killed in a fight last night. The team was staked outside, and apparently he broke loose from the gang line. A few days ago one of Bursey's dogs was so badly chewed up in a scuffle that he cannot be used on the southern trip.

The dog men must take greater precautions. It is a deucedly hard thing to chain the dogs down, but it can and must be done. We shall be hard-pressed for dogs if any rescue efforts are necessary. Gould has already proposed to borrow the two pups, Sky and Ski, which Parker and McKinley have adopted. If he values his life, he had better bring them back. McKinley and Parker will put up a real protest when this plan is suggested.

I have decided to radio Taylor to board one of the whalers with his dogs. The *Kosmos* is leaving New Zealand early, and it is possible that they can relay him and the dogs to the base on a chaser. We shall need dogs badly very soon.

Monday
September 30

After four days of clear, bristling cold weather, another blizzard is on us. The temperature was 63° below this morning, but is rising steadily. It is now 17° below.

Although they cannot possibly reach here before the end of December, we are looking forward to a return of the ships. The men are betting on the day of their arrival; and the largest prizes that are being offered in the camp are the privileges of eating, if the victor, the biggest dinner that the Grand Hotel at Dunedin offers.

We are praying that the ice in the Bay will go out farther than it did last year. Conditions are certainly more promising. Although the edge of the new ice is now between 15 and 20 miles north of us and stretches solidly across north of West Cape, it is badly torn and rafted by pressure, and should go out faster.

The Ross Sea is apparently open far to the north. During the clear spells we constantly saw a dark water sky.

We had another fog today—a light, impalpable mist which greatly reduced visibility.

Tuesday
Oct. 1

Working days are here again.

Breakfast has been advanced to 7:30, and all hands begin work at 8:15 o'clock, "ob" at noon, and supper at 5 o'clock. This gives us a long working day.

We have weighed all the various types of sledges, with the following results:

Airplane sledge made by Strom and Balchen	20½ lbs.
Ski sledges without braces	18½ "
Long Norwegian freight sledge	51 "
No. 1 Strom-Balchen freight sledge	60 "
No. 2 " " " "	60 "
No. 1 Norwegian Army sledge	41 "
No. 2 " " "	41 "
Walden freight sledge, with wooden runners	74 "
Walden basket sledge, with combination runners	80 "

Black has been busy weighing the final list of material that will be carried on the base-laying and polar flights. The sum total of listed material is about 15,000 pounds, including gasoline and the weight of the plane. We have reduced emergency equipment, which includes sledge, food and clothing, to approximately 1,400 lbs. I think that we can still further reduce these weights.

Friday
October 4th

Siple and Bursey have made another long trip by dog team on the bay ice to the north, rounding West Cape and proceeding some distance in the direction of Discovery Bay. The Bay of Whales is frozen much more extensively than we had believed. They did not encounter open water until 20 miles out. The sea smoke was then so dense they could not see any great distance. They sledged over new green ice which had been blown free of drift and was smooth enough, according to Siple, for skating. They also sighted a number of small whales, the first seen this spring.

Saturday
October 5th

More signs of spring.
Strom saw a baby seal, a scrawny, gray-brown Weddell seal, on the ice, and the traces about it and the mother indicated the pup was born yesterday.
Also a flight of Antarctic petrels was seen, flying high.
The wild pups, which, by the way, are nearly as big as their parents, have been down to the Bay, looking over the seals. They were overwhelmed by curiosity, but the boldest of them dared not approach within 20 yards. They will learn rashness soon enough.

Sunday
October 6th

Blackburn, Bursey and Siple have been given the job of rounding up all stray pups and breaking them to harness. They will have their hands full.
The Aviation Unit has been hard at work with snow shovels about the Fairchild, and should have it on the surface within a

couple of days. The mechanics have been wonderful. Day after day, they have worked in temperatures that rarely got higher than 20° above zero.

Overcast and cold, 42° below.

The Supporting Party will be ready to start in eight days.

Monday, March 7th, the Fairchild, its motor oiled, greased and checked, came out of its snow hangar and resumed its old place on the surface. Its folded wings were swung into position, and the plane was secured firmly by ice anchors. Instruments, engine and structure had come through the winter without harm. We then turned our energies toward liberating the Ford, a back-rending effort. On the same day, McKinley took over the responsibility of the administration of the camp, in order that Dr. Gould might be able to devote his whole time to the trail parties, which were nearly ready for the start.

From the 7th of October to the 9th, we had a spell of fairly warm weather, the thermometer registering as high as 3° below; but even had the teams been ready, I was reluctant to start them early, as it was suggested, for fear they would encounter low enough temperatures on the Barrier to turn them back.

Dogs quickly lose their vitality in excessive cold, and the friction of the sand-like snow adds greatly to the weight of the load. As it was, the wind veered from the east to the south on the 9th, and the thermometer tumbled to 47° below zero on the 10th.

After days of a diffused, gray nothing which passed as daylight, in which the world about us took on an unreal and ghostly aspect, oddly lacking in shadows, the sun put on a gorgeous show. The meteorologists, in their terse way, said: "a brilliant, complex halo phenomena occurred on the 9th and the 18th," and let it go at that. When the wind shifted to the south, the canopy of clouds overhead was rent into feathery fragments and sent scudding more or less to the west. The air suddenly became charged with ice crystals, which fell like rain. The sun broke through the shattered cloud fabric which turned yellow and opalescent in its growing power, then an arch more beautiful than any rainbow I have ever seen swept upward, curved, and in a moment the sun was crossed by two great shafts of brilliant light, in the center of which it burned with leaping tongues of flame. On either side could be seen the trembling halos of the mock suns, each impaled on its shaft of prismatic light. Directly opposite the sun was the anthelion, the reflection of the outstretched reach of the cross, a luminous gray pillar rising from the snows of the Barrier.

For nearly an hour we watched this gorgeous display, while the ice crystals that caused it fell in sparkling showers. But as the temperature slid down, and the moisture in the air condensed more rapidly, the fall of crystals became thicker and slowly hid the sun. The gray impalpability again took possession of the scene. And as Owen wrote that night: "we went indoors deeply affected by the beauty and grandeur of this great vision."

On the 9th we also inaugurated Daylight Saving Time (we began to operate on 180th Meridian Time which is about an hour earlier than our time. At this meridian we could use today's date or tomorrow's as we wished). A group of men filled the hole from which the Fairchild emerged so as to eliminate the danger of the planes falling through while taxiing about the camp. Considerable progress was meanwhile made in digging out the Ford. While this work went on, Balchen, Bubier, June, Demas and Roth worked in the chamber in which the nose lay, checking the motors and examing the center section. The first investigation showed that it, too, had come through the winter unscathed; its duralumin structure had endured the low temperatures without so much as a crack. Our hangar was an exceptionally good one. Niches had been cut in the walls of snow and it was possible to work directly on the engines and center sections. Handling metal parts at 25° below, with bare hands, was like handling a red hot stove lid.

Last minute preparations for the departure of the Supporting Party were in full swing. Weather permitting, it was proposed that they should begin their departure next day, October 10th. It was decided, in a conference with Dr. Gould, that the Geological Party should accompany them for several days, in order that the men might not only orient themselves to rigor of the trail, and test out the equipment but also to advance the heavy loads 50 or 75 miles to the south.

Thursday, the 10th, was overcast, with a 10-mile wind from the southwest spreading a draught of cold air from the hinterlands. The temperature fell from 30° to 47° below. The departure of the teams was, therefore, postponed. In a sense, the delay was fortunate, because Gould was suddenly stricken with indigestion, and although he insisted upon making the trip if conditions were favorable he could not have done so without great suffering.

Friday, the wind was still from the southwest, blowing nearly 18 miles per hour, and the temperature was still at 47°. Again the start was deferred.

Saturday, the 12th, the wind shifted to east, rose to a velocity of 30 miles per hour, and drove a first-class blizzard over the camp. When I ventured out in the smother for my daily walk, conditions were so grievous that I could not but be glad that the boys had at least escaped this storm so early in the journey. With the blizzard, the temperature rose from 42° to 12° below, but when the sky cleared it immediately began to go down again, quite as fast as it had risen.

Sunday, the 13th, was cold and clear, with light variable winds, and a temperature of 34° below.

By this time, the men in the Supporting Party were convinced that spring would never come; they besieged Haines for predictions, spent half the time running out-of-doors to see whether or not the weather would repudiate his gloomy words, and the rest making final alterations in their loads. There is one thing about sledging one should always bear in mind: the best plan can always be improved and the task of preparing for it is never really done.

Some of us had meanwhile gone over the plans again, and come to the conclusion that the Supporting Party could take advantage of this bad weather, in a measure, by hauling part of their loads over the bay ice and depositing it on the Barrier slope. The bay ice to the south was wickedly broken up, travelling over it with heavily loaded sledges would be more difficult than they anticipated, and we recommended that they have done with it now, while there was still time for leisurely transport. We further recommended the trip as a test journey and invested the drivers with the responsibility of making the decision on the theory that, as the responsibility for the success of the whole trip rested with them, they should control it from the beginning. Although one or two men dissented, the rest were in favor of the plan.

At 12:30 P.M. o'clock, five teams, driven by Walden, Vaughan, Goodale, Thorne and Bursey, were ready to start. They carried a total load of 4,000 pounds. Each team carried two sledges, one of them empty. The loaded sledge was to be left on the Barrier and picked up at the start of the southern journey. In the party with me were Van der Veer and Rucker, Parker and Owen.

The sledges were off to a flying start, the dogs tearing down the slope to Ver-sur-Mer inlet in an ecstasy of energy. Chunks of snow flew back in our faces, the wind was more than chilly and our heavy clothes did not offer any too much warmth. The sledges struck the bay ice with a great show of speed, and we veered around the southern portal with such impetuosity that I thought, for a moment, the drivers proposed to sheer it off, merely to show how little they cared for such obstructions. Beyond the mouth of the inlet a mighty pressure ridge, towering and distorted, reared its serrated eminence directly across our path and bore due south for about a mile. The teams turned some distance this side of it, and ran parallel to it, between it and the walls of the Barrier. The bay ice was littered with crystals, and the runners scattered them by the thousands.

When the sledges rounded the southern terminus of the ridge, another ridge was found just behind it. "Hi, hi, hi, hi, hi," yelled the drivers, cracking their whips, and we crested it with a surging drive that carried us down the other side at a velocity which was somewhat faster than I had anticipated. However, this raking charge soon spent its force halfway up another incline, and the teams, one after another, slowed down as the dogs dug in for the last, belly-scraping pull.

The trail bore slightly to the west. A short distance on we came to still another pressure ridge, somewhat more complicated than the others, being split into two more or less distinct fractures. Through the first we discovered a fairly comfortable passage, but the second, which we penetrated through a narrow corridor barely large enough to admit a single sledge, sloped sharply down into a gully which was

packed with loose snow. Here every sledge ground to a
halt in a smother of snow. Dogs and men threw in their
strength together, and it took all we had to stir the heavily
loaded sledges. More than once I was of the opinion we
could go no farther.

Thanks to the perseverance of the men and to the dogged
persistence of the dogs, we got free at last. Then the surface
of the ice changed, giving way to rolling waves of ice, resembling furrows, which were caused by pressure. The sledges
bumped over these, booming hollowly over the ice, approaching still another ridge, of an aspect wilder than the rest. As we
could not take this one by assault, we hauled out snow shovels
and fell to the task of breaching it. In spite of the low temperature, shoveling was hot work and we soon were perspir-
ing. At length the men made a sizable embrasure, sufficient
to admit the sledges. On the other side fragments of old ice
had been lifted high above its former level by immense pressure, huge blocks had been up-ended and ice boulders were
strewn over the surface. The boys pushed, pulled and hauled
the sledges through the break, and after an hour's hard work
had moved them all to the other side. A few miles to the
south, the Barrier rolled higher and higher, its surface flecked
with dancing spots of color, and long, mysterious shadows,
suggestive of land which, we knew, was not there, played
over it.

The last stretch of bay ice was badly torn, and we made
our way over it with difficulty. The Barrier, in the vicinity
where we prepared to ascend it, rose in a series of tilted terraces. The first of these was approached by a fairly steep incline, which was surmounted by a jagged ridge. Heaving
and shoving, while the dogs pulled until their red tongues
drooped like flags, we hoisted the sledges to the rim of
the ridge. The stretch beyond was unpromising. A series
of crevasses, some of them open and showing their blue
side, others bridged by snow, lay in our path. Treachery and
grief lay in that tangled waste, and we studied it with respect.

In the center of this disturbance we spotted one of the
flags which had been put up last year, to mark the trail to the
first depots. Otherwise this part of the trail was obliterated,

and it behooved us to move with caution. Walden's practiced
eye, however, made out a likely path, and we decided to essay
it. We had great difficulty in starting the sledges, for the
tractive effort necessary to move them through loosely packed
snow, which was like grit at this low temperature, was much
greater than required on the smooth ice. Time and time
again, we sank almost to the armpits when the crust suddenly
let us through. There was always the unpleasant possibility
that a shallow bridge might admit us altogether.

Descending the farther side of the ridge, we came to a
deep, but narrow crevasse, which investigation showed was
thinly bridged at the point where we proposed to cross it.
Under ordinary circumstances, I confess, I should not care to
try to rush a sledge across it; but these were not ordinary
circumstances. Walden was of the opinion the sledges were
long enough, however, to distribute the load without greater
danger, and we trusted on momentum to lessen the strain.

The first sledge cleared the crevasse in a flurry of snow—
but none too quickly, at that. As the front end rose slightly on
the distant side, the rear runners dipped down and broke a
hole through. One by one, three other sledges made the rush
without mishap. Walden, who brought up the rear guard,
had the heaviest sledge of all. Just as he cleared the edge, the
sledge veered violently and tipped over, pinning him underneath. He fell on the brink of a drop into a second crevasse,
saving himself by clutching hold of the sledge. Without a
word, he scrambled clear, righted the sledge, started the dogs
and resumed his steady trot.

A short distance on we decided to drop the loaded sledges,
and return to camp. We had moved the loads only seven miles,
and it had taken us four hours. We came back on the empty
sledges, making excellent time. But that slight journey left
on my mind an indelible impression. Whatever confidence the
men on the southern parties might have, the fact remained they
carried fearfully heavy loads; and no matter how optimistic
they were, they would find the going very hard indeed, especially with maximum loads at the beginning. I had observed
enough to come to the conclusion that, unless the cold
abated, they would quickly dissipate all their strength during
the first stages of the journey. On my return to camp, I

had a conference with Dr. Gould, and it was decided the parties would not start until the temperature was not lower than 20° below, at which the snow would offer a better sledging surface.

That night we nursed a generous collection of frost bites on the hands and face which were the result of fast traveling with empty sledges on the way back.

Monday
October 14th

Dog teams still in camp.

Temperature was 47° below early this morning, but rose to 21° below. Now it is falling again.

The drivers are impatient to start, but realize this is not the time.

Meanwhile, the camp is beginning to emerge from its winter blanket. The Aviation Unit has retrieved the Ford wing sections from the hole in which they lay and the men have just finished bolting it into position.

Feury and Black are now digging out the snowmobile, and hope to have it in action within a day or two. We intend to send it out on the southern train, on the chance it may be of some assistance in moving supplies from one depot to another. If it proves equal to the Barrier surface, it should help the sledge parties immensely.

There is the greatest rivalry between the crew of the snowmobile and the dog men. Feury and Blackie are boasting that they will take the snowmobile straight through to the Pole, if the road isn't cluttered up by slow-moving dog teams. They are contending with conditions which will test their ingenuity and strength. Frankly, I doubt very much whether the Ford can make much progress in soft snow. However, it is worth a try, anyway. I like their spirit.

Tuesday
October 15th

Both parties started south today.

In the Supporting Party were: Walden, de Ganahl, Bursey and Braathen. Petersen went along to test the radio equipment on the trail and will return with the Geological Party.

Four teams of the Geological Party accompanied them—

Thorne, Vaughan, Goodale and O'Brien. Dr. Gould is in charge. It is planned that the Geological Party will return in two or three days. Each team carries the full southern load, and the trip should give the men just the seasoning and the experience they need.

The weather was splendid for the start: Temperature, 10° below, sky only slightly overcast, and a light wind from the northeast. The sledges moved very easily over the bay ice, and within two hours after the start (which was made at 12:15 P.M. o'clock) the first of them reached the sledges which had been left on the Barrier two days before.

I accompanied them on a sledge driven by Siple, and he gave me what I would conservatively describe as the wildest ride I have ever had. The team was made up of a number of the wild pups which had been broken, none too well, to harness, with Holly as lead. Most of the drivers were of the opinion that the pups were not capable of pulling more than four or five miles at a time, but Siple assured me they were wrong. We started down the inlet as if going to a fire.

Our troubles began. We had twice as many pups as were needed. The traces tangled, the sledge overturned and, worst of all, Holly stubbornly refused to stand still while we tried to straighten out the lines. In desperation, we fastened the dogs down with crow bars and snow shovels until we got things straight.

We had not gone far when the pups tangled the lines again. As I started to get off the sledge, Holly lurched forward, spilling snow shovels, crow bars and me on the ice, and the team went off with bullet-like speed. It travelled nearly half a mile before Siple could bring it to a halt, and by that time I was marching southward with half a dozen crow bars and snow shovels under my arms. I was fond of Holly but she was mightily in wrong for the moment.

After this, however, the pups were on their good behavior and showed a surprising amount of speed over the last stretch; their strength was prodigious. They easily passed some of the bigger teams and carried us up the Barrier well ahead of the rest.

The loaded sledges were coupled on to the other sledges in jig-time, and we all shook hands. I merely told them: "You

can do it if any men can. Every man in camp is back of you
with everything we have. The only thing I ask you to remember is that the life of any man is worth more than anything we can accomplish. That comes first. Good luck, take
the necessary precautions and you will come back O.K. Now
go to it."

Bursey was in the lead, and behind him were de Ganahl,
Braathen, Walden and Petersen. The teams of the Geological
Party were strung out behind.

For quite a long time we watched the line moving up the
slope, disappearing behind one ridge and reappearing on the
crest of another. Presently the figures grew smaller, the calls
fainter, and we lost sight of them altogether.

Their spirit and good cheer were all that could be expected
and more. Their spirit will not break—that I know. But
what their good cheer will be in a few hours may be another
story.

When we turned back to the sledges, we discovered that the
exasperating pups had chewed their harness to pieces and were
running wild. I left Siple and Dr. Coman to the job of rounding them up, and returned on Goodale's sledge.

Matters are moving according to schedule. The Ford engines are being checked, fuel lines renewed and the ship otherwise made ready for the polar flight.

If luck is with us, we shall be off on the base-laying flight
within three weeks.

My concern was realized. Soon after we left them, the
southern parties became bogged in deep drifts and the heavy
loads were almost more than they could bear. The men stripped
off outer clothing, made loops in the lines and harnessed themselves to the sledges, adding their efforts to those of the dogs.
In spite of this, the sledges came to a stop every few hundred
yards, while dogs and men rested to renew their strength.
They radioed that night they were in camp just beyond the
crevasses, 11.8 miles from Little America, having made only
four miles in three hours.

Wednesday, the 16th, they reached 20 Mile Depot after
the hardest kind of pulling. Both parties were in trouble.
Dr. Gould had concluded, when they reached camp, that

it would be impossible for his party to continue farther until the loads were reorganized, and Walden, in command of the Supporting Party, had decided to jettison every scrap of clothing which could be spared. It was decided that the Geological Party should turn back, and that Petersen should accompany them. This would lighten the loads of the supporting Party to the extent of his equipment; but the loss was more than counter-balanced by the 180 pounds of provisions which they had to pick up at the Depot. I was informed by radio of conditions. The following messages were exchanged:

BYRD:

Returning tomorrow as some drastic changes of plans necessary and I want to work them out. Regards.

GOULD.

GOULD:

Whatever new plan is made cannot help but be furthered by your continuing with Supporting Party now that you have started. I suggest that you reconsider going farther for observation of pulling conditions, etc., and to advance your loads. Another day's observation may bring to light some new facts.

BYRD.

BYRD:

Not prepared to go further. Supporting Party will continue with lighter load. Very anxious to talk over situation with you. Regards.

LARRY.

In view of the little time they had in which to accomplish the mission, I was particularly anxious that the Geological Party continue according to plan on this attempt, for the reason that every pound relayed then meant that much less to be hauled when the final start was made. On the morning of the 17th, I asked Dr. Gould to reconsider his decision:

GOULD:

I strongly urge you to make plans where you are instead of returning to make them. This can be done with the help of the radio. Here is a suggestion: Let Supporting Party continue without dropping any loads which are intended to help the Geological Party. You wait where you are until arrival of Crockett, who can come lightly loaded and reach you tonight. He can be convoyed by Strom and Siple who will bring you whatever you need for extended trip. You then proceed with your five teams and advance your present loads, perhaps assisting Supporting Party when you catch up with them. Proceed as far as you think it proper to go and, of course, the farther you go the more it will help your final advance. I think you can go at least 100 miles south. There are a number of things which can be done from 50 to 100 miles where Supporting Party has its heaviest loads, but, of course, you can reason this out better than we can. In other words, my proposition is that you make your plans now and go on with them rather than return here to do so. I am strongly against the Supporting Party making at this early date a decision to accomplish their mission only in part. You must have them succeed completely in order that the Geological Party may succeed completely. I understand, of course, that Supporting Party can drop dog food at 20 Mile Depot and continue to 44 Mile Depot and pick up the same amount of dog food dropped, but they ought not to drop anything that would be vital to success of Geological Party. This is my best judgment after careful thought and thorough discussion. On account of my great confidence in your judgment I will not order you to proceed in accordance with this suggestion, for you may have a better plan, but please let's make a real effort to make plans by radio rather than waste the time and energy to return to camp and simply repeat what we might now be able to do. Cheerio.

BYRD.

BYRD:

We are not prepared to continue as you suggest. Have had great difficulty with stove and unable to fix it here. Supporting Party can continue slowly without changing its mission. All hands here agree that it will be impossible for Geological Party to accomplish mission as planned. More far reaching changes in plans than you suggest are necessary and should be decided promptly. Can't do it satisfactorily by radio. We must return to camp before taking our final departure and believe it best to do so at once and get the whole matter straightened out as it is not simple. Could you have seen man-hauling with the dogs for the last few days as we have, you would realize as we all do we have expected too much of them and must change our plans accordingly. It is the best judgment of all here that the Supporting Party continue and that we return at once. Cheerio.

LARRY.

About six o'clock in the evening, October 17th, the Geological Party returned to Little America, having dropped their loads at 20 Mile Depot. They came back exhausted, thoroughly chastened by the experience and oppressed by the thought that, in its larger aspects, the original plan of the Geological Party was doubtful of fulfillment. Thorne's opinion as to the loads has been vindicated, but the matter was by no means as gloomy as it appeared. The men had paid infinite attention to detail in the planning, and I was convinced that by lightening loads the mission could be accomplished. Dr. Gould returned suffering from the effects of a fall while skiing.

The Geological Party held a conference next morning, at which I was present. There the plan was considered in detail, in the chill light of the recent experience on the trail, and at first glance it appeared there was no alternative save to give up the first plan and lay out a less rigorous programme. But this neither Larry nor I was prepared to do, as long as there was a reasonable hope of success. I repeated then, as I had done on many occasions, the thought that the scientific objectives of the Geological Party were surely of equal importance to, if not of greater importance than the purely geographic investigations of the Aviation Unit; that if this party failed to accomplish the outlined work in the field, the fabric of the whole plan must be weakened, and the value of the expedition the less for it. Much of my hope was in that plan; and I was not yet willing to admit that it should be modified substantially because the first assault failed to carry everything before it. The Antarctic begrudges everything except hardships; no single effort can overwhelm it; only a stubborn, extended struggle can succeed.

I did not propose to tell them how to lighten the loads to accomplish the mission. They could do that better than I. But I did promise every resource at the command of the expedition. The only thing I could not do (and which some men did not understand) was to promise assistance by aviation. I would gladly give it in an emergency; but the few flights we had made the previous fall had convinced me that aerial operations a long distance from base were risky; and that landing away from base should be attempted only when absolutely necessary. I had secretly made up my mind to leave food by plane, but I did not want plans to be based on it.

In order that part of its burdens be lessened, I proposed that the Geological Party give up the idea of assisting the Polar Flight unit in the laying down of a base at the foot of the Queen Maud Range; and to give it sufficient time to accomplish its work, I promised to hold the *City* in the Bay of Whales until February 10; and, if that were not enough, to charter one of the whale chasers attached to the Ross Sea whaling fleet and have it stand by as late as February 25th.

I then left Dr. Gould and his men to work the problem out. I had confidence in them. They were determined, resourceful and courageous men.

It was then proposed that the Geological Party prepare to depart within 48 hours for a second preliminary test trip, with the supplementary purpose of relaying the loads dumped at 20 Mile Depot at least 100 miles south.

That night, Friday, October 18th, Walden reported by radio that the Supporting Party had passed 40 Mile Depot and was now at 44 Mile Depot, having covered 20 miles that day in eight hours' travelling. They took aboard 480 pounds of supplies for the Geological Party. He reported good surface, a strong wind and a temperature just above zero. This was indeed encouraging.

Saturday, the 19th, brought an east wind. At Little America the sky was overcast, and a light snow fell at intervals; but at 44 Mile Depot they reported an all-day blizzard, with heavy drift, which forced them to remain in their sleeping bags.

The following morning the wind abated, the temperature rose above zero, but the fog held and the Supporting Party groped its way well to the east of the mass of crevasses in which Amundsen's party nearly came to grief and which he fittingly named The Trap. In spite of the poor conditions, they covered 20.8 miles. When they struck camp that night a dispatch from de Ganahl, who was navigator and radio operator, said the easting had carried them safely past the area of disturbance, and from their tent they could see two large haycocks at its edge. That night another blizzard overtook them, holding the party in camp until noon, Monday.

Sunday also saw the departure of the Geological Party. It was made up of five sledges—Goodale, Crockett, O'Brien, Thorne and Vaughan,—with Vaughan in charge. Dr. Gould remained in camp to prepare his final plan. That night Vaughan reported by radio that all was well; they had picked up the first loads and were camped at 20 Mile Depot.

Monday, the wind, which had been holding in the east, shifted to the east-southeast, and the temperature dropped fast, ending the warm spell which had lessened the difficulties; that day the Supporting Party logged only 9.7 miles and the Geological Party 11. The first reported a temperature of 17° below zero, the second 40° below and at Little America it reached 25° below, and was still falling.

Tuesday, the 22nd, both parties rose from damp and icy sleeping bags and flung themselves forward again. Vaughan reported his party was now 45 miles south, having made only 14 miles. Birch and Spy, he reported, were weakening and progress was distressingly slow. From the Supporting Party there was no word; but de Ganahl said later they had covered eight miles in six hours of fierce pulling: "It was like sledging on sand. We would go 200 yards and then stop. We camped early with the dogs exhausted. It was bitter cold in the open, but we preferred to keep moving rather than freeze in the sleeping bags."

As these discouraging reports came in—as the weather remained cold and overcast, holding the Fairchild to the ground—gloom descended on the camp. We could not, of course, witness the struggle; but we knew the character of the men who were out on the Barrier, we appreciated their difficulties, and it was as clear as if the scene were before our eyes that only the most wretched kind of going could be holding them back. Surely we could not be defeated so early in the game! Yet the evidence was before our eyes, in the terse messages, the discouragingly low mileage, the hard-wrung admissions of troubles.

On the 23rd Vaughan radioed:

GOULD:

16 miles today. Advise strongly our returning. Birch, Spy, Torngnac, Ski, Amy and Tennant all weakening. Immediate rest

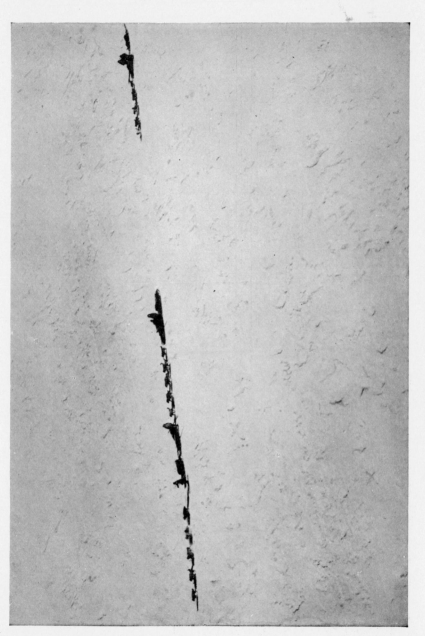

Dog Teams Hauling Loads on the Barrier as Seen from the Air.

THE GEOLOGICAL PARTY.

Left to right, seated:—George A. Thorne, Jr., Frederick E. Crockett, Dr. Laurence M. Gould, Norman Vaughan; *Standing:*—Edward E. Goodale and John S. O'Brien.

THE GEOLOGICAL PARTY AT AMUNDSEN'S CAIRN.

Dr. Gould is reading the note which Amundsen left there in 1912.

necessary if they are to serve us later. Important deficiencies found in gear. Much overhauling necessary.

Gould replied:

VAUGHAN:

Very sorry if you are unable to make 100 miles on this preliminary trip. Can you not try to proceed with lighter loads and let poor dogs run? Must cut our time in field short at least 15 days and you might as well lighten loads accordingly now, but above all else plan to come back from this trip with all the dogs.

Vaughan said:

GOULD:

75 miles is limit at which can bring all dogs back. Think more mileage a hindrance rather than help. Will do whatever you say.

Gould replied:

VAUGHAN:

Please take rest of day or two and see if situation doesn't look better for dogs. Cannot see how we can make 440 miles later if dogs can't do 100 miles now. Don't quite understand what you mean that more mileage a hindrance rather than help. So far you have made exceptionally good time and we have been greatly encouraged here.

Vaughan replied:

GOULD:

Will lighten loads and proceed. Have not been driving dogs to limit in order to save them for final trip. Cannot guarantee to bring all dogs back.

There was no word from either of the southern parties on October 24th. McKinley and Feury made a series of test runs in the snowmobile, for which Czegka had built a new set of wider treads, on the theory that a wider webbing would be effective over soft snow. Even with this, however, the machine became bogged several times, not far from camp, and the two men had to dig it out with snow shovels. On firm crust it was superb. It could then make 20 miles per hour with ease. We were sufficiently encouraged to start it south, in the hope that it might survive the Barrier long enough to mitigate substantially the burdens of the Geological Party. With a clatter of machinery, the snowmobile rolled down the decline to Ver-sur-Mer Inlet. Half the time it was obscured in a blizzard of its own making. After much reconnoitering, McKinley and Feury finally found passage through the pressure ridges to the westward; for the dog trail to the south was absolutely impassable to the snowmobile. McKinley brought out a platoon of snow shovellers and they smoothed out the rough spots. The snowmobile charged the surface, carrying everything before it. It was left south of the pressure ridges, and the men returned to camp, to evolve a means of carrying the Barrier on the morrow. The machine towed three sledges, loaded with food for the bases.

Friday
October 25th

Sky overcast, east wind, temperature 10° below, although zero at noon.

Conditions on the trail are apparently improving. The Geological Party reports that it is 100 miles south, having made good time since lightening the loads.

No word from the Supporting Party. They must have passed the 100 mile mark the day before yesterday.

The *City* has gone into dry dock, Captain Melville reports, for a final overhauling before departure.

Snowmobile is off. McKinley's platoon of snow shovellers, after considerable effort, got the machine up on the Barrier and started it south. Strom is in charge, with Black and Feury assisting him. The snowmobile crew is certainly optimistic. They shot it across the filled-in crevasses like a tank bridging a trench, and scornfully asked McKinley if this was the well-known Barrier of which they had heard so much. I warned them to proceed carefully, and especially ordered Strom to see that Feury, who was driving, wore a life line while crossing crevasses.

Not long ago we heard agonizing groans from the bay, and I think it is a mother seal giving birth to pups. The sound carries wonderfully clear on the still air.

Saturday
October 26th

Better news today.

Walden reported that the Supporting Party made 13.8 miles on the 24th, 11.5 on the 25th and 20 today. Today they laid Depot No. 2 at Lat. 80° 10′ S., Long. 163° 35′ W. They left 200 pounds of provisions.

De Ganahl, in his press dispatch, said the going during the last three days was very hard, with the surface alternating between a granular hard crust and soft patches of drift snow. The wind picked up drift, forcing them to keep up their parka hoods. Apparently it is very cold, but de Ganahl has lost his thermometer and sends as the daily reading "the average of guesses." This has provoked much amusement.

Ten miles south of Depot No. 2 they were forced to abandon one sledge, to get rid of the extra weight.

No schedule with the Geological Party, which is returning to camp.

No word from the snowmobile party.

Little America is quiet. Aviation Unit working on the planes. It is a shame we cannot get some flying in.

Later

Vaughan reports the Geological Party made its second depot 99 miles out last night.

The day's march was 24 miles. Some of the dogs have weakened and are being carried back on empty sledges.

Sunday
October 27th

Three things impress themselves upon my mind as a result of the Geological Party's two trips:

1. Although the original loads were much too heavy, as some believed before the start, the actual situation was by no means as black as it appeared to be.

2. In order to accomplish its mission, the Geological Party had to advance its heavy loads at least 100 miles south.

3. The experience gained on the trail was absolutely necessary in view of the lack of experience of all hands in the party.

The Geological Party should now be able to make its advance as planned.

No word from any of the trail parties today. I am particularly anxious to get in touch with Vaughan, to have him stand by the snowmobile party for a radio conversation so that I can learn what progress it is making.

The snowmobile party is the only unit which has been allowed to go into the field with radio, and I have regretted letting them go. If they keep to the trail, they will be all right, especially as they have dog teams to the north and south of them.

Monday
October 28th

Igloo is in the infirmary again.

With the slickness for which he is distinguished, he broke away this morning and hot-footed it for the wild pups. When he came in he was covered with blood. One of the pups tore out the stitches of the old wound, and he had a new gash on his throat. While Mulroy held him, Dr. Coman took a stitch in the new wound. He could do nothing with the old cut, from which all the flesh had been ripped, and patched it over with cotton.

But Igloo is not at all chastened.

Geological Party came in on the run just about supper time. Men in fine shape, but some of the dogs worn out. On the return trip, they covered 24 miles Saturday, 39 Sunday and 36 today. Vaughan said that the first few days after start were very cold, temperature varying from 40° below to 20° below. Their faces were severely burned and are peeling. Clothes which were soaked with perspiration while travelling froze before they could get them off when they pitched camp at night.

They passed the snowmobile party Sunday, at 11 o'clock, 63 miles from camp. It is apparently getting along as well as was expected.

I wish we had Taylor's dogs here. His latest radio says that the *Kosmos* is lying outside the pack, which is unusually heavy this year.

Tuesday
October 29th

The more I think about the return journey of the Geological Party, the more I am impressed with it. The men made 99 miles in three days, which is one of the best three days' runs on record. There is no need to be pessimistic. Gould is going over the equipment and making ready for the final advance.

Walden reports the Supporting Party at noon today laid Depot No. 3 at Lat. 81° S., Long. 163° 45' W. They are now at the edge of the heavily crevassed area which Amundsen encountered. Fortunately, they have put down most of their loads.

This morning we blasted one of the haycocks to the east of the camp with Trojan powder. These ice formations are as tough as steel. Two cartridges made no impression, but three, when exploded together, opened up a fairly large hole. It exposed a large hollow and a corridor running in the direction of the next nearest haycock. The walls and dome were hung with beautiful crystals, and Dr. Gould discovered the largest crystal we have yet seen. He recovered it carefully and has had it photographed. Several men crawled into the aperture, and followed the tunnel for about thirty feet, at which point it narrowed down, although it continued as far as they could see.

The haycocks which I have examined are dome-shaped and stand about 25 feet high. They seem to be a solid block of ice, covered with snow. Dr. Gould is taking a series of photographs in an attempt to show the development of a haycock from successive condensations around a small vent hole in a crevasse to large pyramidal mounds. So far as I have been able to observe, the haycocks occur at points where there are likely to have been pressure blocks formed in the old bay that was once here. (There is evidence that this basin was once a bay in the Barrier. As a result of the accumulation of snow, it filled in slowly, increasing in height until it became part of the Barrier. In this way, I think, the Barrier renews itself and compensates for the loss of the sections that go out to sea.) The cold air and the warmer sea water below causes fog, and thus the haycocks grow by condensation of moisture.

There is probably enough movement in the ice where the pressure used to be, to keep open water more or less under the blocks.

All the crevasses in the neighborhood appear to be made up of solid green ice from sea level down. No doubt the size of the formation is substantially increased by the accumulation of drift, but in every haycock which we examined we found a central vent hole, through which the process goes on. These haycocks, by the way, are radically different from those found by Amundsen further south, which were roofed by thin crusts of snow.

Wednesday
October 30th

Supporting Party has met dreadful conditions. Walden reported by radio:

COMMANDER BYRD:

Found frightfully crevassed area starting with blind covered chasms without warning 81° 5′ S. Believe it fatal for snowmobile to proceed beyond 81°. Tried to penetrate mass hollow snow and haycocks at 81° 10′, but forced to retrace steps and change course 100 True. Believe we can find crossing to east. No imagination can picture conditions due south of Depot No. 3. Our position dead reckoning Lat. 81° 11′ S., Long. 163° 25′ W.

I answered:

WALDEN:

Sorry to hold you up but you must in some way warn snowmobile not to enter blind crevassed area. You must go back to beginning of blind chasms and leave message in conspicuous place. Better leave messages in several places. This is of vital importance. Tell snowmobile party to return here as soon as possible. Take your time in finding a safe place across crevasses. Safety and care above all else. Mark trail carefully with flags. Congratulations.

The conditions which they had to contend with were made apparent in a subsequent message from de Ganahl:

"The peaceful Barrier showed its sternest front today when the monotony of one hundred sixty miles of unexciting sledging was broken by our efforts to penetrate the maze of crevasses, covered chasms and hollow haycocks eleven miles south of depot 3. The tents were pitched tonight between two pitfalls three miles east of the scene of our escapes from whatever is below the countless hollow crusts over which we passed. The Barrier trembles and roars occasionally as new traps open in this area where the pressure of the ice is equalized. From 81° south this morning a long line of knolls, jagged peaks and rolling domes glistened majestically on the crest of a hilltop stretching east and west. We had gone five miles when Bursey who was leading the roped caravan swung his sled to a halt. His dogs were on the roof of a round hollow pit fifty feet in diameter. There were many such invisible caverns on the ascent of the hill, some filled, some bridged with snow— evidently craters of haycocks opened by released pressure. Soon crevasses, a few open, some filled, most roofed, crossed our path. Five miles of dodging and rushing brought us to a stop. To the south and west were graceful domes, fantastic peaks and black shadows—ugly and forbidding lines of upheaved ice. To the east, a deep valley was crossed and recrossed by scores of the gray depressions we had learned to respect. Well roped we planned a short reconnaissance on foot. Walden stepped away from his sled into a crevasse and sank down to his waist. He was pulled out again and went down into a second. We reached the hill top ridge running south west between villages of haycocks. We proceeded with the teams. In five minutes we were shut in by hollow domes, every step on a thin trembling roof. We crossed a safe looking ridge and slid down ten feet from an open hole with blackness for a bottom and turned the teams to the west. Bursey slipped over the brink of a pit as we crossed a narrow bridge between it and haycocks, but the rope dragged him back. There was a hundred foot hole to the left and countless haycocks to the right. We followed a narrow highway west until a wide, thinly covered crevasse blocked our path to the hopeless area ahead. There was no room to turn the teams between haycocks. Braathen roped and on skis tested the largest and we rushed the dogs around and over the dome to retrace our steps a few hundred yards. Bursey stopped to fix a harness and the surface sank under Braathen's sled. The teams were hurried forward and pulled him to a thicker roof. The route flag slipped through into

space. Below everything was hollow. We tried a valley
with many crevasses but Braathen's experience and short
dodges brought us safe around. Evidences of continual improvement. All believe we will find a way through to the
east.

DE GANAHL."

Thursday
October 31st

The Supporting Party is safely through the crevasses at
last. Thank God for that. They were sorely pressed yesterday.

De Ganahl, in a message today, said they spent the day
reconnoitering through a valley of broken ice honeycombed
by pressure, and reached firm Barrier just as a fog closed in
behind them. He believes it to be the most treacherous area
ever crossed in the Antarctic.

"Great upheavals have taken place here since Amundsen's
time," the message said. "Nothing he describes can compare
with it. It was a restless sleep for all last night, for every
few hours we were awakened by thunder announcing the birth
of a new crevasse and shaking the hollow snow beneath us.

"After an early breakfast Bursey and Braathen retraced
their steps to the northern limit of the crevassed area to place
a warning on the Barrier for the snowmobile party. Then
Walden, Braathen and I, roped and on skis, worked our way
over and around crevasses to the southeast, hoping to find an
opening in the hopeless looking range to the south.

"From the high ridge we had glimpses of the firm Barrier,
but three miles of pitted mountain lay before us. After lunch,
Braathen, Bursey and I proceeded on skis in an effort to
thread our way between open black holes connected by covered
crevasses everywhere. On approaching the range we finally
found a narrow ridge between open chasms leading to a net-
work of canyons on the summit of a large hollow area and
camouflaged by a thin roof of ice. Braathen's skill and experience on skis enabled us to tap our way step by step from
one firm ridge to another. The trail was often two yards
wide, bordered on each side by black ravines or thin-roofed
haycocks. In three hours we marked a zig-zag trail a mile

THE SUPPORTING PARTY.

Left to right:—Chris Braathen, Arthur T. Walden, Joe deGanahl and Jack Bursey.

DeGANAHL (AT THE RADIO SET) AND WALDEN ON THE TRAIL
COMMUNICATE WITH BASE.

THE END OF A LONG HAUL.

The snowmobile party, Strom, Black and Feury, return to Little America after 80 miles of man-hauling.

and a half through the heart of the ridge and returned with doubts as to whether our sledges could get over the bridges, sharp shoulders and steep inclines.

"But there was no other way through, the hills being impassable to the east and west. Teams and men were roped separately and we followed the ragged line of flags. Walden said he had never seen anything like it. We stopped and turned to view the area before fog set in. It seemed as if the gods had been playing with chalk cliffs and left them scattered and broken on the tidy Barrier floor."

I have sent them a message of congratulation. By and large, this is the best piece of work done by the expedition.

Still waiting for good flying weather.

Today is the warmest day in months—above zero all day, and now 12° above. **Cloudy.**

I caused new safety rules to be posted today. All men who leave the camp on walks to the Barrier or bay ice are ordered to sign names and route taken on a pad, so that in case of accident the camp will know in what direction to make a search.

Friday
November 1st

Another warm day, thermometer registering as high as 12° above.

The Supporting Party reached Lat. 81° 45' S., Long. 163° 20' W., today, put down Depot No. 4 and are now preparing to return.

I have begged them to employ the utmost caution in retracing their steps through the crevasses, and to find the snowmobile party at all costs. There has been no word from them since the Geological Party returned.

What a blessing the radio is! Thanks to it there has been such close connection between the base and field parties. I have been kicking myself for permitting the snowmobile party to start out without it.

Saturday
November 2nd

Supporting Party homeward bound. They made 29.9 miles today.

Geological Party has been overhauling its gear and will begin final advance Monday.

Still warm, overcast, moderate east wind. No flying.

Sunday
November 3rd

Supporting Party on the return is safely through the crevasses, which they have named Chasm Pass. Fog blotted out broken features of mountains, but did not hide flags. De Ganahl reports that in the first two camps south of the pressure ridges they heard a continuous rumble of breaking ice, and a narrow crevasse opened up under the tent while Walden and Braathen slept. Walden counted 200 crevasses which crossed the trail within two miles, which does not take into account the crevasses to right and left.

These men, the veteran Walden and the youngsters, have made a magnificent journey.

Still warm and cloudy, wind E.N.E.

Loads for the base-laying flight have been worked out, and we are waiting for good weather to make altitude and speed tests with the Ford, which we will have on the surface within two days.

With the first phase of operations completed, the camp now turned to the task of initiating the others. Monday, November 4th, at 1:30 o'clock P.M., the Geological Party, with Dr. Gould in command, and Vaughan, Crockett, Goodale, Thorne and O'Brien completing the party, began the final advance. They carried fairly heavy loads, which would be increased as they picked up supplies at the various depots, and would reach a maximum load at Depot No. 4. They started with confidence. That night they struck camp at 20 Mile Depot, and a radio from Dr. Gould solved the mystery of the snowmobile party. They met the crew hiking home, painfully hauling a sledge, about 15 miles south. The machine had broken down about 75 miles south, and the crew were forced to abandon it.

I regretted the loss of the snowmobile, but as my faith in it was never great, I was not disappointed. That the men were safe was far more important.

Wilson and snow petrels were now seen about the camp in increasing numbers, heralding warmer weather.

Tuesday, the 5th, was a busy day. The Ford came out of its hangar, under its own power, with the 525 horse power Cyclone in its nose pulling it up the incline while the rest of the camp manned a block and tackle. Balchen was at the controls. He taxied it into position alongside the Fairchild, and the plane was firmly secured by means of "dead men" in case of a blizzard. The Ford was in excellent shape.

The camp prepared to welcome the snowmobile party, whose vaunted promises to conquer the Barrier were not lightly forgotten. As the poor fellows had been man-hauling for eight days, I dispatched Siple, with his team of pups, and Dean Smith on skis to give them a lift home. While they were gone, the conspirators decorated the radio tower and mess hall with streamers and confetti, a number of amusing messages of greeting were posted, a sign "Welcome home" was hung over the entrance to the mess hall, and the cameramen rigged up a dummy camera which they put into position along the path leading to Ver-sur-Mer Inlet. In the midst of these preparations, Siple and Smith returned with the news that the party had spurned the offer of assistance, saying in effect, that in view of the fact they had walked this far, they might as well continue the few remaining miles under their own steam. They were, it seemed, quite chagrined and testy.

In a little while the plodding figures were seen in the Bay. As they came nearer, Very signals were sent into the air, Czegka operated the dummy camera with the utmost gravity and cheers rent the air. The celebration reached its height when a message which Blackie's wife, who of course had not learned of their cruel fate, had radioed from New York, was delivered. It said: "With you every step of the way." The men were tired and burned by the sun, but they took the affair in good humor.

The snowmobile, they said, ran smoothly and fast on firm crust, and did well even on soft snow. But a combination of sastrugi and soft snow proved to be too much. However, the machine got much farther south than I ever expected it would, and as a result of the experience I think a suitable surface machine for Antarctic travel can be designed. The real cause of its difficulty was dirt in the engine, which began to work into the gas lines, so that Feury had to take them down several times, freezing his hands during the operation. The constant bucking weakened the rear end. Two hours after they passed the Geological Party, returning from its second trip, the snowmobile became imprisoned in a soft drift, and after a battle, the rear end expired. Strom shouldered a 40-pound knapsack, Black and Feury hitched a harness to the 300-pound sledge, and they took the trail home.

While the Aviation Unit went ahead with the conditioning of the Ford, both field parties made excellent progress. Wednesday, Nov. 6, Gould reported that the Geological Party was sixty miles south; and the homeward bound Supporting Party, which had picked up tools, radio equipment and personal clothing abandoned on the snowmobile, was only five days' journey from Little America. Under the hood they found, de Ganahl reported with delight, radios from home.

Their progress thereafter was rapid: November 6, they made 30.3 miles; 7th, 26.5, meeting the outward bound Geological Party; the 8th, they were snow-bound in a blizzard which did not touch Little America, making only 9.5 miles, and on Saturday, the 9th, they came in at a great clip, having travelled 46 miles from morning. The same day the Geological Party reached Depot No. 2. Gould reported:

Arrived depot No. 2 this afternoon and spent afternoon changing sledges and loads. High sastrugi and soft snow and very poor visibility have made hard going last two days, but dogs are in better shape than when we left camp. Everything looks bright tonight, including the weather.

The Supporting Party came in, bearded and tired, panting less from exertion than for "ham and eggs," as de Ganahl said. In my diary I wrote:

"I cannot praise Walden, de Ganahl, Bursey and Braathen too highly. They proved that they could defeat the early spring cold, and now their job is done. They went through without a suspicion of a complaint. It was a tough job, on the successful execution of which hangs most of our spring plans. Thanks to them, we may now go ahead with confidence."

CHAPTER XIII

THE BASE-LAYING FLIGHT

THERE was a bit of excitement about the polar plane on November 9th. We were heating the engines with the usual method—that is, using a canvas hood with a funnel leading down to a pressure gasoline stove. Just as the mechanics were ready to start the two outboard Whirlwinds, gasoline dripped on the funnel. It caught fire and spread to the whole hood and engine, and there was danger the flames might reach the tank before we could douse it with pyrenes. This was a bad moment, and it was lucky that we had an all-metal plane. The damage was slight, but involved another day's delay while the mechanics renewed the wiring and Ronne made a new funnel.

Except for an overcast sky, the weather had not been bad for ten days, with the thermometer fluctuating between 5° below and 12° above zero and the wind, never very strong, shifting from south to east. Sunday, November 10th, came in chilly, 17° below, but the air warmed up as the day advanced and a 10-mile wind from the east chased away the clouds, giving us a clear horizon. So we made the first flight of the season.

With Bubier as passenger, Parker took the Fairchild on a test hop. Before he took off, he taxied up and down the field, testing the controls and skis. The surface was quite soft and the skis, the bottoms of which were covered with ice, sank rather deep, but Parker beat down a fairly firm runway after two or three charges and finally wore off the ice. The ship then cleared quite cleanly. When he came down, Smith, Balchen and June each made test hops of thirty minutes over the Bay of Whales, during which the aerial camera, radio and the plane itself were tested. In all, the motor ran continuously for four hours before we called it a day, seventeen men had made flights, and the ship was reported to be in perfect flying trim.

On the following day, the mechanics started the Whirlwinds on the Ford, but the test hop was deferred until the mechanics cleaned out the fuel lines, in which dirt had collected. That night the Geological Party reported it had travelled 26 miles during the last two days, and all was well.

Tuesday
November 12th

No flying today. The Ford was ready to go, but wind shifted to ESE, picking up a slight drift, and sky cloudy.

Brown and Melville report both vessels are making final preparations for southern voyage, and crews in fine condition and eager to start.

Wednesday
November 13th

A splendid day, 14° below, a barely perceptible east wind and perfectly clear horizon.

The Ford went aloft at 3 o'clock this afternoon, with Parker as test pilot, Balchen as engineer and eight passengers.

The plane was off in less than thirty seconds. The big Cyclone in the nose has certainly improved the performance of these ships.

Later, the other pilots took their turn at the controls, and I tested my navigational equipment on a hop 10 miles south of 20 Mile Depot. The depot was very plainly marked, even from the air, and it was possible to see the trail extending indefinitely south.

After supper we loaded the Ford with snow blocks, giving it a load of 13,000 pounds, and took it up on an altitude test, to determine whether it will be able to get us over the mountains. The snow blocks were of known weights and could be dropped before landing. At 10,000 feet the port engine began to skip and the pilots decided to come down. It was bitterly cold at the higher levels.

All hands are now waiting for a ride to 14,000 feet.

Thursday
November 14th

Worked all night, and at 6 o'clock A.M. the mechanics decided to install a new carburetor on the balky engine.

Temperature this morning was 19° below.

Later

An 18 mile wind from the ESE is causing considerable drift. No flying. All hands indoors.

Gould reports the Geological Party camped tonight at Lat. 81° 11' S., on the edge of Chasm Pass, which they will penetrate tomorrow. I wish them luck.

Friday
November 15th

No flying. Warmer today and clear. But mechanics busy installing new carburetor and lagging the gas lines. Following the flags laid down by Supporting Party, the Geological Party passed through Chasm Pass today without "mishap or adventure," Gould reports.

Saturday
November 16th
Morning

Aviation unit worked all last night. It appears that the air bleeds in the carburetor were much too large, causing too much air to be drawn in while the engine turned at intermediate revolutions. The mechanics have soldered the bleeds and drilled the jets a size smaller.

The directional results with the radio compass have been surprisingly good. So, too, with the improvised radio beacon. Hanson's preliminary tests have thus far been limited to a radius of 25 miles, but the signals come in so strong that we are confident that both the radio compass and the radio beacon can be depended upon within a radius of 75 to 100 miles. If we do run into bad weather on the return leg of a flight, these ingenious inventions should be very handy.

Wind shifted from east to east-southeast, growing stronger and picking up drift. Haines found in his balloon runs this morning a 40-mile wind at 10,000 feet and a 125-mile wind at 20,000 feet. So there will be no altitude or load tests today, unless conditions change, which he doubts.

Sunday
November 17th

One of the warmest days in months, 12° above zero, a gentle wind from the southwest and the third clear day in succession.

Ford took off at 10:30 o'clock this morning, with a load of 13,000 pounds. She climbed to 12,000 feet in an hour and one-half, from which height the men in the plane could see the summits of the Rockefeller Mountains sticking up like mounds in the snow.

Then we ran a number of speed, altitude and load tests over a marked course, with revolutions at full throttle and all the way down to 1450 R. P. M.

Later

Have decided to make base-laying flight tonight. The plane is being loaded and we shall take off within an hour. It is only necessary to fill the oil tanks and start the engines.

In addition to fuel and oil necessary for the flight, as well as other equipment, we shall carry 300 pounds of food, 200 gallons of gasoline, 25 gallons of oil and a large gasoline stove (for warming the engines) for the cache. We shall also carry 25 gallons of gasoline and a gasoline stove for the Geological Party. Smith will pilot, June will act as radio engineer and relief pilot, and McKinley will, of course, be the mapper.

It is mighty good to be starting.

Later

No luck. We are too impatient.

Radio conditions have been absolutely dead all day. Every man in the Radio Division has tried his hand at the main set, but failed to raise a station. We have been unable to make contact with the *New York Times,* the ships at New Zealand, the Geological Party—in fact, for the past few hours we have been cut off from the world.

It would be stupid to undertake the flight without radio. So we shall sit still, until the ether returns to normal.

The base-laying flight is one of the most uncertain operations of the whole expedition. If we fail to get down our base, we cannot make the polar flight. If we crack up, we shall not only be forced to give up the polar flight, but we shall also nullify the magnificent work of the Supporting and Geological parties, for the latter party must then put all its efforts into the job of helping us back to Little America.

By the time we get back, if this thing comes to pass, it will be too late to undertake the prolonged flight to the eastward which we plan to make after the polar flight.

Landing away from base in the polar regions is always dangerous, because of the inability of the pilot to judge surface accurately from the air; weather is also an uncertain quantity. This is one of my pet convictions and I would not attempt this landing if it were not absolutely necessary. If the landing can be done, I believe that Dean Smith can do it. He has a tremendous responsibility.

9 o'clock A. M.
Monday
November 18th

The mysterious enervation of the ether is over, and we shall make the flight at once. Engines are turning over and Mulroy has put aboard the fuel cans for the base.

Temperature—several degrees above zero and rising: sky —cloudless: wind—on the surface a 6-mile wind from the southwest, and a quartering 20-mile wind at 2,000 feet according to Haines's balloon runs.

A perfect day for the flight.

Haines said: "You might wait another year for a better one."

We took off at 9:40 o'clock A.M., with Smith at the controls. Thirty seconds after the start, after a run of less than a thousand feet, the three engines lifted our 14,300 pounds of dead weight from the snow, and the plane climbed rapidly, bearing to the south. As the engines took up a steady rhythm, under Smith's deft synchronizing touch, my thoughts and hopes raced ahead. What would we find at the foot of the mountains? A firm, smooth surface? Or a surface torn and marred by crevasses and sastrugi? So much—everything—hung in the balance.

Little America, a few dark roofs and a mass of trodden snow, dropped steadily astern, the radio towers became mere black pins against the white, and the Ross Sea, open, black, and strewn with icebergs, stretched indefinitely to the northern horizon.

Our altitude was 1,200 feet, and Smith kept the plane at this height for some time. For more than a year, we had been wondering if we could follow the dog team trail from the air. We had discussed the problem backward and forward and were now about to find the answer.

Down below, the southern trail wound through the crevasses southwest of Little America, but we could not see it. Reaching the Barrier, we had to search for the trail, and for a time I thought we were not going to be able to follow it. Finally we sighted it—a thin, broken, ribbon. The sun compass checked with the direction of the trail. We could, therefore, keep on an exact course with the sun compass, when and if we missed the trail, and sooner or later would pick it up again. Smith had to keep some distance to the right or left of the trail in order to see it at all.

We saw 20 Mile Depot, a few snow blocks surrounded by a welter of footsteps. Over the beacons the western sun threw long gray shadows.

Visibility was excellent. The atmosphere was wonderfully smooth.

McKinley, who was just getting ready to send his cameras into action, touched my sleeve, pointed down and grinned. In the center of the trail lay a dark hulk, the forlorn wreck of the snowmobile.

Snow, snow everywhere, rising and falling in swelling folds, meeting the blue of the sky with a sharp clear line.

We passed Depot No. 2 at a speed in excess of a hundred miles per hour. We could see the crevassed area long before we reached it. I had been intent on navigating when suddenly Dean turned in his seat and wiggled his finger. Dark shadows appeared in the smooth floor of the Barrier ahead—the crevasses. As we approached, the pattern evolved. What a frightful mess it was! It was a frozen whirlpool. Even under the softening influence of vertical vision and altitude, the horrible nature of the surface was apparent. The area was traversed by massive pressure ridges and crevasses, the sides of which showed black and blue in the sun, and the shearing movement of the Barrier had wrought destruction of millions of tons of frozen ice and snow. Had the guns of half a dozen armies played upon the scene, they could not have worked as much destruction.

To the east a mass of crevasses was spread fanwise, furrowed and partly drifted over.

Here for two days the Supporting Party had risked its necks; and we were over it in two, perhaps three minutes. I almost felt ashamed.

From the surface the crevassed area appeared to them to stretch indefinitely from east to west. But from the air we saw that it was not more than 25 or 30 miles from end to end, and a fine route around it lay to the eastward.

Amundsen had reported two high peaks to the eastward in Latitude 82 degrees. He did not name these peaks, and thought they were part of Carmen Land. I searched for them with binoculars, but could not see them. Did the Barrier continue indefinitely to the east? I decided that on the return flight, as well as on the polar flight, we should have to investigate this area.

Smooth and undulating, the Barrier stretched to the south. The crumbled dome of Depot No. 4 was underneath.

"We ought to meet the Geological Party any minute," I shouted.

"I see them now," McKinley answered.

Five teams, scattered and each making its way alone, were headed up a long, rolling rise in the Barrier.

"They haven't heard us yet," McKinley shouted.

That was apparent, for they had not turned. Smith brought the ship down in a long, curving glide. The poor devils, we saw quickly, were having a hard time. Some of the men were in harness, pulling with the dogs, and the sight of their bending backs, the separation of the sledges, the very, very slow progress told everything. They had picked up a maximum load at Depot No. 4, and the men had their toes dug in and the dogs had their bellies to the snow trying to keep the sledges moving.

"Must be cold down there," McKinley yelled. "They have their parkas up—can't hear the engines."

We passed them at 300 feet, swinging low in salute, and caught sight of two or three white faces lifted up.

"Don't cheer, boys," June said, "the poor devils are dying."

If ever a conclusive contrast was struck between the new and the old methods of polar travelling, it was then.

We dropped them a bag of letters and miscellaneous equipment and continued on. Smith had done a fine job in keeping to the trail, which was always elusive. On the few occasions when we lost the trail, the sun compass took the plane on a bee line until we sighted it again.

A little later to the southwestward a magnificent peak appeared in the sky. It was the strangest mountain I have ever seen. It lacked body and base. It was a towering, truncated, gray-black peak pinned against a cloudless sky. Halfway down it ended, with a clear line of breakage, against the shimmering brilliance of daylight, as if the agency responsible for its structure had started to build it from the top, grew tired when the job was half done and left it there, like Mahomet's tomb, between earth and heaven. A mirage, I thought.

Then another peak, a third, a fourth, then a whole line of them popped suddenly in the sky, at least 150 miles away, trending laterally across our path; and the same shimmering light played underneath. Could they be—why, surely they must be—the mountains between the range that Amundsen saw on his polar journey (Crown Prince Olav) and those which Scott and Shackleton saw from Beardmore Glacier.

For the first time in history the entire sweep of this majestic mass which buttresses the polar plateau was visible to human eyes. Smith gradually lifted the plane to 2000 feet, and the beauty and the extent of this range were more fully shown.

Fold upon fold, peak upon peak, the range rimmed the polar plateau, bending in a broad sweeping curve to the east. I studied them through my glasses. Some black rock showed, a charred and weathered black which gave the peaks an air of ageless sturdiness. Here and there the blue-white stream of a glacier cut through the ebony; and one glacier, larger and more beautiful than the rest, which could be seen almost at the limit of vision, I took to be Beardmore Glacier, up which the parties of Scott and Shackleton had climbed, with infinite patience and pain, in search of a highway to the Pole. But of course I could not be sure; it is always difficult to recognize from the surface a mountain according to written description; but from the air it is well-nigh impossible.

Slowly, now, the Queen Maud Range came into view: first a few lone peaks dancing above the cylinder heads in the arc of the propeller; then dark shoulders of rock draped with snow; then, finally, a solid mass of mountains cut and riven by glacial streams. Here, indeed, was what we had come so far to see.

Spread out on the navigation table were Amundsen's charts, a number of photographs ripped from his book, and scribbled notes taken from his descriptions.

Here was a subject which de Ganahl, one of the expedition's navigators, and I had discussed exhaustively on many occasions. Would it be possible to recognize from the air the mountains which Amundsen had seen and described according to their characteristics as seen from the ground? Amundsen had repeatedly confessed that under different conditions of visibility he failed to recognize mountains which he believed he knew well. It was absolutely necessary that I know exactly where we were when we prepared to land for the base. Thus far I had recognized nothing, but I had confidence, however, in the sun compass and drift indicator. I knew that we were flying in a straight line south.

I searched first of all for Mt. Fridtjof Nansen—"15,000 feet[1] . . . a blue-black look . . . a mighty hood of ice that raised its shining top . . . the immense Mount Nansen"[2] and then for its eminent companion, Don Pedro Christophersen . . . "farther to the east . . . more covered with snow . . . but the long, gabled summit was to a great extent bare,"[3]

[1] Amundsen, "The South Pole," ii, p. 45.
[2] *Ibid*, ii, 44.
[3] *Ibid*, ii. 30.

and for Axel Heiberg Glacier . . . "that rose in terraces along their sides . . . fearfully broken and disturbed[1] . . . the great main ice field . . . stretching right up from the Barrier between the lofty mountains running east and west."[2]

But I recognized nothing. We were heading for a glacier which I took to be Axel Heiberg because I had confidence in Albert Bumstead's sun compass. There was a great mountain mass ahead, a trifle to the starboard bow, and there was an even larger mass to the right of it. There were huge mountains on the port bow too. At the foot of these high mountains were rows of even, pyramidal, black foothills like Arab tents struck at their feet.

But another mountain had shouldered its mass in sturdy prominence against the rest, a stately, glittering cone. Could this be Ole Engelstads? I studied Amundsen's description of it. ". . .Ole Engelstad's a great snow cone rising in the air to 19,000 feet[3]" . . . Mount Wilhelm Christophersen and Mount Ole Engelstad formed the end of Axel Heiberg Glacier, "two beehived-shaped summits, entirely covered with snow."[4] No, this peak did not fall into that description. It must be— I hastily riffled the photographs, refreshing my mind with detail in them as we advanced steadily toward the range.

A queer thing happened as we approached. The cone of the mysterious mountain gradually separated itself from the mountain mass on the port bow and the shape of the mountain changed before our eyes. It had ceased to be a cone. From the northern peak a ridge ran far back, to the south, and the effect then was that of a tented arch. I saw, at the moment, a definite structural similarity with the picture of a mountain on my table—ah, Ruth Gade.[5] It was a gorgeous mass, rising 14,000 to 15,000 feet.

Here was one thing on which to hang our position. There could be no doubt that the photograph I held in my hand and the one I was looking at were the same. From it I worked to locate the other mountains. The big mountain mass on the starboard bow must be the great Nansen. But wonders, there was an even greater mass to the right of Nansen, seen in its

[1] Amundsen "The South Pole," ii, 44. [2] Ibid, ii, 47.
[3] Ibid, i, The First Account, xiii.
[4] Ibid, ii, 54. [5] Ibid, ii, 30.

length, perhaps for the first time. I concluded that Don Pedro Christophersen and Ole Engelstad must be hidden behind Nansen. Axel Heiberg Glacier was ahead and Liv's Glacier to the right. Good! Now we knew where we were.

It seems almost absurd, as I look back upon it, to have been standing thus, staring one moment at a far-flung shield of snow-draped rock, and the next at a few words and photographs, striving to put them together. If ever I saw the inadequacies of words I did then. *Cones, summits, peaks, flanks, ridges, turrets*—scramble them together, add a dash or two of adjectives, and one has, at best, an approximation. Here we had the thing before us, in all its wonderful complexity. Even photographs were misleading; for with every mile of our advance the shapes and attitudes of the mountains changed and became almost irrecognizable.

It was then past two o'clock.

Ever since we had passed the crevasses, I had searched for signs of Carmen Land and the mountain range which Amundsen believed connected Carmen Land to King Edward VII Land and South Victoria Land.[1] We not only failed to see the "two lofty white summits" or the "appearance of land" to the southeast "in about 82°,"[2] which he reported on the return journey from the Pole, but we had not yet caught sight of the chain of mountains which he first saw at 84°,[3] on the way in, and later as he stood halfway up the mountains and paused, before he renewed the ascent, for a backward glance at the Barrier.[4]

Of this fascinating area not a trace had yet appeared.

This was the more surprising as we were approximately over Amundsen's route and had naturally a more extensive field of vision.

New personalities emerged in the mountains ahead of us. To the left of Ruth Gade two snow-swathed peaks, of almost exactly the same shape, began to stand out from the rest. A conservative estimate put their heights at from 10,000 to 14,000 feet. Behind these the highest peak, curved to the southeast and the foothills continued endlessly to the eastward. Here and there I could see the blue-white glint of glaciers against

[1] Amundsen, "The South Pole," i, "The First Account," xviii.
[2] *Ibid,* ii, 170–171.   [3] *Ibid,* ii, 31.   [4] *Ibid,* ii, 45.

the soft, velvet-black of exposed rock. And once or twice I was quite sure that I saw, behind the tops of the glacier, the white floor of the plateau. But of that I could not be certain. It was quite likely, I warned myself, that the imagination conjured up what the eye was most eager to see.

The colossal mass to the right of Nansen was unlike anything that Amundsen described. It was easily the most impressive mountain of the lot. It did not have Nansen's chill sculptured profile. This was consolidated mass, with the frowning ramparts of a fortress. It was at least 20 miles in length.[1]

To the right, the peaks and spurs of Crown Prince Olav Mountains continued to South Victoria Land. Behind the first outposts I had seen a second range, with peaks higher and more superb than those in front.

Smith edged slightly toward the western portal of Axel Heiberg Glacier, where we planned to make the base. The Barrier underneath became more rolling, its level stretch giving way to a series of swelling undulations.

We drew within a few miles of Nansen's approaches, and saw that the surface, in the vicinity of Axel Heiberg Glacier, did not appear as favorable for landing. We headed to the westward and found, 15 miles or so in that direction, deep, fan-shaped crevasses, which were from 10 to 50 feet from edge to edge and partly drifted, marring the surface of the Barrier. The area was impossible for a landing. We kept these crevasses to the westward and flew south for a few minutes. The eastern portal of Liv's Glacier was several miles to the west.

Anxiously we studied the surface. It was not at all promising. Everywhere the Barrier was scored with the wave-like formations of sastrugi, and these, for the most part, appeared to be so high and rough as to forbid the attempting of a landing. However, several miles north of Nansen's foothills, the western peaks of which served as the eastern portal to Liv's Glacier, there was a pool of fairly level snow: there we decided to lay the base.

We dropped lower. I let go a smoke bomb to get the

---

[1] This mountain was named Fisher Mountain, after the Fisher brothers of Detroit.

wind direction, and its column leaned slightly on a gentle easterly. Then we dropped four bombs in line, as a means of determining our distance above the snow. As we turned and came into the wind, I had a fair view of Liv's Glacier. Amundsen had wondered what this glacier was like. The main channel, which was astonishingly wide, curved behind Nansen's foothills and rose, in a series of escalated ice falls, some of which were at least 200 feet in height, to a great elevation. Far up it seemed to bend slightly to the west, disappearing behind the arm of Nansen and the bulking shoulder of Fisher Mountain.

The moment which we had looked forward to with apprehension was at hand. Everything depended upon this landing, and Dean Smith carried a heavy burden on his shoulders. When such moments come, the time for worry is passed. One feels calm, calmer than when planning for such a critical project. We had gone as far as mere planning could carry us, and the result rested with Fate. There was no thought of physical danger. We were oppressed only by the fear that if things went wrong now the whole expedition would suffer.

I had supreme confidence in Smith. He brought the plane down with rare caution. The surface was rough, and I was more than thankful that the new skis were long and wide. Had they been narrower and shorter, we might easily have stubbed or smashed them on the razor-backed sastrugi which traversed even the less disturbed spaces.

Just before the skis hit, Smith nosed the plane into a power stall. We landed at a speed of about 50 miles per hour and the Ford was severely tested on the rough, very hard snow before it came to a stop. Smith's landing was perfect. We had surmounted the first big obstacle between us and the Pole.

Smith remained in the cockpit, carefully nursing the engines, while June, McKinley and I prepared to build the depot. I paused long enough to take several sights of the sun, which gave us a longitude line on the chart and indicated that we were about where we thought we were. That done, I pitched in and helped the others unload.

Building the depot took very little time. We simply piled

the cans of fuel and oil and the bags of food in a high mass.
The food, however, we covered with snow blocks. The gasoline stove for which the Geological Party had asked was set
on top of the mound, which was several feet above our heads.
We finished with some satisfaction at this southernmost base
in the world. I named it after Josephine Ford—the same
name which was given to the North Pole plane.

"Well, that's done," June said. "Boy, what scenery!"

To the north the Barrier invaded the horizon. The rolling
troughs and crests which seemed none too conspicuous from
the air were immense. Nansen's group of foothills had become full-fledged mountains, which effectively shut off Nansen from view.

How much more—and yet how very much less—the surface traveller sees. And how different the point of view.

The area in the vicinity of the base was heavily scored
with sastrugi. Those nearby which we examined were quite
deep and firm, and curved up to a sharp icy overhang. Quite
plainly they showed that the prevailing easterly winds in this
area were severe at times. There was, to our surprise, little
evidence of recent movement in the ice in the immediate
vicinity except where a few glaciers debouched from the mountains. Farther to the west, where Liv's discharging stream,
freighted with millions of tons of ice pouring from the
plateau, met the Barrier we saw a series of huge crevasses
which ran in parallel cracks more or less to the northeast.
These were partly drifted over.

The engines purred constantly. Smith, who was anxious
about fuel consumption, slid back one of the windows in the
cockpit and yelled: "We'd better not hang around here too
long."

We hustled into the cabin, and rose in a long glide and
headed east. With the first phase of flight operations successfully accomplished, I was eager to make a thorough investigation of Carmen Land. It was my intention to fly at least
100 miles to the east. McKinley's camera went into action
again, mapping the face of the Queen Maud Range as we
flew parallel to it.

The main structure of Queen Maud, we saw, trended to
the southeast, and presently we saw the same smaller range

we had seen before, which extended indefinitely to the east-ward.[1]

The Ford had risen to an altitude of 3,000 feet and we had visibility to the east for at least 50 miles. Again I looked for Carmen Land, but in vain. I could see only the Barrier rolling endlessly to the east. A great pressure ridge or perhaps a mirage may have misled Amundsen into believing that land was there. So, from a geographical point of view, the base-laying flight had great significance in that we were now able definitely to extend the known limits of the Barrier at least 100 miles to the east. But I did not want to announce this until we had made still further investigation.

At this moment, as we stood again on the threshold of discovery, June, who had been sounding the fuel tanks, moved down the cabin and told me, with a grave face, that the fuel supply was dangerously low.

I shouted: "How can that be! Surely we must have gas for nearly seven hours' flying."

June took off his glove and raised four fingers, "Very heavy consumption. Don't know why."

When we were about an hour out from Little America June had discovered a fairly rapid leak near the hand fuel pump underneath the pilot seat. He had plugged this with chewing gum and then dammed it with heavy tape. At the time, we believed it had stopped the flow.

There was nothing to do but turn back at once. We should have to run for it, as it was. Smith turned the plane, and as it wheeled I stared up the valley of a steep mountain glacier which debouched from Nansen's flank. Far up, over a saddle where Nansen appeared to merge with a second mass of foothills, I caught sight, for a moment, of the blue-white flooring of Axel Heiberg. From it a mighty ice fall descended to the mountain glacier.

Studying it, I was moved to wonder if we could hurl our heavily loaded plane over its pass, which we could not see. I looked at it anxiously, and wished that I might be able to see what lay hidden in the heights.

We swung over Josephine Ford cache, turned north and I laid a straight course for Little America. There could be

[1] These were named the Charles V. Bob Mountains.

no following of the southern trail on the return trip. With a diminishing fuel supply, a straight line recommended itself overwhelmingly. We should depend wholly upon the drift indicator, the sun compass (and astronomy if necessary) to get us back. Fortunately the weather continued excellent, the sun was visible and as long as it was there I could get a line on it with the sun compass.

I glanced for a last time at Liv's Glacier, and the idea occurred that it might offer better passage over the "Hump" than Axel Heiberg.

Far to the west a tracery of cloud crept over the highest peaks.

We flew now at an altitude of about 2,000 feet, with the engines turning over at the most economical revolutions, while Smith endeavored to "lean" the mixture as much as possible.

I studied the eastern horizon with my glasses. Still no signs of Carmen Land.

I sent Smith a message: "We will pick up the trail just north of the crevasses."

We were over the crevasses shortly before 7:00 o'clock, and sure enough at approximately the point at which the calculations indicated we sighted the trail. We were then about 150 miles from Little America.

About fifty miles on, the engines began to miss. Directly ahead was an area which Thorne and de Ganahl, both of them flyers, had reported, on their return from their dog team journeys, was impossible for landing. It was furrowed with sastrugi, and we could see that the surface was still very rough.

Smith worked the throttles anxiously, trying to restore the engines to their former fluency, but to no avail. All three stopped at once. June looked up from the main gas tank. "No gas," he yelled in the sudden quiet that followed the cessation of the engines.

Smith brought the plane down in a superb manner, squeezing the last inch of altitude from the glide. We barely crept over the edge of the worst area and landed with a bump. Nevertheless everything held. Luck and a fine piece of work by Smith saw us through.

It was then 7:29 o'clock.

THE CREVASSES AT LAT. 82° 12′ S.

(Photo by Captain McKinley.)

Fisher Mountain (in the Background) as Seen from a Great Distance.

The moment the plane stopped, all hands scrambled out, snatching empty cans from the racks in the fuselage and made ready to drain the oil from the engines. We pulled out the plugs and caught the warm oil as it fell. A goodly percentage of it went into the cans, but a considerable amount fell on us. In a very short time we were reeking with oil and unquestionably the dirtiest persons within thousands of miles. The oil congealed on our clothes and we were very uncomfortable.

June assembled the emergency radio set and tried to send an S.O.S. to the camp, but for some reason, which we were unable to determine at the time, he could not raise the operator.

We then set up a tent not far from the plane, and tried to get some rest. It had been a busy day. But we could not remain still for long, for we were greatly concerned as to the safety of the plane. If a blizzard should come before we could get in touch with the camp, we might lose it. The weather, however, remained perfectly clear and calm.

About 11 o'clock, when we were on the verge of giving up the hope of establishing communication with the camp, and when McKinley's arm was about used up in cranking the hand generator, we heard the sound of an airplane. It was the Fairchild, with Balchen and Petersen. It made an extremely rough landing and taxied alongside. Balchen was piloting and Petersen was radio operator. To our delight Balchen reported that he had 100 gallons of fuel aboard.

"When we heard the transmitter stop," Balchen said, "we knew you had come down and figured you were about 100 miles out. Haines waited to hear from you by radio, and then decided to send the Fairchild out. Lack of gas, we decided, brought you down."

Our joy at seeing Balchen and Petersen was equalled only by our respect for Haines' good judgment.

This incident illustrates the value of radio. Had Balchen not known our position, searching for us in that vast expanse of snow would have been as hard as trying to find the proverbial needle. The radio men, at Little America, who had been listening in on the flight, heard the engines stop. Knowing the rate of speed at which we were flying, Balchen was able to figure out our approximate latitude; and knowing that we had been following the trail, he knew our longitude. For a second time, our rescue plans functioned smoothly.

Balchen and Petersen immediately unloaded the fuel cans and we dumped them into the Ford's wing tank. Then the Fairchild took off for Little America, expecting us to follow.

When we began to figure out the high fuel consumption, we realized that we had been a bit hasty in promising to follow. Not knowing exactly the cause of this excessive consumption we were afraid that the 100 gallons would not be sufficient to carry us back to base. Another forced landing might prove disastrous. We decided, therefore, to fly two-thirds of the distance to the base, select a good place to land and there await the arrival of more gas.

It had turned colder and we had a difficult time getting the engines started. We heated them first with the blow torch and then the three of us threw our weight on the long crank which turns the inertia starter. We finally managed to get one engine going but were then so fatigued we were almost reluctant to tackle the second. When we finished cranking and thrust home the pin which engages the engine, instead of the whine of high speed revolutions which we waited to hear, we heard instead a blank silence. We tried again, and yet again, but without success. The "booster" had frozen solid and we were guests of the Barrier for the night. We stopped the first engine and tried to renew radio communication with the camp.

McKinley crawled into the fuselage and went to sleep. We found him sprawled across a four-inch upright, sleeping as soundly as if he was in a feather bed. Smith served a supper of cocoa and biscuits, the predominant taste of which was oil, and we arranged watches for the night.

For a time we were baffled as to the cause of the excessive consumption. It did not seem possible that the small leak near the fuel pump could have caused it alone. It was finally decided that the jets were still too large.

June worked on the radio set all night, having finally taken down the transmitter in an attempt to locate the trouble. He found a rupture in the high tension lead in the hand generator. Smith, who is a capable operator, relieved him, and June finally crawled into his oily sleeping bag. My bag I stretched on the snow, and slept fairly well.

We were still waiting at 7 o'clock the next evening. Not long afterwards June made contact with the base. I sent a message to Bill Haines, asking him to send out the Fairchild with more fuel and another man to help us crank the engine. Haines replied instantly that the Fairchild had left some time ago, with more gas and oil, and should reach us very soon. Bill thought of everything. A moment later June heard the transmitter of the Fairchild and we established communication. Balchen was piloting and Petersen was radio man.

A few moments later Balchen landed safely. We borrowed the booster from the Fairchild, got the three motors started in jig time and took off. At 2,000 feet we met a walloping 30-mile tail wind and rode it to Little America, swinging above the wireless towers a few minutes before midnight. The Ross Sea, to the north and east, was choked with drift ice.

An hour later Balchen returned in the Fairchild, and the incident, which had been full of potential dangers, was closed.

The mechanics took over the Ford, and we turned in. We were ready, then, to tackle the polar flight.

Meanwhile the Geological Party, burdened down by heavy loads, was making heavy going of it to the mountains.

Saturday
November 23rd

The mechanics have made the necessary engine adjustments on the Ford, and it is ready to go.

All gear is ready. We are waiting now for the Geological Party to reach the mountains and a favorable weather report from Gould.

The Geological Party reached Depot No. 5 tonight.

Sunday
November 24th

McKinley's photographs of the Queen Maud Range and the mountains to the westward are excellent. I have notified Gould by radio that I shall drop him a batch of these photographs when we pass over him on the way to the Pole. They will give him a much clearer idea of the area than he can get from the surface. At least, it may simplify his geological work.

Monday
November 25th

Sky partly overcast, temperature as high as 12° today. The wind is a gentle southwesterly.

The Geological Party has the mountains in sight. Gould reports they put down Depot No. 6 this morning and are pushing ahead. He reports also that they have had no sun for three days.

The sun is absolutely necessary on the polar flight, not only from the point of view of navigation but also of survey photography.

We must wait.

Tuesday
November 26th

Still cloudy here.

Gould reported at 6 A.M. that "a heavy cloud bank to the south completely hides the mountains."

So we must defer the start. We cannot risk an assault on the "Hump" unless the air is absolutely clear. It will be a close squeeze as it is, just with the heavy load, without the added danger of colliding with an unseen mountain peak.

For the 1000th time I have calculated expectancy and performance. We can do it by the skin of our teeth.

The total weight of the Ford, including personnel, is nearly 15,000 pounds.

Wednesday
November 27th

This execrable cloudiness continues. The temperature was 6° below this morning but has since risen above zero. The wind is ESE. A 30 mile wind and heavy drift were reported by Gould this morning.

We have asked the Geological Party to stand by until 1 P.M. for a radio schedule to advise us on weather.

Later

Gould radioed at 1 o'clock that the weather at the foot of the mountains is "excellent," with a five mile wind from the southeast, and a few thin clouds above the mountain peaks.

It looks good.

Midnight

In its 10 o'clock P.M. report the Geological Party says the weather continues unchanged—"excellent."

Haines is making his charts. He believes that within another ten or fifteen hours we shall have the weather we want.

It would be asking too much to demand perfect weather throughout the flight. A south wind, for example, which generally brings clear skies, must of necessity be a head wind on the outward trip, when the Ford will be carrying its heaviest loads. But a north wind, which might provide a very helpful boost, unfortunately brings as a rule clouds formed by the condensation of the warmer air from the water as it strikes the Barrier.

As I have done on equally critical occasions in the past, I shall have implicit confidence in Bill Haines. He knows exactly what we need, and will not give the word until conditions are adequate.

CHAPTER XIV

THANKSGIVING DAY, November 25th, gave us what we wanted. At noon the Geological Party radioed a final weather report: "Unchanged. Perfect visibility. No clouds anywhere." Harrison finished with his balloon runs, Haines with his weather charts. The sky was still somewhat overcast, and the surface wind from the east-southeast. Haines came into the library, his face very grave and determined. Dear old Bill, he always takes his responsibilities seriously. Together we went out for a walk and a last look at the weather. What he said exactly I have forgotten, but it was in effect: "If you don't go now you may never have another chance as good as this." And that was that.

There were a few things to be done. Every possible thing that could happen and some that could not possibly happen we had attempted to anticipate and prepare for. First, I delivered to Haines, who would be in charge of the camp during our absence and until the return of Gould, a set of instructions suggesting his procedure in case we should fail. It was, of course, necessary to anticipate this contingency. There were, besides, a number of sealed instructions, to be opened only if no word came from us within a fixed period. These provided for the organization of a relief expedition, the allocation of responsibility, the return of part of the expedition to the United States and the messages which a thoughtful man must leave behind before undertaking such a flight. These last I gave to Lofgren, who had served the expedition faithfully and than whom there is no squarer or truer man.

The mechanics, Bubier, Roth and Demas, went over the plane for the last time, testing everything with scrupulous care. A line of men passed five-gallon cans of gasoline to

326

several men standing on the wing, who poured them into the wing tanks. Another line fed the stream of gear which flowed into the plane. Black weighed each thing before passing it on to McKinley and June, who were stowing the stuff in the cabin. Hanson went over the radio equipment. With de Ganahl I made a careful check of the sextant and the watches and chronometers, which were among the last things put aboard. For days de Ganahl and I had nursed the chronometers, checking them against the time tick which was broadcast every night from the United States. We knew their exact loss or gain. We had to know. An error in time would put the Bumstead sun compass off and our geographical position as well.

No thoroughbred went into a race more carefully, scrupulously groomed than was the Floyd Bennett before the polar flight. Responsibility for its performance rested with no single man. It lay on the shoulders of the whole camp. It was a sobering responsibility, and I think that every man felt it in his heart.

We were done with these details shortly after three o'clock. At the last moment we decided to take aboard an additional 100 gallons of gasoline. There was no telling what kind of winds we would meet. If head winds, then the extra quantity of fuel would be invaluable. If not, we could dump it overboard before we reached the "Hump."

The total weight was approximately 15,000 pounds.

Haines came up with a final report on the weather. "A twenty-mile wind from the south at 2,000 feet." It meant clear skies to the south. I went into my office and picked up a flag weighted with a stone from Floyd Bennett's grave. It seemed fitting that something connected with the spirit of this noble friend who stood with me over the North Pole, on May 9, 1926, should rest as long as stone endures at the bottom of the world.

There were handshakes all around, and at 3:29 o'clock we were off. The skis were in the air after a run of 30 seconds —an excellent take-off. I was greatly relieved. A calm expectation took hold of my mind. Having started, we were certainly going to get somewhere.

There was a flashing glimpse of the men clustered near the runway—those splendid fellows whose willing help and indestructible spirit have never faltered, no, not once—and we faced the south.

The moment the Ford leveled off the impalpable haze with which we had contended so often confused the vision, and we lost several precious minutes before we found the trail. But if Haines' predictions were correct, this would not last for long.

Our course was laid along the meridian of the trail, which at that point was 143° 45′ W. Although the trail did not always follow that meridian, it would bring us finally to Axel Heiberg Glacier.

The sky began to clear, under the sweeping movements of a southeasterly wind, and presently blue sky showed ahead. Haines was right, as always. Slowly gaining altitude, we passed 20 Mile Depot, then 44 Mile Depot.

From time to time we lost the trail, as our altitude changed or our distance from it varied slightly. But invariably by steering a straight course with the Bumstead sun compass we picked it up again.

Presently the northern edge of the crevasses was underneath. The trail then followed meridian 163° 42′ W. The wind was still from the east and it was necessary to nose the plane 10° to the left of the course, to make good a straight course to the south. Had there been any one below to see, he must have been surprised at the sight of a plane headed well to the east but flying steadily to the south. With this diagonal push tending to press us from our course it was necessary to check the course frequently with the drift indicator.

Had you been there to glance over the cabin of this modern machine which has so revolutionized polar travel, I think you would have been impressed most of all—perhaps first of all—with the profusion of gear in the cabin. There was a small sledge, rolled masses of sleeping bags, bulky food sacks, two pressure gasoline stoves, rows of cans of gasoline packed about the main tank forward, funnels for draining gasoline and oil from the engine, mounds of clothing, tents and so on, *ad infinitum*. There was scarcely room in which to move.

June had his radio in the after bulkhead on the port side. From time to time he flashed reports on our progress to the base. From the ear phones strapped to his helmet ran long cords, so that he might move freely about the cabin without being obliged to take them off. His duties were varied and important. He had to attend to the motion picture camera, the radio and the complicated valves of the six gasoline tanks. Every now and then he relieved Balchen at the wheel, or helped him to follow the elusive trail.

McKinley had his mapping camera ready to go into action either on port or starboard side. It was for him and the camera he so sedulously served that the flight was made. The mapping of the corridor between Little America and the South Pole was one of the major objectives of the expedition.

Balchen was forward, bulking large in the narrow compartment, his massive hands on the wheel, now appraising the engines with a critical eye, now the dozen flickering fingers on the dials on the instrument board. Balchen was in his element. His calm fine face bespoke his confidence and sureness. He was anticipating the struggle at the "Hump" almost with eagerness.

It was quite warm forward, behind the engines. But a cold wind swept aft through the cabin, causing one to be thankful for the protection of heavy clothes. When the skies cleared, the cabin was flooded with a golden light. The sound of the engines and propellers filled it. One had to shout to make oneself heard. From the navigation table aft, where my charts were spread out, a trolley ran to the control cabin. Over it I shot to Balchen the necessary messages and courses. On receiving them, he turned and smiled his understanding.

That, briefly, is the picture, and a startling one it makes in contrast with that of Amundsen's party which had pressed along this same course eighteen years before. A wing, pistons and flashing propellers had taken the place of runners, dogs and legs. Amundsen was delighted to make 25 miles per day. We had to average 90 miles per hour to accomplish our mission. We had the advantages of swiftness and comfort, but we had as well an enlarged fallibility. A flaw in a piece of steel, a bit of dirt in the fuel lines or carburetor jets, a few hours of strong head winds, fog or storm—these things, remotely beyond our control, could destroy our carefully laid plans and nullify our most determined efforts.

Still, it was not these things that entered our minds.

Rather it was the thought of the "Hump," and how we should fare with it.

Soon after passing the crevasses we picked up again the vast escarpment to the right. More clearly than before we saw the white-blue streams of many glaciers discharging into the Barrier, and several of the inner and higher snow-clad peaks glistened so brightly in the sun as to seem like volcanoes in eruption.

Our altitude was then about 1500 feet.

Now the Queen Maud Range loomed ahead. I searched again for the "appearance of land" to the east. Still the rolling Barrier—nothing else.

The quartering wind from the southeast blew with fluctuating direction and velocity, imparting an angle of drift as high as 20° at times.

At 8:15 o'clock we had the Geological Party in sight—a cluster of little beetles about two dark topped tents. Balchen dropped to an altitude of about 750 feet, and McKinley put overboard the photographs of the Queen Maud Range and the other things we had promised to bring. The parachute canopy to which they were attached fluttered open and fell in gentle oscillations, and we saw two or three figures rush out to catch it. We waved to them, and then prepared for a settlement of the issue at the "Hump."

Up to this time the engines had operated continuously at cruising revolutions—1580 R.P.M.'s for the big center engine, 1600 for the smaller engines outboard. Now Balchen opened them full throttle—1750 R.P.M.'s for the center engine, 1700 for the two outboard—and the Ford girded its loins for the long, hard, fighting pull over the "Hump." We rose steadily. We were then about 60 miles north of the western portal of Axel Heiberg, and holding our course steadily on meridian 163° 45' W. with the sun compass.

I watched the altimeters, of which there were two in the navigation compartment. The fingers marched with little jumps across the face of the dial—3000 feet, 3500, 4000, 4500. The Ford had her toes in, and was climbing fast.

Drawing nearer, we had edged 30° to the west of South, to bring not only Axel Heiberg but also Liv's into view. This was a critical period. I was by no means certain which

I should choose. I went forward and took a position behind Balchen. We would figure this thing out together.

The schemes and hopes of the next few minutes were beset by many probabilities. Which would it be—Axel Heiberg or Liv's Glacier?

There was this significant difference between flying and sledging: we could not pause long for decision or investigation. Minutes stood for gasoline, and gasoline was precious. The waste of so little as half an hour of fuel in a fruitless experiment might well overturn the mathematical balance on which the success of the flight depended. The execution of the plan hung on the proper judgment of the route over the "Hump."

True, we had a 40 percent safety factor over fuel needs to the Pole and back. This, of course, was a theoretical margin. It was a precaution against depletion resulting from head winds, and its value could not be weakened by a mistake in judgment. In fact, head winds had already exhausted some of this reserve.

Yet how well, after all, could judgment forecast the ultimate result? There were few facts on which we might base a wise decision. We knew, for example, that the highest point of the pass of Axel Heiberg Glacier which Amundsen reported was 10,500 feet. We would know, in a very few minutes, after June had calculated the gasoline consumption, the weight of the plane. From that we could determine, according to the tables which we had worked out and were then before me, the approximate ceiling we would have. We would know, too, whether or not we should be able to complete the flight, other conditions being favorable.

These were the known elements. The unknown were burdened with equally important consequences. The structural nature of the head of the pass was of prime importance. We knew from Amundsen's descriptions and from what we could see with our own eyes, that the pass was surrounded by towering peaks on each side, extending much higher than the maximum altitude of the heavily loaded plane. But whether the pass was wide or narrow; whether it would allow us room to maneuver in case we could not rise above it; whether it would be narrow and running with a torrent of down-pressing wind which would dash a plane, already hovering at its peak of maximum efficiency, to the glacier floor—these were things, naturally, we could not possibly know until the issue was directly at hand.

I stood beside Balchen, carefully studying the looming fortress, still wondering by what means we should attempt to carry it. With a gesture of the hand Balchen pointed to fog vapor rising from the black rock of the foothills which were Nansen's high priests—caused no doubt by the condensation of warm currents of air radiated from the sun-heated rocks. A thin layer of cloud seemed to cap Axel Heiberg's pass, and extended almost to Liv's Glacier. But of this we were not certain. Perhaps it was the surface of the snow. If cloud, then our difficulties were at hand. Even high clouds would be resting on the floor of the uplifted plateau.

There was, then, a gamble in the decision. Doubtless a flip of the coin would have served as well. In the end, we decided to choose Liv's Glacier, the unknown pass to the right, which Amundsen had seen far in the distance and named after Dr. Nansen's daughter. It seemed to be wider than Axel Heiberg, and the pass not quite as high.

A few minutes after nine o'clock we passed near the intermediate base, which of course we could not see. Our altitude was then about 9000 feet. At 9:15 o'clock we had the eastern portal on our left, and were ready to tackle the "Hump." We had discussed the "Hump" so often, had anticipated and maligned it so much, that now that it was in front of us and waiting in the flesh—in rock-ribbed glaciated reality—we felt that we were meeting an old acquaintance. But we approached it warily, respectfully, climbing steadily all the while with our maximum power, to get a better view of its none too friendly visage.

June, wholly unaffected by the immediate perplexities, went about his job of getting the plane in fighting trim. He ripped open the last of the fuel cans, and poured the contents into the main tank. The empty tins he dropped overboard, through the trap door. Every tin weighed two pounds; and every pound dropped was to our advantage. The fumes filled the cabin, offending one's stomach and eyes. June examined the gauges of the five wing tanks, then measured with a graduated stick the amount of fuel in the main tank. He jotted the figures on a pad, made a few calculations and handed me the results.   Consumption had thus far averaged between 55 and 60 gallons per hour.   It had taken us longer to reach the mountains than we had expected, owing to head winds. However, the extra fuel taken aboard just before we left had absorbed this loss and we actually had a credit balance. We had, then, enough gasoline to take us to the Pole and back.

With that doubt disposed of, we went at the "Hump" confidently.

We were still rising, and the engines were pulling wonderfully well.   The wind was about abeam, and, according to my calculations, not materially affecting the speed.

Liv's Glacier was before us almost in its full sweeping entirety—a Niagric torrent doomed to rigidity, with frozen whirlpools and waterfalls.   Far ahead it bent in a wide curve to the west of south.   About thirty-five miles away it disappeared into a vague white surface—could it be the plateau? We then had nearly the whole of Nansen's foothills on the left.   One of these formed the eastern portal of Liv's Glacier. When we first saw them on the base-laying flight, they had seemed to be high and imposing mountains; but now they were obscure and small.   Nansen was on the left, to the southeast, and filled the horizon.   The marbled walls of Fisher Mountain, with its company of stalwart foothills, was on the right, crowding into the horizon on the southwest.   The ice line of the glacier, where it met the Barrier, was quite distinct; but the immense crevasses which we had seen before were softened and subdued by the difference in altitude, and now resembled the fluted surface of a washing board.

The floor of the glacier rose sharply, in a series of ice falls and terraces, some of which were well above the (then) altitude of the plane.   These glacial waterfalls, some of which were from 200 to 400 feet high, seemed more beautiful than any precipitous stream I have ever seen.   Beautiful yes, but how rudely and with what finality they would deal with steel and duralumin that was fated to collide with them at 100 miles per hour.

About ten miles up, the glacier was given over to terrific crevasses, where the weight of the flow carried it against solid rock.

At this point the stream of air pouring down the pass

roughened perceptibly. The great wing shivered and teetered as it balanced itself against the changing pressures. The wind from the left flowed against Fisher's steep flanks, and the constant, hammering bumps made footing uncertain. But McKinley steadily trained his 50-pound camera on the mountains to the left. The uncertainties of load and ceiling were not his concern. His only concern was photographs—photographs over which students and geographers might pore in the calm quiet of their studies. Had we gone down in a tailspin, I am sure that McKinley would have operated his camera all the way down.

The altimeters showed a height of 9600 feet, but the figure was not necessarily exact. More likely than not, the barometric principle on which it operated was influenced by local changes in pressure. Nevertheless there were indications we were near the service ceiling of the plane.

The roughness of the air increased and became so violent that we were forced to swing slightly to the left, in search of calmer air. This brought us over a frightfully crevassed slope which ran up and toward Mount Nansen. We thus escaped the turbulent swirl about Fisher, but the down-surging currents here damped our climb. To the left we had the "blind" mountain glacier of Nansen in full view; and when we looked ahead we saw the plateau—a smooth, level plain of snow between Nansen and Fisher. The pass rose up to meet it.

In the center of the pass was a massive outcropping of snow-covered rock, resembling an island, which protruded above and separated the descending stream of ice. Perhaps it was a peak or the highest eminence of a ridge connecting Fisher and Nansen which had managed through the ages to hold its head above the glacial torrent pouring down from the plateau. But its particular structure or relationship was of small moment then. I watched it only with reference to the climb of the plane; and realized, with some disgust and more consternation, that the nose of the plane, in spite of the fact that Balchen had steepened the angle of attack, did not rise materially above the outcropping. We were still climbing, but at a rapidly diminishing rate of speed. In the rarefied air the heavy plane responded to the controls with marked sluggishness.

It was an awesome thing, creeping (so it seemed) through

the narrow pass, with the black walls of Nansen and Fisher on either side, higher than the level of the wings, watching the nose of the ship bob up and down across the face of that lone chunk of rock. It would move up, then slide down. Then move up, and fall off again. For perhaps a minute or two we deferred the decision; but there was no escaping it. If we were to risk a passage through the pass, we needed greater maneuverability than we had at that moment. The pass was uncomfortably narrow. Once we entered it there would be no retreat. It offered no room for turn. If power was lost momentarily or if the air became excessively rough, we could only go ahead, or down. We needed power, and there was only one way in which to get it.

June, anticipating the command, left the radio and put his hand on the dump valve of the main tank. A pressure of the fingers—that was all that was necessary—and in two minutes 600 gallons of gasoline would gush out. I signalled to wait.

Balchen held to the climb to the last degree of safety. But it was clear to both of us that he could not hold it long enough. Balchen began to yell and gesticulate, and it was hard to catch the words in the roar of the engines echoing from the cliffs on either side. But the meaning was manifest. "Overboard—overboard—200 pounds!"

Which would it be—gasoline or food?

If gasoline, I thought, we might as well stop there and turn back. We could never get back to the base from the Pole. If food, the lives of all of us would be jeopardized in the event of a forced landing. Was that fair to McKinley, Balchen and June? It really took only a moment to reach the decision. The Pole, after all, was our objective. I knew the character of the three men. They were not so lightly to be turned aside. McKinley, in fact, had already hauled one of the food bags to the trap door. It weighed 125 pounds.

"Harold, a bag of food overboard," I said to June. He signalled to McKinley. The brown bag was pushed out and fell, spinning, to the glacier. The improvement in the flying qualities of the plane was noticeable. The Floyd Bennett took another breath and renewed the climb.

Now the down-currents over Nansen became stronger.

The plane trembled and rose and fell, as if struck bodily. We veered a trifle to the right, searching for helpful rising eddies. The issue was still in doubt and Balchen's irritation with the inexorable laws which limited our altitude waxed and grew profane. The head of the pass was still on a level with the plane's line of flight. Balchen was flying shrewdly. He maintained flight at a sufficient distance below the absolute ceiling of the plane to retain at all times enough maneuverability to make him master of the ship. But he was hard pressed by circumstances; and I realized that unless the plane was further lightened, the final thrust might bring us perilously close to the end of our reserve.

"More," Bernt shouted. "Another bag."

McKinley shoved a second bag through the trap door, and this time we saw it hit the glacier, and scatter in a soundless explosion. Two hundred and fifty pounds of food—enough to feed four men for a month—lay on that lifeless waste.

The sacrifice was the saving factor. The plane, literally, rose with a jump; the engines dug in and we soon showed a gain in altitude of from 300 to 400 feet. It was what we wanted. We would clear the pass with about 500 feet to spare. Balchen gave a shout of joy. It was just as well. We could dump no more food. There was nothing left to dump except McKinley's camera. I am sure that had he been asked to put it overboard, he would have done so instantly; and I am equally sure he would have followed the precious instrument with his own body.

The next few minutes dragged. We moved at a speed of 77 nautical miles per hour through the pass, with the black walls of Nansen on our left. The wing gradually lifted above them. The floor of the plateau stretched in a white immensity to the south. We were over the dreaded "Hump" at last. The Pole lay dead ahead over the horizon, less than 300 miles away. It was then about 9:45 o'clock (I did not note the exact time. There were other things to think about).

Gaining the plateau, we studied the situation a moment and then shifted course to the southward. Nansen's enormous towering ridge, lipped by the plateau, shoved its heavily broken sides into the sky. To the right of it Ruth Gade's tented arch gradually became, as we watched, a white inverted porcelain bowl. A whole chain of mountains began to parade

The South Polar Plane, the "Floyd Bennett," Its Skis Covered by Drift.

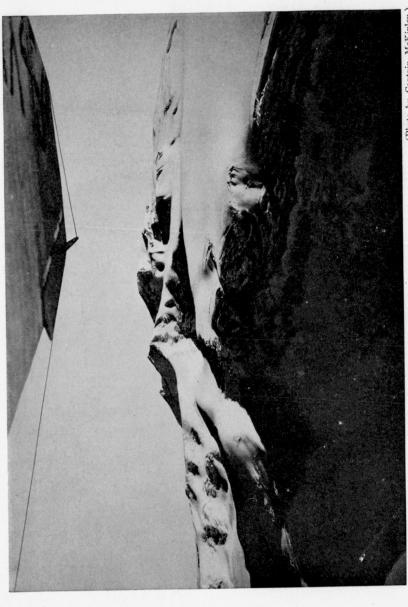

(Photo by Captain McKinley.)

OVER "THE HUMP."

The South Polar Plane over the head of the pass of Liv's Glacier on the way to the Pole. Altitude about 10,500 feet.
The top of Mt. Nansen, which is on the left, is 15,000 feet high.

across the eastern horizon. How high they are I cannot say,[1] but surely many of them must be in excess of 15,000 feet, to stand so boldly above the rim of the 10,000 foot plateau. Peak on peak, ridge on ridge, draped in snow garments which brilliantly reflected the sun, they extended in a solid array to the southeast. But can one really say they run in that direction? The lines of direction are so bent in this region that 150 miles farther on, even were they to continue in the same general straight line, they must run north of east. This is what happens near the Pole.

However, such preoccupations did not bother us then. We were on a flight of discovery, and wanted to see things and record them. To bring them nearer, we had soon edged the course slightly to the east of the southern course we had taken. McKinley's camera, which had never ceased to operate, trained on them, taking a succession of oblique, overlapping mapping photographs. Far to the left I made out what appeared to be the largest glacier we had yet seen, discharging into the new range we had first observed on the base-laying flight.

We laid our line of flight on the 171st meridian.

On the right was a range, which appeared to trend to the south nearly to 87° and more or less parallel to and perhaps a little beyond the 180th meridian—a line of low-hung peaks standing above the swelling folds of the plateau. Now, with the full panorama before us, in all its appalling ruggedness and gothic massiveness, we had a conception of the ice age in its flood tide. Here was the core, the center point of the Antarctic ice sheet. How deep it lay under us, whether 1,000 feet or 8,000 feet, we could not tell. But deep it must be, thus to dominate nearly all but the highest peaks which rimmed it, like the walls of a dam. Seeking an outlet to relieve its incalculable pressures, it presses through the passes which become glacial spillways, and makes for the sea. The parade of the mountains, the contrast of black and white, the upreaching peaks and the trisulcated troughs of the glaciers, the plateau spreading to an illusory horizon—it was something never to be forgotten.

[1] These heights will be established, however, after the necessary and involved mathematical processes have been applied to McKinley's photographs.

The plateau seemed to be falling in a slope to the south. Our altitude was then between 10,500 and 11,000 feet. We were "riding" the engines, conscious of the fact that if one should fail we must come down. Once the starboard engine did sputter a bit, and Balchen nosed down while June rushed to the fuel valves. But it was nothing; to conserve fuel, Balchen had "leaned" the mixture too much. A quick adjustment corrected the fault, and in a moment the engine took up its steady rhythm. Moments like this one make a pioneering flight anything but dull; one moment everything is lovely, and the next is full of forebodings.

The drift indicator showed a variable wind from the east. To compensate for it, we had to point the nose of the plane an average of about 12° to the east, in order to steer a straight course for the Pole. The influence of the drift on the course was always a bothersome element. It had to be watched carefully, and any change in the angle of drift detected at once, so as to make good a straight course south. Fitted in the floor of the plane was a drift indicator which McKinley used in connection with his photographic work, and during the flight he constantly checked the drift with me. Whenever I noted any change in the direction or strength of the wind, I would steady Balchen on his course with the sun compass, first shaking the trolley line to attract his attention, then waving him on to the new course.

The basis of these calculations was the ground speed; and owing to the impossibility of determining the height of the plane above the snow, this value was not easily accessible. The altimeters register altitudes, only in reference to sea level. There is a way, however. By timing with a stop watch how long it takes a crevasse, sastrugi or smoke bomb to run the length of the drift indicator wire in the floor of the plane, and then turning north and passing over the object again, timing it a second time, it is possible by mathematics to get the speed.

Consequently, I spent a great deal of time kneeling on the floor of the plane, sighting sastrugi whenever I detected any change in drift. It was by no means a comfortable position. The temperature had dropped steadily since we reached the plateau, and when I opened the trap-door a torrent of sub-zero atmosphere swirled in, numbing my face and hands.

These readings showed that while the engines were cruising at about 100 miles per hour, the plane was actually moving over the snow at the rate of 90 statute miles per hour.

The character of the plateau surface varied from time to time. There were stretches of smooth, soft snow, colonies of domed haycocks and arrow-headed sastrugi. To have been forced down in these latter areas would have been as dangerous as being forced down in a rock-strewn field. From the time we reached the plateau its level appeared to fall gently toward the Pole; the altimeter showed that the Ford was maintaining a fairly steady ceiling at approximately 11,000 feet, and the plateau fell farther below.

While the mountains on the left were still in view, I attempted to shoot the sun with the sextant to get its altitude. This would give us a sun line which would cut our line of flight and at the point of intersection tell us what the sun had to say about our progress. The air, however, was slightly rough; the powerful center engine, laboring to keep the heavy load at an altitude of two miles, produced a weaving in the plane; and the most patient efforts failed to bring the sun and the bubble together long enough for a dependable sight. This was bothersome, but relatively unimportant at the time. We were quite confident as to the accuracy of the dead reckoning, and hoped that conditions would improve in the vicinity of the Pole.

From time to time June "spelled" Balchen at the controls; and Balchen would walk back to the cabin, flexing his cramped muscles. There was little thought of food in any of us—a beef sandwich, stiff as a board, and tea and coffee from a thermos bottle. It was difficult to believe that in recent history the most resolute men who had ever attempted to carry a remote objective, Scott and Shackleton, had plodded over this same plateau, a few miles each day, with hunger—fierce, unrelenting hunger stalking them every step of the way.

Between 11:30 and 12:30 o'clock the mountains to the eastward began to disappear, gradually of course, dropping imperceptibly out of view, one after another. Not long after 12:30 o'clock the whole range had retreated from vision, and the plateau met the horizon in an indefinite line. The mountains to the right had long since disappeared.

At 12:38 o'clock I finally shot the sun. It hung, a ball

of fire, just beyond *south* to the east, 21° above the horizon. So it was quite low, and we stared it in the eye. The sight gave me an approximate line of latitude, which placed us very near our position as calculated by dead reckoning. That dead reckoning and astronomy should check so closely was very encouraging. The position line placed us at Lat. 89° 4½′ S., or 55½ miles from the pole. A short time later we reached an altitude of 11,000 feet. According to Amundsen's records, the plateau, which had risen to 10,300 feet, descended here to 9,600 feet. We were, therefore, about 1400 feet above the plateau.

So the Pole, the mysterious objective, was actually in sight. But I could not yet spare it so much as a glance. Chronometers, drift indicators and compasses are hard task-masters.

Relieved by June, Balchen came aft and reported that visibility was not as good as it had been. Clouds were gathering on the horizon off the port bow and a storm, Balchen thought, was in the air. A storm was the last thing we wanted to meet on the plateau on the way back. It would be difficult enough to pass the Queen Maud Range in bright sunlight; in thick weather it would be suicidal. Conditions, however, were merely unpromising: not really bad, simply not good. If worse came to worse, we decided we could out-race the clouds to the mountains.

At six minutes after one o'clock, a sight of the sun put us a few miles ahead of our dead reckoning position. We were very close now. The sight was a check, but I depended more on the previous sight. At 1:14 o'clock, Greenwich Civil Time, our calculations showed that we were at the Pole.

We turned right and flew three or four miles. Had we turned right just before reaching the Pole, one could say that we had turned westward; but having reached the Pole we really turned northward, because all directions at the South Pole are north. We now reversed our direction, which had been northward, and flew toward the Pole again. Our direction then was southward, although at right angles to our previous line of course, which was also southward. It is difficult, therefore, to speak of directions during these maneuvers. For example, the moment we crossed the Pole again after this second change of course our direction, which

(Photo by Captain McKinley.)

ON THE WAY TO THE POLE.

The huge mountains that rim the polar plateau to the eastward. They are very far in the distance.

(Photo by Captain McKinley.)

THE PLATEAU IN THE NEAR VICINITY OF THE SOUTH POLE.

When this photograph was taken the altitude of the plane above the plateau was about 2,000 feet, and above sea level nearly 11,000 feet.

had been southward, instantly became northward, although we were still on the same straight line.

We continued on the same straight line of flight for about six miles, and this took the plane about three miles beyond the original line of flight we had followed from the mountains. Then we cut diagonally across an extension of our line of flight, which we hit five miles beyond the Pole. At 1:25 o'clock we turned back—toward the Pole and Little America.

It is a confusing place, this imaginary point, the South Pole. All time meridians converge there. A person unfortunate enough to be living in the vicinity would have difficulty in telling just what time to keep. Time is reckoned by the interval between two successive crossings of the sun over the meridian at the place at which the time is reckoned. As all meridians intersect at the South Pole, there is no particular meridian. The sun circles the sky at the same height above the snow horizon, and this height changes only an imperceptible amount every twenty-four hours. Directions, as we reckon them, would likewise mean nothing to this unfortunate creature. For unless he were travelling either north or south, it would be impossible for him to walk in a straight line and still retain the same direction. His direction would change noticeably every few minutes; and to keep his original direction he would be forced to follow a spiral course.

A few minutes after the turn I opened the trap door and dropped over the calculated position of the Pole the small flag which was weighted with the stone from Bennett's grave. Stone and flag plunged down together. The flag had been advanced 1,500 miles farther south than it had ever been before our expedition reached the Antarctic. June radioed the following message to Little America: "My calculations indicate that we have reached the vicinity of the South Pole. Flying high for a survey. Byrd."

The altimeters indicated our altitude as 11,000 feet.

For a few seconds we stood over the spot where Amundsen had stood, December 14, 1911; and where Scott had also stood, 34 days later, reading the note which Amundsen had left for him. In their honor, the flags of their countries were again carried over the Pole. There was nothing now to mark that scene; only a white desolation and solitude disturbed by the

sound of our engines. The Pole lay in the center of a limitless plain. No mountains were visible. In the direction of
Little America visibility was good, and so it was on the
left. But to the right, which is to say to the eastward, the
horizon was covered with clouds. If mountains lay there,
as some geologists believe, they were concealed and we had no
hint of them.

And that, in brief, is all there is to tell about the South
Pole. One gets there, and that is about all there is for the
telling. It is the effort to get there that counts.

We put the Pole behind us and raced for home.

The mountains to the eastward came into view again,
one by one. But whereas before the southernmost peaks had
stood out clear and distinct, they were now confused by haze
and clouds. The clouds were travelling fast, threatening to
close in ahead of us, and if we valued our skins, it behooved
us to beat them to the pass.

We were then riding the 168th meridian to Axel Heiberg
Glacier. It was my intention to return somewhat to the eastward of the original course, in order to bring within range
as much new territory as was possible. McKinley, who had
photographed the area to the eastward on the way to the
Pole, was then mapping the area to the westward. By that
time his camera must have seemed almost as heavy as the
mountains he was photographing. But his efforts never
slackened. When the highest mountains to the eastward
came into view, he mapped them as well.

Time began to crawl. It was a case of hitting the pass
of Axel Heiberg Glacier ahead of the clouds or being sorry.
The wind was then astern and helping us considerably. At
first it maintained a fairly steady direction, then shifted and
hit the Ford dead astern. Of course, its direction varied
from time to time. Our speed increased. About two o'clock,
seeking a still stronger wind aloft, we climbed several hundred
feet and here found a fairly stiff following wind. With that
boosting us, we hurried over the plateau. At three o'clock
Balchen opened the throttles wide and a short time later we
climbed about 400 feet higher. At this level the wind was
even stronger. We commenced to make a speed better than
125 miles per hour. Our altitude was between 11,500 and
12,000 feet.

About half past three o'clock Balchen's face broke into a smile. Ruth Gade's conical turret was off the starboard bow. There was Nansen off the port bow. Soon W. Christophersen came into view, a small rounded dome between Ruth Gade and Nansen. The charts, photographs and descriptions which I had culled from Amundsen's book, as well as the photographs which McKinley had taken on the base-laying flight, were before me: and as each new prominence appeared and fell neatly into its expected place, we were delighted. Our return course had been straight and our position coincided with our dead reckoning position. The flight was almost done. Best of all, the pass was clear.

We edged to the left, to bring Axel Heiberg's corridor into view. Then we changed course to the right, to examine a depression to the right of Ruth Gade. While moving toward it, we noticed still another pass to the left of Ruth Gade, apparently the most accessible of all, and decided to make for that. The maneuver brought Don Pedro Christophersen into full view. He was a good-sized fellow. But how very beautiful was Ruth Gade!

A few clouds were beginning to gather in the passes to the right and left. We had out-stripped the main advance.

By 3:50 o'clock we had passed over the head of the glacier, sinking lower all the time, and glided down the shattered terraces between the precipitous sides of Ruth Gade and Don Pedro Christophersen. The glacier we were following debouched into Axel Heiberg. The air in places was very bumpy, and the loose gear in the plane was tossed about rather wildly. Nansen's noble summit showed above Don Pedro Christophersen, a stern but kindly spectator of the descent.

We emerged from the glacier shortly after four o'clock.

June finished with his calculations of the fuel supply and reported there was a slight margin over needs. There was enough, then, to make further inquiry into Carmen Land, so we continued to the eastward. McKinley, I decided, ought to photograph the area.

We were now over the Barrier, and we could see how the shearing movements of the Barrier, where it pressed against the feet of the mountains, had resulted in very deep and extensive crevasses in several areas. What mighty pressures must be at work, to rip that tough fabric as if it were silk. The extensions of Queen Maud Range and the new mountains which we had seen on the base-laying flight were on our right, a solid rampart extending to the south of east. They were almost wholly covered with snow and some were broken by glaciers of considerable size and beauty. Indeed, what is, I think, one of the most beautiful glaciers in the world lies about 30 miles from our mountain base. I saw it for the first time then and was struck with its wild loveliness. It was wide and curving, a glacial river, and we could look up into it for miles.

The flight proved what I already knew to be true. Carmen Land does not exist. McKinley photographed the Barrier where Amundsen believed it lay, and we then turned westward, looking for the base.

Soon after we turned I became puzzled by the unfamiliar aspects of the mountains in the port beam. They appeared to be unlike any that we had seen. Yet my calculations placed us eastward of Ruth Gade. Could it be that we were off the course? Surely it did not seem possible that we could have gone so far astray in such a short time. I stared at the mountains and racked my brain. Where in the world, I asked myself, is Ruth Gade? All four of us conferred for a moment. My companions, who evidently had not been watching the course carefully, were unanimously of the opinion that the base was still farther to eastward. For a few frightful seconds I was uncertain as to the validity of my course. If the base were really to the east of us, then I was the world's worst navigator. For my calculations showed that it was to the west.

As I unrolled my charts, my eye caught on a penciled notation in the corner of one. It said: "Remember that the appearances of mountains change according to the position from which viewed." Amundsen had been misled on a number of occasions by this illusion, and my experience on the base-laying flight had caused me to take this warning as a controlling principle. The night before the start of the polar flight I wrote the warning on the chart.

While I watched these strange mountains, the peaks began to change their shapes. This unfamiliar eminence—why, it was Ruth Gade in a new attitude. There was Nansen. And there, of course, were Nansen's foothills.

With these points established, finding the cache itself was a matter of a few minutes. We edged over to Liv's Glacier, made several turns at lower altitudes, and finally spotted it. June, who had been a member of the base-laying party and therefore knew the character of the surface, brought the plane down smoothly. The skis touched the surface at 4:47 o'clock.

Taking the fuel aboard was quite a problem. Each can had to be broken open and poured, one by one, into the wing tanks, and we soon tired of lifting them to June, who was doing the pouring. It was six o'clock before we rose from the Barrier and headed north, on the last leg of the flight. By that time the out-riders of the storm clouds were creeping over the mountain rim to the east. They were too far away to be troublesome.

We steered a straight course for Little America, and made no attempt to pick up the trail, which was to the east. But our course converged with the trail a few miles north of Little America. We flew by sun compass and drift indicator and made a perfect land fall. Again the sun compass had done its job.

We had Little America's radio spires in sight at ten o'clock. A few minutes later we were over the administration building, swinging west to come in for a landing. A last survey showed that the Bay of Whales was still choked with ice, the northern edge of which extended almost to West Cape. At 10:08 o'clock, November 29th, the Ford's skis touched snow, and the flight was over.

Sunday
November 29th

Well, it's done. We have seen the Pole and the American flag has been advanced to the South Pole. McKinley, Balchen and June have delivered the goods. They took the Pole in their stride, neatly expeditiously, and undismayed. If I had searched the world I doubt if I could have found a better team. Theirs was the actual doing. But there is not a man in this camp who did not assist in the preparations for the flight. Whatever merit accrues to the accomplishment must be shared with them. They are splendid.

CHAPTER XV

EASTWARD BEYOND THE HORIZON

THE completion of the polar flight left the expedition as far as operations were concerned with only three major objectives unachieved—(1) the geological and geographical survey of Gould's party, (2)—an accurate ground survey of the Bay of Whales, and (3)—the further investigation of the new land to the eastward. The first of these was on the threshold of accomplishment. Sunday, December 1st, Dr. Gould notified the base by radio that his party was camped at the foot of Liv's Glacier, having spent the previous day in negotiating crevasses which "made the memory of those back between 81° and 82° seem like playthings for children." Dr. Coman and Quin Blackburn, who had had considerable surveying experience, had been detached to do the second. As for the third, we were already in preparation for an extended flight.

Apart from the attraction which any unknown area holds for an inquiring mind, the land to the eastward drew us, as it had drawn many before us, with a magnetism peculiar to itself. It is the central mystery in a continent of mysteries. For many years a school of geologists and geographers has held the theory that the Antarctic is not one continent, but two; perhaps not a continent at all, but a series of epicontinental islands which, to borrow a phrase from Sir Douglas Mawson, may have been "overwhelmed and united by a flood of glacier ice and between which the sea would flow were the ice to melt."[1] There were many bases for this supposition. The almost identical indentations cut into the continental structure by the arms of Weddell Sea and the Ross Sea are looked upon by some authorities as evidence of separation.

[1] Mawson, "Problems of Polar Research," 258.

Is there a low-depression channel underneath the glacier cap through which the sea flows between them? Geological investigations have shown certain wide dissimilarities between East and West Antarctica, which would seemingly support the assumption. There is, on the other hand, circumstantial evidence on which it is argued to the contrary. The question stood posed, and the answer, it was believed, might be found in the vast unexplored area between King Edward VII Land and Graham Land.

Hence, our desire to get over there, in spite of the fact we had been driven back thrice by sea and twice by air.

Monday
December 2nd

Warm today, 15° above zero, with a gentle southwest wind. The higher temperatures are causing havoc to the old tunnel systems, which we no longer use. An incautious traveller who passes over them is liable to find himself dumped with scant ceremony into the basement.

The Geological Party reports that it attempted to climb Liv's Glacier, but was forced back by crevasses and ice falls. They have now decided to attempt the ascent via Axel Heiberg. Today they march to the eastward.

Tuesday
December 3rd

Still warm, partly cloudy. No word from the Geological Party.

Camp very quiet.

Wednesday
December 4th

Real summer weather, 27° above zero.

Gould reports that he is unable to find our mountain airplane base, despite the photographs which we dropped to them on the polar flight. He said; "Never saw a place where distances so deceptive. Much worse than desert." He explained that the fine last day's march to the mountains, when they covered

35 (geographical) miles, was due to the fact that they thought the distance was only 15 miles. They are now camped at the foot of Axel Heiberg Glacier.

Dr. Gould added a special news item: "Freddy Crockett's appetite has now been eclipsed by those of Mike Thorne and Norman Vaughan. That *is* news."

Thursday
December 5th
Later

I think we shall make the eastern flight tomorrow. Haines believes that weather conditions are improving. No announcement will be made, however, until we are absolutely certain. The false starts before the polar flight almost broke the heart of the personnel.

Parker will be the pilot, and June and McKinley will go in their accustomed capacities. We will use the Floyd Bennett.

This flight may be the most important flight of all.

On the morning of the 5th, Haines made a series of balloon runs which showed a slight southerly drift up to 10,000 feet. The day was clear and warm, with a light southwesterly wind on the surface. The plane was ready, and at 10:50 o'clock in the morning we took off. In the tanks was fuel for 12 hours flying. I laid a course which would bring us about five miles to the north of Scott's Nunatak.

We climbed to an altitude of approximately 2000 feet.

The Ross Sea was open, except for scattered pieces of pack and a few icebergs in the distance. During the previous weeks the wind had blown rather steadily from the south, and this no doubt had driven the pack farther north. It was a perfect time to send a ship through, but the *City,* alas, was still in New Zealand.

We were surprised to note how little the shape of the Barrier had changed since our last flights. We carried, of course, the survey photographs which McKinley had made the previous summer, and what change there was, was almost imperceptible. For example, a V-shaped bay which I had noticed before and remarked would probably be gone when we returned, was still in position, unchanged.

(Photo by Captain McKinley.)

IN THE GRIP OF THE ICE AGE.

The Polar Plane, on the Return from the Pole, descending the Glacier. Mt. Don Pedro Christophersen on Left.

(Photo by Captain McKinley.)

Coasting Down the Glacier, with Ruth Gade on the Right, on the Return from the Pole.

Hal Flood Bay was underneath at 11:40 o'clock. We were then at an altitude of 4500 feet, and visibility was approximately 80 miles. While the horizon was not as distinct as we had hoped for, neither was it obscure. Conditions of visibility were far better than on the previous flights, indeed they were splendid, and we went forward with keen confidence. The Ford was making more than 100 miles per hour at cruising revolutions.

A little before noon we had the Rockefellers abeam. We were cutting across Cape Colbeck's hump on a Great Circle course. Here we observed the crevasses which Prestrud described, and they appeared to be very extensive and disturbed. South of Colbeck the continental ice sheet was very roughened and undulating. Far to the north the fine, glittering clarity of the snow's edge met the burnished copper of the sea. The water was slightly ruffled, and here and there an iceberg floated suspiciously near a jagged break in the Barrier, suggesting recent "calving."

Not long after we had the Rockefellers abeam we sighted the Matterhorn. Now it stood out perfectly, whereas before it had been partially masked by clouds. It was off the starboard bow, and made a brave and compelling sight on the snow pedestal on which he stood. This time we saw what we had not seen before—that high land lay in rolling swales about the Matterhorn.

Parker continued to climb, and at 12:27 o'clock we were 5000 feet above and about 5 miles north of Scott's Nunatak, with a splendid bird's panorama of this unknown area spread beneath.

To the north the continental ice sheet ended in a most unusual formation of ice tongues, which licked into an outer band of shelf ice. From our great height it was difficult to believe that these out-jutting tongues rose probably 200 feet above sea level. Under the vast pressures exerted from the hinterland they had pushed out over the sea, and huge pieces had broken off, forming ice islands, some of which were grounded and others imprisoned in the layer of shelf ice which was anchored to the coast line. These islands were terribly crevassed and split.

Beyond the rim of shelf ice a consolidated mass of pack ice

was pressed. The pack was much broken up and seemed to be held in position by the long arm of Cape Colbeck.

We then had the whole chain of the Alexandra Mountains below us and to the right. They were far smaller and less extensive than we had expected. None of them appeared to be more than 2000 feet high.

We could now see into the great blank space on the chart which I had studied hundreds of times and wondered about.

About 12:40 o'clock the thing we were looking for emerged grudgingly from the translucent horizon—first a mountainous mass a few degrees to the right of our course, which at the moment was 55° right of north. It was a considerable distance to the eastward. As we drew nearer other peaks loomed up, and there was the suggestion of a long range. It was, we knew, a first class discovery.

Even the charted areas that were then ending were quite inaccurately placed on the map, for at this point the ice line continued more to the northeast than north, as shown on the charts. In fact, between the plane and the new land was a stretch of open water. A straight line course recommended itself at once, although it did seem a risky venture to take a land plane over this pack-strewn area. A forced landing could have had only one ending. However, to have followed the circuitous route along the coast line would have taken much too long, so we held on to the course that took us across the sea.

As we moved out and away from the coast line we could see with surprising clearness how the belt of water-borne shelf ice was attached to the seaward-moving masses of continental ice. This shelf ice appeared to be a miniature barrier half way in size between old bay ice and barrier. The fringe was, for the most part, from 25 to 50 miles wide; here and there the ruptured rounded dome of an ice-island showed in the shelf ice to the right. The land ice terminated in a barrier-like formation, with chalk-white cliffs 200 to 250 feet high in places. Behind these the ice sheet rose and fell undulating to the east and south. Matterhorn gradually disappeared on our right.

As the Ford moved farther on, we could see where the pack behind us was jammed in a mass of débris against the fore-shore of Cape Colbeck. The new ice skirting the shelf ice on the seaward side was quite broken and shallow in places, and the darker shadow of the water was visible underneath it. The pack littered the sea like paper scraps; there were a few fairly extensive floes; but for the most part the loose ice appeared to be granulated and fine.

Steadily we bore away from the coast. When we were 20 miles out, June, looking down at the open sea, turned and went through a series of gestures which plainly indicated swimming. True, there had been little enough bathing in Little America during the winter; but the suggestion left the rest of us cold. The engines sang without a break, and their music was the sweetest and most satisfying sound that we wanted to hear.

We saw one immense floe standing out to sea, a cemented piece of old thick sea ice and new thin ice which had apparently separated from the main sheet at the same time. It was at least twenty-five miles long and ten miles wide, a very substantial recruit to the pack. It was badly cracked, and along the lines of cleavage one could see where it was beginning to disintegrate.

There were 35 miles of open water in the direction of our line of flight. This we crossed.

A few minutes after one o'clock, we reached the edge of the shelf ice and soon afterwards were over the 150th meridian, the eastern boundary of the British claims. We were advancing at the rate of 100 miles per hour over an area which had been unseen before, unknown and unclaimed. Here was the romance of geographical exploration; and seeing this land at last, after so much hoping and trying, brought deep satisfaction. The mystery to the eastward was beginning to yield. Aviation was doing what surface craft had for many years been failing to do. Best of all, every foot of this area was being recorded precisely and in its full perspective by McKinley's camera.

The Ford's altitude was then about 5,000 feet. Wisps of cloud vapor swept underneath, and their shadows were like dirty finger marks on the ice.

We changed course more to the northward at 1:13 o'clock, to enable McKinley to keep the coast line in his survey photographs, a most important consideration in the discovery and mapping of a new area.

The mountain masses to the eastward had been steadily enlarging. Against the horizon they extended north and south as far as the eye could see, an irregular steel-gray bulwark. The nearest peak was at least 60 miles away, but at our altitude could be seen quite distinctly. The mountains were large and I could not repress a feeling of joy over the discovery.

Most important of all, what I took to be the white elevated floor of a plateau showed behind the range. In this new land, then, there was perhaps a counterpart of the mighty plateau in South Victoria Land and about the Pole.

The coast line now bore sharply to the eastward for 20 or 30 miles, but its general direction was northeasterly. Our northerly course took us approximately parallel to the mountain range, which runs north and south, and we continued on it for about 60 miles, then changed course again to the eastward, to bring the mountains nearer.

McKinley's delight was beyond words. Everything of which an aerial surveyor dreams were before his camera in one grand profusion—a new and undiscovered land, excellent visibility, a well marked coast line which would give him a fixed altitude (sea level) for scientific determination and a scenery unlike any other known to man.

After we had flown to the east for a few minutes we saw a peak emerging from what we took to be shelf ice. It was a great distance off. We headed in its general direction, but it did not draw appreciably nearer although we flew towards it about 20 miles. It was too far away to be investigated without the sacrifice of considerable time, which we could not give without jeopardizing the larger purposes of the mission.

At 2:10 o'clock we swung to the southward and flew again approximately parallel to the mountains. Just as we made the turn, June was certain that he saw the sea to the northward of us turn sharply to the eastward. If it did, I failed to see it. The mountain range continued on to the northward and some of the mountains curved to the eastward as far as I could see with the glasses, and that was at least about 70 miles. It was undoubtedly a large range. Though we were still a great distance from these mountains they stood out clearly and beautifully. The peaks of some

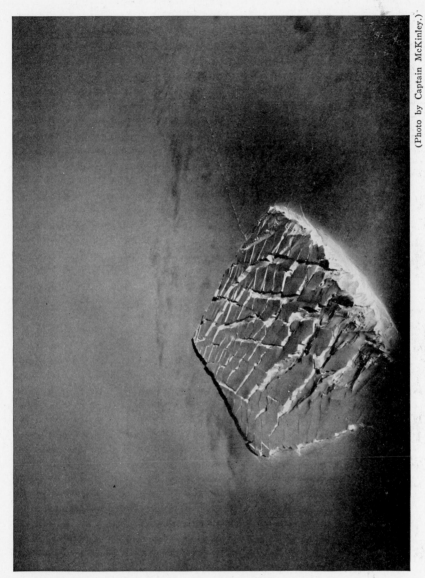

An Ice Island Seen on the Flight to the Eastward.

(Photo by Captain McKinley.)

(Photo by Captain McKinley.)

OPEN WATER IN ICE COVERED LAND DEFIES THE ICE AGE.

This photograph was photographed by Captain McKinley during the flight to Maria Byrd Land

of them were surely 10,000 feet high. Bursting through this rampart was a superb glacier. Cold and blue, it lay between two gray-black walls, and in the center of the stream stood a high black peak. Actually, it must have been about 4000 feet. The glacier itself was about 15 miles across its mouth and it was like a great white river flowing between smooth black cliffs.

After paralleling the coast line for about 60 miles, we steered various courses to investigate and photograph a number of ice islands and rock islands which we thought we saw in the Ross Sea. But they were too far off and we desisted. What they are I do not pretend to know. So many explorers more experienced than I have made mistakes in the claiming of lands that I was determined to claim discovery only of those things which could be and were recorded by the unforgetting and unassailable memory of the camera.

About three o'clock we turned south again.

The surface between our line of flight and the mountain was very much disturbed. It advanced toward the mountains from the sea in a series of wave-like ridges, which were cracked and broken by pressure.

Dim shapes began to loom up in the southeastward, suggestive of land. They were not unlike the pyramids of Egypt in the odd looming which is characteristic of Antarctic visibility.

Of all the flights I have ever made, none was so full of excitement and profit as this one. An air of impending drama foreshadowed every mile of progress. North, east, south and west—everything that was there was unseen and untrodden and unknown. It seemed to be very important, and yet one could not exult. Nature had worked on such a large scale and with such infinite power that one could only gape at her handiwork with open mouth and say: Holy smoke!

For here was the ice age in its chill flood tide. Here was a continent throttled and overwhelmed. Here was the lifeless waste born of one of the greatest periods of refrigeration that the earth has ever known. Seeing it, one could scarcely believe that the Antarctic was once a warm and fertile climate, with its own plants and trees of respectable size.

Here, too, in this glacial flood is a counterpart of the immense ebbs and flows of ice over the earth which profoundly

affected mankind. "But for the Permo-Carboniferous glaciation of India, Australia, South America and Africa, with the
accompanying cooling of the remainder of the world, gigantic
insects might have dominated the world. But for the cooling
of Cretaceous and Eocene times, it appears quite likely that
mammals might yet be insignificant tribes, leading a precarious
existence at the mercy of the Jurassic horde of reptiles. Refrigeration has again and again involved extinction of
specialized races and vivification of more generalized and
newer types. Insects gave place to reptiles, reptiles to mammals and—to bring the history up to date—the dominance of
man coincides remarkably with the coming of the great cooling of the Pleistocene, the effect of which upon the climates
of the world is still apparent." [1]

Here, too, is the receding flood of a once much greater
flood. One could not help but speculate, with a sense of thank-
fulness that by that time the matter will probably have no personal interest, on what new destiny Nature has in store for the
lowly mammal when the pendulum reaches the point of turn.

There was great beauty here, in the way that things which
are also terrible can be beautiful. Glancing to the right, one
had the feeling of observing the twilight of an eternity. Over
the water and submerged land crept huge tongues of solid
ice and snow, ploughing into the outer fringe of shelf ice
and accomplishing wide destruction. There were cliffs that
must rise hundreds of feet. Once I caught sight of a cliff
as it fell into the sea. From the great height of the plane it
was just a small pellet falling from a toy wall. Not a sound
penetrated through the noise of the engines. Yet thousands
of tons must have collapsed in one frightful convulsion. To
the right were the mountains, cold and gray, and from them
fell, in places, ice falls which were perhaps 500 feet in height.
The figure is arbitrary. They may have been more, or less.

We had sighted the Matterhorn again and advanced steadily toward it, studying the mountains on our left. The farther
we went, the more we became impressed with the rolling
character of the land. In one place, where the surface was
quite high, we made out a patch crossed by rippling lines;
these were pressure ridges, no doubt covering an area perhaps 20 miles in length. I saw then that the mountains con-

[1] Priestley and Wright, "Problems in Polar Research," 334.

tinued in an uninterrupted chain to the southward, and this whole enormous area definitely joined the land we had seen on the eastern flight.

On our port bow we saw extraordinary lakes of open water, showing in velvet-black pools against the irregular pattern of the ice, in ice covered land. I call them lakes, but it is possible they were channels or inlets. Just why these lakes should defy freezing I could not understand. It may be that strong currents keep them open. Certainly it does not seem that they can be the result of thawing—not on a continent where the temperature only rarely rises above the freezing point.

One of the lakes lay to the northeastward of Matterhorn. We changed course so that McKinley might photograph it. Drawing nearer, we saw that on its northern side was a high snow cliff. Its southern edge was bounded by a curious ice or snow formation which rose and fell regularly, like waves. The crests of these waves must have been at least 300 feet high.

A series of these pools of open water lay to the eastward.

After passing over the lake we changed course to the westward, to bring the Matterhorn before McKinley's camera. By then McKinley had photographed 200 miles of the new mountain range, and our own vision, helped by glasses, had seen even farther.

The purposes of our trip, then, were realized.

We changed course again, a few degrees to the left, to investigate more patches of open water which lay, as near as I could judge, 50 miles from the open sea at the point where it met the shelf ice.

Matterhorn slowly made felt its splendor. From its cone-like eminence a slightly less elevated ridge ran to the southeast, about to the 150th meridian, according to a rough estimate.

We passed the Matterhorn to the north at 4:45 o'clock. To the northeast of it was a violently disturbed area. Even from 5000 feet the crevasses seemed monstrous. They lay in long, almost perfectly drawn furrows, and some of them must have been at least 200 feet across. Here and there the black depths of pits and craters showed. Scott's Nunatak was in sight, and between it and Matterhorn the surface was high and rolling, suggestive of land.

In the course of the flight we had circled the nunataks of Alexandra Range and photographed them from all sides.

We were then well inland, homeward bound. Presently the Rockefellers were in view, a scattering of peaks throwing long shadows. A few stratus clouds floated near them.

Parker opened up the engines and we struck across familiar territory.

At 6:20 o'clock we landed at Little America. Parker had made a splendid flight.

Friday
December 6th

The flight to the eastward was more successful than I had dared to hope.

From a geographical point of view it was eminently satisfactory. It proved the existence of land in that area—an immense landfall.

It extended the outline of the coast and lifted a great section of it from the realm of fiction. McKinley has now surveyed and mapped a 400 mile stretch of the Barrier line and coast line.

It provided the new land first discovered on the flight of February 18th with a coastal access.

The survey photographs which McKinley made will be interesting and important to glaciologists fifty and one hundred years from now. For they are a permanent record of ice conditions in 1929, and the extent of the changes which will undoubtedly occur during the intervening years can be clearly drawn. Here, again, is an example of the new precision in modern exploration.

The discovery of land explains, in a measure, why all attempts to penetrate this region by sea have failed. With a northwesterly wind, the northern extension of the coast, whether as an archipelago or as a solid mass, would be jammed with ice, which would collect and consolidate in impenetrable quantities. At this time, I am inclined to lean toward the belief that there is an archipelago somewhere to the northward of the newly discovered land, which feeds the pack in that vicinity. This alone, it would seem, can account for the stupendous quantities of ice discharged.

However, discovery is only the beginning. It merely brings to light a reality. It is now the job of the geologists to take it apart and find the inner secrets. How it would delight Larry Gould to make a study of that fascinating problem. But there is no time for it on this expedition.

If he can cross the 150th meridian during this trip and enter the new land to the east of his course, it will be an excellent contribution. I am reluctant to suggest an extension of his journey, which will be long enough anyway; but I am sure that when he has assimilated the importance of the eastern flight, he will see the value of the trip and will suggest the extension himself.

To the new escarpment I have given the name Edsel Ford Range. Mr. Ford has been a consistent supporter of my efforts in exploration and aviation. More than that, he is a dear friend.

To the new Land I have given the name Marie Byrd Land, after my wife, who has backed and helped me every foot of the way, who has shouldered much of the burden of the expedition and whose understanding has made my many expeditions possible.

Saturday
December 7th

Warm and partly cloudy.

The Geological Party is camped on the north side of Mt. Nansen, having ascended the west side of Axel Heiberg Glacier yesterday. It is snowing hard there.

McKinley is developing the photographs taken on the polar and eastern flights. They are excellent, and show the unusual character of this area in detail and relationship which no pen nor brush could equal. It paid us handsomely to await good weather and visibility, and to put our faith in prophets Haines and Harrison.

Monday
December 9th

Gould's Party continued to climb up Mt. Nansen, reaching a height of 7,500 feet. At 6,500 feet Crockett found what Gould is sure is lichens. This may be the farthest south at which life has been discovered.

I have delegated Siple to the job of collecting twenty Adelie and Emperor Penguins for zoos. If it is possible, we shall bring them back to the United States alive. We had a dozen of them, last year, but they all got away. They are shrewd devils and can escape faster than Houdini. We have built a pen for them in the hole formerly occupied by one of the Ford's wing tips, but I don't think they will stay long.

The ice in the Bay of Whales is still holding and as yet gives no sign of going out.

Friday
December 13th

No word from the Geological Party for two days.

Saturday
December 14th

The Geological Party was on its regular schedule to-night. They have been held in camp by a heavy snow storm. Gould reports they found our mountain cache last Thursday. The wind had scattered the empty gasoline tins and a pair of snow glasses was found fifty yards from the cache. He says the weather has continued cloudy and squally.

It would seem that we made the polar flight just in time.

The Geological Party is now working to the eastward and will penetrate Marie Byrd Land—that is, beyond the 150th meridian.

Sunday
December 15th

Siple and Mulroy took a sounding in Ver-sur-Mer Inlet today and 1,600 feet of line ran out before it registered bottom.

So Little America has been afloat. However, we have always been convinced of that.

A baby Crab-eater seal was found on the bay ice last night and has been put in a pen. He will presently join the distinguished group of specimens. He is a scrappy little fellow and when aroused makes a queer whistling sound.

Wednesday
December 18th

We are getting ready to break up the camp. Today Black began to collect all equipment not in use—that is, equipment not necessary for operations. By getting things ready now we may escape much confusion at the end.

It appears that both the *City* and the *Bolling* are in for another struggle with the pack. The whalers report that ice conditions are worse than any within their experience. A chaser was sunk in the pack on the 15th, according to a radio message which Petersen overheard, and the factory ships find the going very hard.

Consequently, I have sent a message to Brown and Melville suggesting that departure of both ships be held up until conditions improve.

We are hoping to make another flight to the eastward of Queen Maud Range. This, together with a flight to the westward of Little America, should clear up the aviation activities of the expedition. Weather, however, remains unfavorable.

A light rain in the form of mist began to fall late yesterday and continued intermittently today.

Friday
December 20th

The Geological Party reports that it is camped at Lat. 85° 27′ S. and Long. 147° 30′ W. Gould says: "Have completely proved that Carmen Land does not exist." They have penetrated Marie Byrd Land and are the first men to set foot on American land in the Antarctic.

The area is, therefore, claimed for the United States and may be considered to extend to the Pole. It appears that the Barrier lies between Gould's position and the land we discovered.

Tomorrow Gould will begin his march to the westward. He has done a fine job.

Wednesday
December 25th

A white Christmas, and a warm one. The temperature today was 31° above zero, and Tennant even had trouble bringing the ice cream to the freezing point.

The day was celebrated appropriately. There was a Christmas tree wrapped in cotton, and festooned with cigarette papers, chewing gum, cough drops and other knick-knacks: Taffy Davies took the part of Santa Claus, and though a cotton beard hid his jovial face, it could not disguise his precious accent.

There were even cigars and cigarettes, and George Black produced a pound of candy for every man. This *is* luxury. The party enjoyed the following quatrain; dedicated to the cook:

"Use one ounce of chicken to each pair of pups,
If they pop out of dishes, just serve 'em in cups,
And if we're out of mutton this glad Christmas-tide,
I'll season and serve 'em with some tender rawhide."

*Thursday
December 26th*

The Geological Party had its own thrilling Christmas on the Barrier. They were camped near Mt. Betty, which Amundsen had ascended on the return from the Pole, and Dr. Gould decided to investigate it. He found the cairn which Amundsen had built, and in it the matches, the can of kerosene and the note he and his party left behind, 17 years ago. [1]

Petersen translated the note, which said: "Arrived and encircled the South Pole Dec. 14–16, 1911. Have confirmed Victoria Land so that it is most likely that King Edward VII Land has no connection at 86° south latitude with Victoria Land. Also shows this land continues in a colossal mountain range toward the south. Could see this enormous mountain range to 88° south latitude and most likely from its appearance it continues further in the same direction over the Antarctic Continent. Passed this cache on our return from the South Pole with provisions for 60 days, 2 sledges and 11 dogs. All well."

Roald Amundsen.

We have been informed by radio that a small airplane attached to the whaler *Kosmos,* which has Taylor and his dogs

[1] Amundsen, "The South Pole," ii, 159. "—We built a great cairn, and left there a can of 17 litres of kerosene, two packets of matches—containing twenty boxes—and an account of our expedition."

aboard, has been lost. The pilot, Leif Lier, and a passenger, Dr. Ingvald-Schreiner, took off for a short flight on Christmas Day, but failed to return. The plane was equipped with pontoons and carried fuel for six hours. On the following day (they are a day ahead of us because they are west of the 180th meridian) the sea rose and a thickish fog hampered the chasers which were sent out to search for the plane.

At the time the *Kosmos* was lying north of the pack. The master, Captain Andresen, had intended to use the plane in scouting for whales.

What a pity we can give no aid! The position of the *Kosmos* is more than 800 miles to the north of Little America, and the Ford, even if it were equipped with pontoons, the possession of which would alone justify taking her on such a long water hop, has not a sufficient radius of action to allow her to make an effective search. Our hands are tied.

What has happened we cannot tell. No doubt the plane was forced down by engine trouble, for visibility, according to Captain Andresen, remained clear and the pilot was skillful. It is unlikely that he became lost. A number of the men here, including Owen and Petersen, knew the pilot, and so the tragedy strikes personally. For I believe it is a tragedy. Even assuming the landing was made safely, the plane could not long exist in the heavy seas which ran on the following day. I can imagine no worse predicament than to be forced down in the vicinity of the pack.

Saturday
December 28th

No trace of the missing flyers. Apparently Lier had intended to make a flight to the Balleny Islands. Captain Andresen wirelessed yesterday that he had found an entry in the pilot's diary, dated December 26th, the date of his disappearance, saying that he would fly to the Balleny Islands if weather permitted. In all, sixteen chasers have been searching for the plane. All but two have been recalled, and these have been dispatched to search the waters adjoining the islands. The flyers carried emergency rations for only two days. I am sure they are lost. Dr. Barnes, who is coming down on the *City,* has been asked to volunteer as physician aboard the *Kosmos,* to take the place of the doctor who was lost. There are

400 men on the *Kosmos* and the attendance of a doctor is necessary. I am sure that Dr. Barnes will agree to go.

The pack itself shows no signs of relenting. I am afraid it will be a more serious problem this year than last year. Petersen, our radio man, who is maintaining a regular schedule with all the whaling ships, says the veterans are unanimously agreed that this is the worst ice year they have ever known.

Two whaling factories have at last forced their way through the pack, after a very strenuous voyage, the *Nilsen Alonzo* and the *Sir James Clark Ross*. The *Southern Princess* was turned back by heavy pack at 69° S.

Both the *Kosmos* and the *C. A. Larsen* are still waiting to the north of the pack, reluctant to attempt the passage until conditions improve.

Ole Andersen, a gunner on the *Ross,* has informed Petersen that the pack is the hardest he has ever seen—it is largely heavy, hard ice, green and glassy. How the *City* can make her way through such ice is beyond me. Nevertheless, she must try.

Tuesday
December 31st

The Geological Party is homeward bound. In his daily message Gould says that they were camped 45 miles north of the mountain. They are on the old trail, following the snow beacons which they erected on the outward journey.

I cannot speak too highly of the splendid work these men have done. The trip, when finished, will be the longest sledge journey ever undertaken for purely geological investigation. Once the party started the final advance, it continued without a hitch. The weeks, even months, of care and study that went into their planning have born fruit. They were greenhorns when they started, but they carried on like veterans.

Tonight the year will have run its course. And thanks to all hands a great deal of work has been accomplished. Certainly it is doubtful whether much more could have been done, everything considered. That, after all, is the test.

The weather lately has been quite warm, and on the 27th and 28th the temperature was, for a few hours, above freezing. The wind was from the northeast. It shifted to the southeast, then to the east, and is now blowing softly from the south-southeast.

The ice in the Bay of Whales is beginning to disintegrate. It still has a long way to go, though. The northern edge is still eight miles from the camp, and a great deal of thick *old* ice lies between. We watch it quite as anxiously as we watched it last January. If it goes out no farther, we shall have a difficult time hauling the materials out to the ship. One thing is certain: there will be no further experiments with the Barrier as a pier. The taste of that memory is still strong.

In another month, God willing, we shall be on our way back.

Wednesday
January 1st

The New Year begins inauspiciously enough. This time, last year, the *City* was at the Barrier. This year she is still at Dunedin. Even the *Larsen,* for all her tremendous horse-power, is just beginning to try to force the pack. It's a tough situation all around. There is a possibility the *City* may be unable to get through. As a last resort we might try to induce one of the whalers to come down here and take the winter party aboard. But this would be an emergency measure. Having continued so long with our own resources, we ought to carry on alone as long as possible.

This much is certain: another winter here, with our depleted supplies, would work great hardships. Worst of all at least two of the men cannot, I believe, survive a second winter. They must be protected.

I have already opened negotiations with several of the whaling captains with a view to covering our retreat if the *City* should be blocked. Surely this is the prudent thing to do. It may be that I am unduly pessimistic, but there are elements in this situation which recommend that every avenue be kept open.

We are fortunate to have Petersen as radio operator. A former operator on Norwegian whaling ships, himself a Norwegian, he knows most of the operators on the ships to the north. With their captains' permission, they keep him posted on developments, and as a result we have an accurate picture of what is taking place in the pack. We would be in a bad way without him. The masters of these ships are most generous in their cooperation.

Sunday
January 5th

The *City* has started south. Melville reports: "We sailed from Dunedin at 2:30 P.M. but owing to the severe southerly gale blowing outside and heavy seas did not proceed, but will wait until weather and sea moderate. Barometer low but rising gradually."

The good old *City* is in the thick of it from the start. Wait until she meets the pack. Then we shall see the stuff she is made of.

Monday
January 6th

Melville says they dropped the pilot boat at 9 o'clock this morning. Weather clear.

Come on, *City!*

CHAPTER XVI

DEATH OF A CITY

JANUARY found us on tenterhooks. The *City* was plow-ing south, meeting one storm after another, advancing to the greatest battle of her always rugged life. Three huge whal-ing factories, the *Kosmos,* the *Southern Princess* and the *C. A. Larsen,* were still north of the pack, prowling along its edge, waiting for wind and tide to accomplish what they dared not attempt even with their powerful engines. South of the pack were the *Nilsen Alonzo* and the *Sir James Clark Ross,* watch-ing it with anxiety. Gould's Geological Party, its job done, was racing home from the Mountains. And at Little America the winter party had its ears bent to the radio, which was handling the heavy traffic flowing from these separated units, telling of daily, and in many cases hourly, developments. There were grimness and excitement in the situation. The pack was an inscrutable, implacable resisting force stretched solidly between the parallels of 68° and 70° S.

Would it also be our jailor?

I admit frankly that no situation—not even the struggle up the pass of Liv's Glacier—brought the worry that this one did. For we were anxious to get home. Our work was done, and waiting was trying after months of great activity. But this would have been nothing had we not been worried over the physical condition of several men. There were some of us who were prepared to spend another winter at Little Amer-ica, regardless of the outcome of the *City's* struggle with the pack, to continue the scientific work of the expedition. The plan had already been discussed. But for others the issue which hung in the balance was perhaps a matter of life and death. If the *City* failed to get through, at least one man might not live to see a second spring. Mason, the radio operator, had been developing symptoms of appendicitis.

365

McKinley, too, was troubled with the same thing. Their illness had not progressed sufficiently at that time to inconvenience either of them very much, but it was a cause of alarm to the rest of us. The physical condition of a third man had gone down steadily since the winter. He had lost weight rapidly, his nerves were worn out and he was neither happy nor well.

So far as the fundamental needs were concerned, the expedition could endure a second winter at Little America. There were seals, penguins and skua gulls with which to replenish the meat supply. We had an adequate amount of dehydrated vegetables to see us through. This contingency had been anticipated and prepared for. Nevertheless, an extended stay, if it were to come to pass, must work real hardships, with nothing but pipe tobacco left and that almost gone and the supply of luxuries such as butter, sugar and canned milk scarcely sufficient to last another month.

More, there were some men—I can count them on the fingers of one hand—who were sick of the Antarctic, who were counting the days when they should return to the United States and looked forward to the *City's* arrival as a release from hard and unprofitable existence. Temperamentally and physically, a second winter, especially an enforced second winter, would have tried their patience and temper more than sorely.

Truth to tell, I doubt whether there was a single man, myself included, who was really eager to stay. The Antarctic, when all is said and done, is no pleasure resort. Even the very few modern conveniences which we had introduced had scarcely relieved its hardships. The hardest kind of existence that any organism has cut out for itself on this planet is that of the Emperor penguin, Mr. Cherry-Garrard has said. And even he has the sense to abandon it before winter comes. The Antarctic offers little enough solace, stimulation and satisfaction to a scientist and explorer with work to do. When that work is done, it seems the loneliest, most God-forsaken spot on this globe. Doubtless it is.

So, through the miraculous agency of the radio and the unremitting efforts of Mason and Petersen, we followed the skirmishing between the pack and the vessels which lay outside; and as conditions grew worse instead of better and as it became apparent that this was perhaps the worst ice year in a decade, there were some who felt like going out there and trying to hammer it apart with their fists.

Monday
January 6th

The Geological Party is coming fast. They camped at 82° 16' shortly after two o'clock this morning. Soft snow has made the going rather hard these last few days, but men and dogs are apparently well.

I informed Gould today of the developments to date with respect to the *City of New York,* the whalers and the pack. It was hard to give them bad news on top of such an arduous journey.

If the *City* is here before February, we shall be in luck, according to present indications. There has been no improvement in the pack during the past week.

The dear old *City* is right in the thick of trouble. Captain Melville radioed today: "Terrific southwest gale all night. Squalls of hurricane force. Rain, hail and a very high sea. Hove to under sail. At present moderation indicated." Then later: "8 A.M. Am under sail and steam. Ship laboring heavily in high seas. All well. Regards."

Thursday
January 9th

No schedule with the Geological Party today.

The *City's* noon position was Lat. 47° 28' S., Long. 172° 25' E. Weather fine and the ship under both steam and sail. Her position is about 123 miles south of Tairoa Head.

Our penguin farm will be the end of Siple.

For the past month he has had about a dozen Emperors and about half a dozen Adelies in the pit formerly occupied by one of the Ford wing tips. Not the same ones all the time, however. That is the trouble. The shrewd little creatures get out every time. They spurn kindness and attention; they pay no heed to the inducements of civilization and the offer of a fine berth for their declining years in an American zoological garden. They refuse food, even though Siple and Bursey have lured them with canned meat, frankfurters,

sardines and strips of seal meat and blubber nicely cut up.
They rebuff these advances, and the moment their captors'
backs are turned try to scramble from the pit. And by means
of some extraordinary occult power, they almost always succeed.

When the first batch escaped, Siple hoped to keep the
others in by setting a ring of bamboo pickets, the points of
which were pointed in, about the rim of the hole. But the
rogues shoved them aside with their bills. Then he massed
gasoline drums about the hole, and caught a third batch.
But every day one or two of them mysteriously disappeared.
Exactly how they escaped we did not learn until Thorne came
in one day with the news that he had seen a new flock of
penguins waddling about the camp. Siple, suspecting the
worst, rushed out and found half his penguins gone. Two
were in the act of scrambling over the backs of the rest, whose
bodies were heroically massed in a kind of a pyramid at the
bottom of the pit—a sacrificial altar, if you will. The penguins in the bottom cannot escape, of course. Poor devils, I
have already begun to regret having promised to bring them
north.

Friday
January 10th

The Geological Party is camped on the southern edge of
the crevasses at 81° 16′ tonight, having been impeded since
Wednesday by soft snow and fog.

The *City* logged 100 miles during the last twenty-four
hours. That's the way to do it.

Saturday
January 11th

We have decided to begin preparing for loading operations
at once. The more we examine the situation, the more it becomes apparent that we are confronted by abnormal ice conditions. It will be touch and go whether we shall be able to
get north this year. As if the extraordinary thickness and
density of the pack were not trouble enough, the ice in the
Bay of Whales continues to hold. If anything, it is worse
than last year. The northern edge is at least 8 miles from Ver-

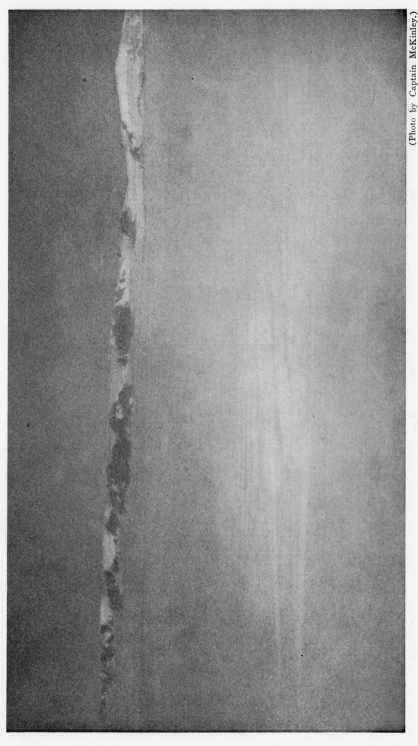

An Unusual Glacier of the Edsel Ford Range Divided by a High Pillar of Rock.

(Photo by Captain McKinley.)

These mountains were more than 50 miles away when the photograph was taken. This range was photographed by aerial survey camera for 200 miles. It is a high range and probably a very long one. This is part of the new land claimed for the United States.

WHALES TRAPPED IN A CRACK THAT SUDDENLY OPENED UP AT THE BACK
DOOR OF LITTLE AMERICA.

sur-Mer Inlet. It was so widely ridged and cracked that we believe it would go out much quicker this year; but on the contrary it remains fast and stubborn. If there is no improvement before the *City's* arrival, and I doubt if there will be, we certainly will have neither the time nor the dogs to carry our supplies over that distance. There are only two good teams in camp. A third team is out with Dr. Coman and Blackburn, who for several weeks have been making a survey of the Bay of Whales, and Gould has five more, making a total of eight available for loading.

We made a study of the bay ice today and came to the conclusion that the ice is more likely to begin to go out along the western side of the Barrier than on this side. We have, therefore, decided to begin moving part of the equipment to Floyd Bennett Harbor by sledge teams, so that when the *City* arrives as little time as is possible will be lost in loading here. McKinley has been put in charge of this operation. A camp will be made about a mile in from the mouth of the harbor. Heaven help them if the ice starts to go out with a rush while they are on the bay ice. It may be perverse enough to carry out bay ice, harbor ice, camp and all. But I doubt very much that this will happen. There was no movement of ice in Floyd Bennett Harbor last year; and, to judge from the characteristics of the ice, there has been none for many years. Nevertheless, the men have been ordered to sleep on the Barrier.

The *City's* run under sail today was 140 miles.

Sunday
January 12th

Gould says the Geological Party is camped tonight in the middle of the crevasses, awaiting better weather before continuing. Fog shut down on them as they reached the worst area, and Dr. Gould decided to camp rather than risk his men and sledges in trying to grope through the area in the fog. According to Gould, the area has changed considerably since they went through it on the outward journey, and much of the old trail has disappeared. I imagine they are in a very tight corner.

The *City* made 83 miles during the last 24 hours. Her last position was Lat. 52° 15′ S, Long. 175° 31′ E. She is now under steam, wind having failed.

I am still holding the *Bolling* at Dunedin, until conditions improve. Captain Brown is tearing his hair out. If the *Bolling* were an armored cruiser, he could not be more eager to pit her against the pack. She is just an ordinary metal ship and we cannot afford to risk her in such heavy pack. Although she is protected in the bow her stern sheets are more than ordinarily vulnerable. It is my opinion that Brown was extremely fortunate in bringing the *Bolling* through on the first trip. Judging from the present experience and the experience of other exploration parties in the past, the conditions under which a small metal ship can be safely sent through the pack are not always available.

Monday
January 13th

The Geological Party is still camped in the crevasses, held by fog.

The situation with respect to the pack is really alarming. Both the *Ross* and the *Nilsen Alonzo* report very poor fishing, whereas the whalers to the north are finding good fishing. Moreover, the gunners on the *Ross* and the *Nilsen Alonzo* report that the few whales they have caught are scarred, showing that even the whales had a fearful battle trying to get through the pack. In my opinion, the *Ross* and the *Nilsen Alonzo* will start north very soon. If they go, the only source of immediate aid within eight hundred miles is lost. I shall therefore send a request for a chaser on the next radio schedule.

Tuesday
January 14th

Captain Andresen, of the *Kosmos,* radioed today that he did not expect the pack to open up before the end of January or the beginning of February. He said also that he would not attempt to move his ship south until the pack opened. Fishing north of the pack, he added, was excellent, and so he has nothing to gain by attempting a passage.

We can, therefore, expect no help from that quarter, if the *City* fails.

Today I addressed strong messages to Captain Vermeli, of the *Nilsen Alonzo* and Captain Thorstensen, of the *Ross,* describing our predicament and asking them if it would be practicable to send two chasers to the Bay of Whales, to take off our equipment and the sick men in the event of an emergency.

Until the situation resolves itself, we must develop and hold every avenue of escape.

Apart from the protection of the sick men, what worries me most is the disposition of our equipment. If the *Bolling* is unable to get through, we shall be out of luck, that's all. The *City* cannot accommodate 42 men, as well as her own crew, and all the supplies here, a large part of which is valuable.

Wednesday
January 15th

The whole story of today's development was told in the ironic note which Petersen posted on the bulletin board:

"To the anxious public:

"S.S. *Ross* is leaving now—but NORTHWARD. Swallow it, boys. But don't worry if our own ships can't get through. The *Ross* says: WE WILL GET THROUGH AND GET YOU ALL, SO DON'T WORRY.

"*Alonzo* is still in the Ross Sea. She also says: DON'T WORRY.

"S. S. *Kosmos* said: Heard *Ross's* message to you this morning and add: Don't worry. We won't leave you behind."

PETE

The anxious public, which follows Pete's messages on the bulletin board as crowds used to mass in front of the bulletin boards of newspaper offices in July, 1914, took the news hard.

But the rest of the camp was more amused than anything else.

The one bit of good news came from Gould's party.

With dog food running short and tired of trying to outwait the fog, they retraced their steps and made a new trail around the crevasses. Twelve miles on they picked up the trail and are now camped at 80° 27′ S "with all going well."

They should arrive within five days. I am relieved.

Thursday
January 16th

Today I renewed my petition to Captain Vermeli, of the
Nilsen Alonzo, asking him to send a chaser to the Bay of
Whales to pick up a number of men and the more essential
equipment. It had been arranged previously that he should
send a chaser with supplies which he took aboard for us at New
Zealand, and so I think he will do this.

At the same time I instructed Captain Brown to be ready to
start the *Bolling* south by Saturday.

It is a blow to pride to have to call for help, but the circumstances leave no alternative. The whaling masters can ill
spare the time to succor exploring parties, whose troubles are
no fault of theirs. Every day lost from fishing when fishing is
good means a sacrifice of $30,000 to the owners and stock-
holders. As the crews' wages are in the nature of a bonus, the
cost of assisting us must come, in part, from their pockets, unless we are prepared to pay it ourselves.

Later

Captain Vermeli's reply is at hand.

ADMIRAL BYRD, WFA

Your message received. I have no doubt that the ice will
break up in a week or so, so your ships will get through. As the
whales are very scarce in the Ross Sea this year we are now going
through the ice pack again. If your ships should not get through
we will do our best to help you. Kind regards.

VERMELI.

And that is that. I hope that Captain Vermeli is right.

Still Later

There is another message from Captain Vermeli:

ADMIRAL BYRD, WFA

I quite understand your situation. However the situation on
our behalf is this. We have now been lying here for more than
a month and during this time caught very few whales. We have
hoped all along the whales would appear, but in vain. All this
time we used quite a lot of coal and fuel oil and we have very

An Antarctic Skyscraper Ventures into the Bay of Whales.

THE *City* IN HER TOUGHEST BATTLE.

This photograph was taken on her last journey to the Bay of Whales, when nearly 200 tons of ice accumulated on her.

small quantities left of both. This week we received reports that the whalers outside find fishing good. For this reason we now are on our way north, but if you are absolutely hard up for food we shall send a chaser down. In that case it means stopping the whole expedition and we shall have to stay here another week. Regards.

I sympathize with his point of view, but our needs are also important.

Again I renewed our request for a chaser, but when he next answered the *Nilsen Alonzo* was already in the pack and he therefore could not send it.

I have made known the facts to the camp in a memorandum. In my opinion, the *City* has but one chance in ten of making the passage—the *Bolling* has none.

Worst of all, the *City* has apparently started south without sufficient coal to see her through a sustained battle with the pack. Why this happened is beyond me. I have instructed Brown to take on another 50 tons for her, and am now radioing the *Kosmos, Southern Princess* and *Larsen* which are still north of the pack, to see if they can spare a few tons.

Saturday
January 18th

The Geological Party reported today it will reach Little America some time tomorrow afternoon. Thus will end a magnificent journey. They have now been gone three months, and it will be good to have them in camp.

Petersen has prepared the following summary of today's developments, which he posted on the bulletin board:

"*S.S. Ross* has been stuck in the pack since yesterday afternoon, and is still stuck. Ice is up to 36 feet thick, packed hard, and impossible to move. It is likely the belt of thick pack ice is not more than 25 or 30 miles wide Snow yesterday with northwest wind, but today clearing and wind shifted to southeast, which ought to cause some movement in the ice.

I have laid the facts bearing on the situation before Captain Railey, who is in charge of expedition affairs in New York, suggesting that he sound out the owners of the *Nilsen Alonzo* with a view to determining whether or not they are willing to order the ship to return and pick us up, in case the *City* is unable to run the pack. I have urged Railey particularly to keep the matter confidential. As a matter of fact, our position is by no means unsafe. Not yet at least. Prudence suggests, however, that our lines of transportation be kept open. I have made this quite clear.

The need is simply for patience—patience and control of the situation.

At 9:30 o'clock on the morning of January 19th, the sledges of the Geological Party were seen defiling across the Barrier slopes. We gave them a royal welcome, for they had done a wonderful job. It was not the fact of having sledged 1500 miles that was remarkable. It was the fact that these men had started this punishing trip as green, from the point of view of experience, as bay trees. They went through with the dash and élan of youth. To that they added resourcefulness, and stubbornness. I doubt that few veterans could have done as well. For the measure of the trip lay in the balancing of what was planned in advance and what was actually done: if anything, they exceeded the plans. How fit they were may be judged from the fact they made 34 miles on the last day's march and were travelling strong when they reached Little America.

Thorne was in the lead, on skis. Behind him came Gould, with a bristling beard and wearing a red and white sash about his waist. O'Brien was behind him, and then Vaughan. Goodale brought up the rear-guard. What they had endured had left its mark on their faces and bodies. They were lean, hard, grizzled and dirty. The most jovial, tattered and unwashed group of pirates that ever disgraced a quarterdeck would have blushed at the appearance of our scientists. That men could become so dirty on the tidy surface of the Barrier was incredible. Of course, it was soot from the stoves. Gasoline was much too precious to be wasted in melting snow for bathing. "A bath—and Paradise," Goodale yelled. They thronged into the mess hall, pillaging the precious pots of water which Tennant had stored for kitchen use; and as the layers of grime flaked and dissolved, we saw, as through a glass darkly, how very well and strong they looked.

With the men re-united for the first time in more than

three months, we forgot for a time the uncertainty which lay over the pack, but not for long. Thereafter it was with us every waking hour. If, during the winter, we had discussed every subject under the sun, some of us now concentrated on one. Sooner or later the pack edged into every conversation. How long will the pack hold? Can the *City* get through? Would it be worth while to risk her in the face of unfavorable conditions? Can and will the whalers really come through the pack? "What's new?" was the first question. And for days the answer was "nothing." The radio room was a magnet that drew the more fretful men. Here Petersen posted the messages from the whalers and the *City*. There was the thought in the back of several minds that important and bad news was being concealed, which was not the case at all. For example, June, Smith and Crockett, who were operators, could overhear the dots and dashes as the radio men sent and received them.

But, on the whole, as any serious situation does, the affair yielded its lightest side. There was far more joking over the situation than dismay. There was formed the Harbor Board, so called after the organization of that name which handles marine activities at Dunedin; and this committee met every night for lengthy discussions and mad proposals. As a result the pack and this train of consequences became unreal and ludicrous.

Meanwhile Captain McKinley went forward with his plans for demobilizing Little America. This was a difficult problem in itself. If both the *City* and the *Bolling* reached the Bay of Whales, the problem would simply be one of loading. If only the *City* made the passage, then the problem was one of selection. From the beginning of January I had scant hopes that the *Bolling* would get south of the pack, and began to prepare accordingly. Orders were issued to the various departments to begin listing all material in their charge under three classifications of importance. Class A. was to include records and valuable scientific apparatus. Classes B. and C. were progressively lower ratings of material. Three general piles were to be made of the supplies and records, according to these classifications, so that if and when the *City* arrived alone, the most important stuff could be put aboard her at once. As the material accumulated, the dog drivers, under the direction of McKinley, began to transport it to the camp at Floyd Bennett Harbor. The camp was approximately 10 miles from Little America, and as the trail wound back and forth around the pressure ridges the task of moving supplies was no less troublesome than when we first landed in the Bay of Whales.

January 20th, the *City* came within sight of the *Kosmos,* but a gale from the north stirred up such a heavy sea that she could not come alongside.

The *Bolling* put out from Dunedin the same day, the *Ross* was still stuck in the pack, beset by storm and fog, and the *Nilsen Alonzo* had plowed within 25 miles of the northern edge of the pack. Once more the whaling companies renewed their pledge to stand by with assistance. For this I was grateful. But assistance would come high. It would cost $500,000 to bring a whaling factory ship to the Bay of Whales. Dollars and cents—they were the commanding elements in the situation. Let me make this point clear: the whaling masters were neither reluctant to come to our aid nor mercenary. I knew most of them, and a finer group of men never walked the deck of a ship. And we, on the other hand, had neither the right nor the desire to pass the cost on to their crews, owners and stockholders. No matter what the cost, we were prepared to move our sick men to civilization, if it meant pledging everything we had or ever would have. That was an inescapable responsibility, and it was only fair that we should be ready to carry it alone.

A thick, heavy fog extending to higher altitudes put a stop to flying in January but on the 20th Captain McKinley finished mapping the Bay of Whales. On the following day I also flew to the westward, to continue the study of the Barrier. With me went Captain McKinley, June and Petersen. We used the Ford. We took off at 2:12 o'clock P.M. and followed the coast line to the west. Visibility was excellent. There was a scattering of clouds in the distant west. The Ross Sea was spattered with bergs and fragments of pack.

Discovery Inlet was underneath at 3:05 o'clock. As we circled it at an altitude of 2,000 feet, the thought occurred to me that here was one of the most interesting bays in the world. Entrenched most probably behind a submerged ridge

of land, it resisted the stubborn and inexhaustible surges of
the ice sheet which would engulf it and remained one of the
few apparently permanent spots on the front of the moving
Barrier. We confirmed what we had learned when we first investigated Discovery, in 1929; that while the outer part of it
runs east and west, as the charts show, an inner member
bends to the south. Between the tips of a V-shaped formation
which forms the eastern wall of the outer bay, we saw a deep
crack, sufficiently extensive to suggest that it extended to the
bottom of the Barrier. Here, it would seem, the millions of
tons of solid ice and snow resting on submerged land had
split under its own weight.

We headed due south, studying the Barrier. Mile after
mile, the snowscape remained unchanged—fairly flat, smooth
Barrier. Just before four o'clock we sighted a faint ruffling
in the surface—crevasses—to the westward, and at 4:02 o'clock
we changed course to bring us nearer. The surface for several miles was quite broken, and the movement apparently centered about a series of fairly high ridges, running eastward
and westward. McKinley and June were certain that they saw
black rock showing through, but I thought it was merely the
shadows thrown by ridges. The ridges were at Lat. 80° S. and
Long. 173° E—almost due west of the area through which the
dog teams had struggled. This was an important discovery in-
asmuch as it indicated that the Barrier in the vicinity either
rested on the ocean bed or on an ocean peak. It was another bit
of knowledge about the Barrier and when all the bits are finally
put together, the mystery of the Barrier will be explained.

After flying about 12 miles to the westward, we turned east
for a few minutes and then headed south until 4:30 o'clock.
Far in the distance the Barrier began to rise, in swelling undulations, suggestive of a gradual inclination of the ocean
flooring.

McKinley photographed this area, and we then turned for
home, cutting diagonally across the Barrier. The return was
without incident.

During the flight, however, a very important message from
Captain Railey, who was moving heaven and earth for us
at New York, asking for information about the pack,
was relayed by radio from Little America. Petersen radioed

my reply and it was relayed at once to New York City. I cite this merely as an example of how effectively the modern organization of exploration can keep in touch with its affairs.

The next few days brought no end of troubles and excitement. First of all, there was the fear in my mind that Captain Melville might be persuaded against his better judgment to attempt to force a passage before the ice was sufficiently open. If he failed and the *City* became beset, there would be need of relieving her as well. Stout as were her old sides, her engines were much too weak to contend with very heavy pack. Then, too, reports were conflicting. It was almost impossible to know exactly what was going on within the broad reaches of the pack. One master dismissed it airily; "a good south wind," he said, "would break it up over-night." Another said: "it is the toughest pack we have ever seen." Come what may, I was determined the *City* should not start south as long as the situation remained confused. In the United States our friends, alarmed over our position, began to hammer through official channels for immediate action. Immediate action was not necessary; we did not want official action. There still remained, at that time, nearly a month for the *City* to try to carry off the job on her own resources. At the most, we desired only assurances of cooperation.

To cap the matter, sensational newspapers in the United States picked up a false report from an amateur radio operator that not only had the *City* reached the Barrier, but the entire expedition was hastily embarking. Had that report been true, nothing could have pleased us more. However, it was solemnly posted on the bulletin board in the mess hall with the explanation: "interesting, if true."

From the *Nilsen Alonzo* came word that she was stuck in the pack again, surrounded by a belt of very heavy ice. She had not come through the northern passage unscotched. Her bow, we learned, had been badly injured in forcing movements, and the Captain was unwilling to risk the weakened structure in further assaults until conditions improved.

The *Ross,* we learned, had injured her propeller in the battle.

If these great vessels, with their wealth of horsepower, commanded by masters long versed in the lore of the pack, could not go through without injury, is it any wonder that we were reluctant to throw at this time the *City* into a final struggle?

By the 26th, the *Ross* and the *Nilsen* were in open sea, north of the pack, and we were in the possession of the facts bearing on the situation. Both Captain Thorstensen, of the *Ross,* and Captain Vermeli, of the *Nilsen Alonzo,* reported heavy, hard ice and advised us not to order the *City* through before the middle of February. A final analysis came from the veteran ice pilot of the *City,* Bendik Johansen:

January 28

No. 42 WFBT
AMDIRAL BYRD, WFA

. . . After talking with Captain Vermeli, I also saw Captain Andresen and Captain Nilsen. The pack ice is very heavy from (Lat.) 68° S. and 70° S. and extends west towards the western shore of the Balleny Islands. From 68° to 69° it is heavy, dangerous old ice, with hard ice foots. South of 69° it is only year-old ice, which is also heavily packed but less dangerous. For the *City of New York* there is no danger in going through, but we will have to take our time in going through. We still have four weeks on which to figure. The *Eleanor Bolling* ought not to try to force the pack. Captains Andresen, Nilsen, and Vermeli are of the same opinion. I think the *Bolling* ought to stay on the outside of the pack and be ready in case anything happens. It would be wise to have support behind in case the whalers should have finished whaling before we get out. I wouldn't advise you to take the *Bolling* through at all. I would start here and go in about 68° S. and 178° E. and follow the meridian true south. Cannot tell about exact conditions until we are there. Ice conditions can change within an hour. I firmly believe that we will be able to get in and out. Regards.

JOHANSEN.

With these reports in hand, the confusion that had hung over the situation was dissipated. February 10th, therefore, was set as a tentative date for the raising of the siege.

Coal, the curse which had dogged us before, lifted its ugly head. More than once I had reason to regret the limited capacity of the *City,* but never did I rue it as much as then. During the time she was lying off the pack, she was under steam most of the time, and this unexpected consumption was beginning to deplete her reserve. The radio department swung into action again, and we tried to borrow as much coal as could be spared from the whalers. The *Larsen* offered 55 tons and the *Kosmos* 25, the latter giving us what was left, beyond immediate needs, of her galley supply. As these vessels are all oil-burners, they carry only enough coal to supply their chasers; and at this advanced stage of the season they had precious little to spare. For that matter most of them had not enough for their own requirements.

I therefore decided to order Captain Brown to take the *Bolling* back to Dunedin, take on as much coal as she could safely hold, and return to the pack. Thus, if the *City* came out of the ice with depleted bunkers, we would have a reserve supply at hand. But the *Bolling* had already reached the pack on January 29th, and Captain Brown, in his indomitable way, plunged right in, sending me the following message:

ADMIRAL BYRD, WFA

We are in the northern edge of the ice pack and have coal aboard for 32 days. I recommend that we go through. I assure you I will not endanger the ship or crew. Give us a chance to try this. Regards.

BROWN.

Twenty-four hours later the gallant *Bolling* and her crew, who through a cruel turn of affairs were destined to shoulder most of the dirty work of the expedition, had turned their backs on the pack and were steaming northward. This was a bitter blow to all hands on the *Bolling,* but the way Brown, McGuinness, Adams and the crew took it was typical of their spirit to the end. Had there been no other way, I am sure they would have taken the *Bolling* through, if they had had to berth it in sections in the Bay of Whales.

On the 29th we were notified by our government and the Norwegian government that the Norwegian whaling companies had agreed to render us assistance in case it was needed with the provision that we agree to reimburse the companies for whatever losses were incurred. The heavy item was insurance. The insurance alone necessary for the protection of the whaling ship during the passage would be, we learned, between $200,000 or $250,000.

February came in, dark and gloomy, with the hint of impending winter in the air and a darkening of the sky at night.

A WELCOME SIGHT.

The *City of New York*, only her upper works showing above the sea smoke, returns to the Bay of Whales. The first thing the men at Little America had seen from civilization in a year.

A strong cold wind blew from the south, and the sound of the sea beating on the Barrier cliffs to the north was plainly heard, January went out in a heavy snow storm, and the whole camp was blanketed. Even the Ford lay half-buried. Fire broke out in the radio storeroom on the 6th, when gasoline spilled from the blow torch was ignited. It was put out with small damage, the incident being chiefly distinguished by the fact that one of the pups ran off with my windproof trousers, which I was indiscrete enough to lay aside while helping to put out the fire.

Continuing southerly winds had begun to break up the pack. February 6th, the *City* went alongside the *Southern Princess* and took aboard fifty tons of coal. That evening Captain Melville decided to try his luck. He tackled the pack in the vicinity of the 179th meridian and headed south. The going for fifty miles was very difficult. The ice was tightly packed and interlocked with immense bergs. In places it reached a thickness of twenty feet. On at least two occasions the *City* barely wriggled from a dangerous squeeze. "We just hammered and hammered," Captain Melville said. "We would make a few feet and stop, then back up and charge again. Sometimes we would gain a mile at a time through a lead, and often make no impression at all." Johansen, in the crow's nest, "conned" the pack and inevitably, when it seemed that retreat was the only alternative, he discovered a saving lead. The pounding continued all night and most of the next day. On the 7th, however, the ice lightened somewhat, open water became more frequent and toward seven o'clock in the evening the ice commenced to heave so violently that Captain Melville was certain they were nearing open sea. The wind stiffened, bringing snow squalls and cold, and as fast as they pushed through it the mushy ice froze into solid new ice six inches thick, which greatly impeded their progress. At eleven o'clock the look-out sang out he had seen the open sea. Beset by ice propelled by a south wind, they stubbornly pressed on, and at midnight entered the Ross Sea. The wind by then had reached almost hurricane force. Captain Melville sent the following message:

ADMIRAL BYRD, WFA

We are in the Ross Sea. Estimated position at 8 A.M. Lat. 69.30° S., Long. 178° E. Hove to in clear water. Severe southerly gale of hurricane force and heavy swell. Have passed through 60 miles of new pancake ice varying in thickness up to six inches. With a low temperature and calm, the ice pack will become impassable. Therefore strongly urge that base party be prepared to leave on arrival as any delay might prove serious. With more favorable conditions we should arrive at Bay of Whales in five or six days.

It had taken the *City* thirty-seven hours and twenty minutes to make the passage. She had caught the pack at just the right time. Patience had been rewarded.

We sprang to the task of breaking camp with delight. The men were divided into groups, and the following memorandum was posted:

February 8th, 1930

The following is the list for details of loading, McKinley will be in charge at the ship.

Any one desiring relief from any one of the following details will obtain permission from either McKinley or Gould.

The following men will go to Floyd Bennett Harbor Sunday morning. These men will make camp and sort supplies:

Black (in charge of the loading of sledges and sorting supplies.)
Chips Gould (carpenter and will also help sort supplies.)
Mulroy (will sort supplies.)
Feury (cook and will help sort supplies)

The following men will go to Floyd Bennett Harbor on Monday:

Balchen (in charge of camp)
Demas   (sorting supplies)
Parker   (sorting supplies)
Smith   (radio operator and helping with supplies)
Details after the ship's arrival.

At Floyd Bennett Harbor: The following men will load dog teams:

Black (in charge of loading)
Feury (cook and loading)
Demas
Harrison

At ship:

Strom (in charge of stowing and securing cargo on ship.)
Balchen (will assist Strom)
Chips Gould (will put up additional standee bunks on ship.)
Haines (will assist Chips Gould)

The following men will be under the direction of the man in
charge of loading at the ship:

Blackburn	Mulroy
Bubier	O'Brien
Clark	Parker
Czegka	Roth
Davies	Smith
De Ganahl	Thorne

Dog drivers (Note: these men will sleep and eat at Floyd
Bennett Harbor)

Alexander	Goodale
Braathen	Walden
Bursey	Vaughan
Crockett	

If only 23 hours are available for loading all hands will work
straight through. If the ship is here longer than that the watches
will be divided 12 and 12.

Mail will be given out immediately after ship gets under way
for home.

Members of the Winter Party will be excused from all details
on board ship for 24 hours after sailing.

R. E. BYRD

With the posting of that order Little America began to disintegrate before our eyes. Men were busy packing clothes and
gear. The scientists were crating their records and instruments. The sound of hammering continued with unabating
enthusiasm. And with the dissipation of uncertainty, spirits
mounted wonderfully.

The *City,* however, found the Ross Sea in an evil mood.
A few minutes after Captain Melville reported reaching open
water, the wind stiffened to hurricane force and gusts reached
velocities in excess of 100 miles. The air ran with snow and
visibility shut down to zero. The *City* met the storm head-on
and managed to steam six miles south of the pack. Here her
engines could not prevail against the seas, and she was driven

back. A small storm tris'l was set to keep her head to the seas, which were treacherous.

As she retreated slowly, a new danger appeared. The ship was driven into a spur of the pack, and in the darkness, immense floes, rising and grinding under the combined force of wind and seas, towered menacingly at the crests of the waves. Because the rudder and stern sheets are the most vulnerable points of the *City,* it was necessary to bring her head into the ice. Melville swung her to port. Although the engines were full on, she failed to come around quickly in the face of the tremendous seas and in a moment tons of green water swept over the rail. The deck cargo shifted, heavy steel fuel drums broke away from their lashings and charged into the bulwarks and rails, smashing them; the bags of coal washed into the companionways, blocking them so that the men below were trapped and the decks were raked unceasingly by a cross sea.

In the darkness, they were driven into the pack. The stern, poised high, came down with fearful violence on a floe. A moment later another large mass of ice smashed against her starboard quarter. "I thought, for a moment, the blow had finished her," Captain Melville said. But the stout old *City* took it with no more than a shiver, and Melville stopped the engine to save the propeller. "Had one of those floes, sliding up and down those towering seas, crashed on the deck, it would have crushed it to pulp," the radio operator, Berkner, said.

Captain Melville worked the ship farther into the pack, and the swell decreased. But even with bare sticks, she made more than six knots backwards. The wind at times reached a velocity of 100 miles per hour.

The gale lasted for 24 hours, and during that time the *City* clung to the lee of the pack, waiting for it to subside. The following afternoon the sea calmed somewhat, and the *City* ventured south again. The Ross Sea was choked for twenty miles with new ice which had been blown from the south, and the ship had some difficulty traversing it. The temperature had fallen to zero, and new ice was forming in their wake. There has been no sun for three or four days and the proximity of the vessel to the magnetic Pole rendered the compasses all but useless.

The sky cleared and for two days the *City* drove south at a goodish clip. Then the gale struck her again, and this time nearly finished her. On the night of the 10th a sou'easter sprung up, cold and raw. By morning it had reached almost hurricane force. Snow fell continuously, and the spray whipping from the choppy sea froze on the decks and rigging as fast as it fell. Captain Melville, recognizing the danger, ordered the crew to clear the ship with axes and hammers; but the ice formed faster than they could chop it away. The next day she was actually going down a few feet by the head under the load of ice. A cylinder of ice, ten feet thick, covered the bowsprit and the martingale; and the mass of ice on her decks brought her so low that every other sea boarded and swept her from fore to aft. The engine was cut to half speed to lessen the impact of the seas against the head gear. Erickson was injured in a daring attempt to smash the ice from the bowsprit. If the bowsprit gave way, the topmasts and rigging must have come crashing down. The ship had actually gone down two feet under the load of ice.

The gale continued for four days, with scarcely a break, and during that period, which was surely as trying as any that Providence could inflict upon a wooden ship, the *City's* plucky crew never wavered once. How hard the battle was we did not realize at Little America. There were hints of it in the meagre messages that flew between the base and ship, sandwiched in between discussions over mattresses, knives and forks, bedding, food, plates, bunks and the like—things we should have to take along to eke out the supplies of the *City*, which was scarcely equipped to handle 60 men.

February 13th

Our dead reckoning position is Lat. 76° 22' S., Long. 179° 54' W. Just one continuous southeast blizzard. Force 9 and 10 and a rough, confused head sea. Ship laboring heavily in sea way. Practically hove to with engines at full speed. Regards.

MELVILLE

February 15th

The vessel is iced up in the worst condition I have ever seen a vessel. We have been running under full steam into a living gale of wind ever since we left the ice pack. We have had no sun for a week and our positions are only approximate. Our head gear is

so heavily iced up that at present we are looking for the first shelter
to clear ship of ice. On the outside of her hull from the water
line up there is approximately two feet of ice. Heavy pitching.
We are hampered by heavy seas in our efforts to keep the ship
clear of ice. The leak in the stern remains unchanged, but it is
not serious. I am in full control of the situation and will advise
you of any change.

MELVILLE

On the night of the 15th the situation reached a crisis.
The men were worn out. Everything that could be spared
had been thrown overboard to keep her afloat. The *City* was
taking green water aboard every other roll. And Captain
Melville, after a conference with Johansen, reached the conclusion that unless shelter was gained before morning, they
would be forced to run with the gale in search of shelter to
clear ship. Johansen went on watch, and toward the end he
made out land to the westward through a break in the clouds.
It was the cone of Mt. Erebus, an active volcano, with a
feathering vapor streaming from her crater; and the land
which they sighted was Ross Island. They had been driven
more than 300 miles off their course. Presently they could
see to the westward the lower peaks of South Victoria Land.
Melville edged the ship in toward the shelter, and in the morning had her in the lee of the Barrier. Her decks were then
nearly level with the sea, and her hull, rigging and spars were
encased with a solid coating of ice which, in places, was three
feet thick. More than 200 tons of ice lay above the water
line of this 500 ton ship. That the *City* did not go down, I
think, is due to the skill of Captain Melville and ice pilot
Johansen, the courage and unswerving loyalty of her crew,
and the stout heart of the old ship herself.

We at Little America breathed a sigh of relief
when Captain Melville reported, on the morning of the 16th,
that the men were chopping the ship clear of ice, and he was
proceeding eastward.

Captain Brown had meanwhile started south from Dunedin,
and such was his hurry to get into the fray that he started
off without a pilot, and ran the *Bolling* ashore. "Sorry," said
Brownie. "Trying to save time. Expect to be off at 10 P.M."
They floated the *Bolling* off on the flood tide. She was undamaged and Brown came south at once.

Sunday
February 16th

Little America is about ready to pass out of existence.

For the past eight days the sledges have been moving in a steady line to Floyd Bennett Bay. McKinley and Black have the stuff gathered in three piles. Nearly half the camp is now living there. Feury has built a mess hall from dog crates, and an upturned ski from the Ford serves as a mess table. Two lines of tents face each other, and with tons of gear piled behind them it is like a refugee camp.

The ice has been moving rapidly lately, and the western edge is scarcely a *hundred yards* from the mouth of Floyd Bennett Harbor. It will make an excellent pier.

McKinley has handled this thing very well.

Winter cannot be far off. The temperature has been falling steadily, and the Bay has been full of sea smoke for days. We shall get out just in time. And yet, with the end so near, I am rather sorry that it is over. I shall miss most of all the informal life and the understanding of men which only an expedition of this kind can bring out. Nowhere else can the qualities of friendship and unselfishness be so fully nurtured.

Monday
February 17th

The *City* is making excellent time, with clear sky and open sea, although contending with a strong westerly set in the current. She will arrive some time tomorrow afternoon.

The last things were moving out of Little America today. The camp is very quiet tonight—there are just a few here— the rest are at Floyd Bennett Bay. "Doc" Coman has remained, to keep watch over Mason. Mason is doing quite well, although in constant pain, and we have decided not to attempt to move him until the *City* is fully loaded and ready to go.

His condition is really precarious. Dr. Coman does not think it will be necessary to operate. If it is some of us must make up our minds to remain here another year—Mason could not be moved for at least three weeks.

It is a pity that we cannot take the airplanes. However, the aviation gang has anchored them securely on the top of a wind swept ridge about three-quarters of a mile to the eastward of the camp. They faced the planes into the prevailing winds and we hope that they will not be buried by the snow for several years to come.

The skis have been covered with snow blocks, the tail lifted and the wings set at a negative angle of attack. I don't think the planes will come to harm. There is one advantage in this climate: where there is no melting there can be no rust.

More ice went out of the western side of the Bay today, and the edge of it lips the mouth of Floyd Bennett Bay. The *City* can dock less than a mile from the piles of supplies.

I cannot speak too highly of the dog drivers—Walden, Goodale, Crockett, Vaughan, Bursey and Blackburn. It is they who have borne the burden of transport from the beginning; and for the past week they have worked like demons. The trail is very soft and dangerous, with open pools of water, yet they have performed as efficiently as ever.

Well, another twenty-four hours will tell the story.

Tuesday
February 18th
Eight o'clock

The *City* is in.

An hour ago—6:45 o'clock P.M. to be exact—Melville radioed that the ship was in the Bay of Whales, making for the West Barrier. A few minutes later the camp at Floyd Bennett Harbor radioed she was in sight, her topmasts showing through a heavy mist. She came alongside the ice a few minutes ago, and June has begun to load her.

The camp will be deserted in a few hours. I am remaining here to send a last few radio messages to the United States, which Petersen is handling. The last message from WFA will go to Mr. Adolph Ochs, publisher of the New York *Times* from the station named after him.

The place has never been so quiet, nor has it seemed so large and barn-like. The bunks are empty and stripped of everything. The fire in the stove has gone out. Mason is curled up in a bunk and the "Doc" is talking quietly to him. Vaughan is sitting nearby. Ten miles away the loading is in full swing. In all frankness, I hate to see it end.

McKinley lowered colors for the last time. There was only one of us there to salute them as they came down.

At 9:30 o'clock this morning Melville gave the order to cast off. The *City* nosed her way through loose ice in the Bay of Whales and then stood out to sea. We are now making our way along the Barrier, headed for Discovery Inlet.

These last hours have been the most rushed of all.

Early this morning, I came down to the ship on Vaughan's sledge. As we rounded the point of Ver-sur-Mer Inlet, we met Blackburn on his way back to pick up Dr. Coman and Mason. The air was quite raw and cold, with the hint of fog in it. We saw the *City* moored alongside the bay ice, and the loaded dog teams scurrying between it and the camp in Floyd Bennett Harbor. I met Captain Melville and congratulated him on bringing the ship through. The *City* still bore the marks of her struggle. Her bow, rigging and decks were still swathed in ice, and the sheathing was scarred where heavy floes had struck her.

McKinley, Gould, June and Black had the loading problem well in hand. They had been working all night, and most of the important records and scientific equipment were already aboard. All hands pitched in, and the supplies marched up the wooden plankings in a steady stream.

Taylor and the dogs, which he had brought down were more than helpful in the rush of loading.

At 9:30 o'clock the last piece was put aboard. Then the dogs were released from the sledges and taken on the ship, as were the penguins which we hope to bring back alive to the United States. We cast off.

Now that we have started the Antarctic is showing its most beautiful side. The sun is shining, lighting up the Barrier cliffs, bringing out its lovely blue shadows and tints. It seems to say: "You see, I am not half so bad as I am painted."

We are passing through slush and pancake ice. The Bay of Whales was freezing as we left. In another week, I think, we would have been there to stay—at least until another year had passed. All hands are stowing gear below decks and securing the deck cargo.

We shall attempt a passage of the pack at the 178th meridian. The *Larsen,* after penetrating the pack for twenty miles, has withdrawn because of heavy ice and the difficulty of maneuvering. She is heavily loaded. The *City* was indeed fortunate to get through.

Thursday
February 20th

We took our departure from Discovery Inlet early this morning, and our noon position was approximately 50 miles northwest of it. The *Bolling* has reached the edge of the pack, and is now standing by the *Kosmos.*

Weather continues good. We are meeting patches of new ice.

Tuesday
February 25th

Last night we dogged through scattered fragments of the pack. It is much farther south than we had expected to find it. However, it is quite light and we are making excellent time. If luck is with us, we shall meet the whalers tomorrow. We are heading for the *Kosmos* and the *Bolling.*

I am desperately anxious about Mason, whose condition has not improved. If it becomes necessary to operate on him aboard the *City,* he hasn't a chance in a thousand to survive.

Our noon position was Lat. 70° S., Long. 178° E.

Wednesday
February 26th

We are out of the pack at last. It was tough going for a while—but really not bad. Recent southerly winds had massed a lot of ice against the southern edge of the pack. This was thick enough to impede us considerably—in fact, stopped us once altogether. Then a walloping 35-mile wind came out of the south, and literally pushed us through. We set all sails, and with the wind behind us plowed through, gaining an open lead. Later the *City* averaged as high as five knots going through rotten ice, patches of which are at least four feet thick.

When night fell, the ship hove to. The lead we were fol-

lowing had narrowed down and rather than run the risk of
crashing against a heavy floe in the darkness we decided to
wait until daybreak before continuing. In the morning conditions were much better, and the northern edge of the pack
was made up of loose floes. We turned westward and are
making for the *Kosmos*.

There has been no sun for several days, and we are proceeding by dead reckoning. The slush was freezing behind us
as we quit the pack.

Friday
February 28th

Homeward bound.

Early this morning we came alongside the *Kosmos* and
transferred Mason and Taylor's dogs. The *Bolling* was
nearby. I cannot describe how strange it was to see new
faces after these many months.

Poor Mason went up in a basket operated by a winch, and
after him went the dogs. One crate fell between two ships,
but the dogs were saved. The sea was quite rough, and we
used a couple of dead whales as bumpers between the two
ships. The odor was simply terrible.

I paid my regards to Captain Andresen and to Dr. Barnes,
who, in volunteering to serve aboard the *Kosmos* is living
up to the best traditions of the expedition. The *Kosmos* has
excellent hospital facilities and Mason is certain of good care.

A heavy swell was running and we had a most difficult
time to find water smooth enough to permit the *Bolling* to
come alongside. We tried it first in the lee of a huge iceberg
but the water was much too rough and we were finally forced
to enter heavy pack which was quite dangerous to the unpro-
tected rudder posts of the *Bolling*. However, the sea was
quieter there.

The journey is almost run. In a few days we shall see
Dunedin and our friends. Then home. The mission is done,
and well, I hope . . . I hope it sincerely, principally for these
men who have gone each step of the way with me. They have
given two years of their lives to the service of science, a hard
and grudging master, and it would be a pity if their sacrifice
were neither understood nor appreciated.

To what is already written I can add little more. There is
the wish, however, to restate our debt to the men who showed
the way in the Antarctic—to Scott, Shackleton, Amundsen,
Mawson, and the rest of that fine company. There is the
wish also to put an end, once and for all, to the journalistic
practice of referring to our efforts as the "conquest" of the
Antarctic. The Antarctic has not been conquered. At best we
simply tore away a bit more of the veil which conceals its
secrets. An immense job yet remains to be done. The Antarctic will yield to no single expedition, nor yet to half a dozen.
In its larger aspects, it still remains, and will probably remain
for many years to come, one of the great *undone* tasks of the
world.

CHAPTER XVII

THE GEOLOGICAL SLEDGE TRIP

BY DR. LAURENCE M. GOULD

IN his original plans for sledging operations southward from Little America, Admiral Byrd had expected to have the dog teams proceed directly south to the Queen Maud Range at the foot of Axel Heiberg Glacier. En route they were to establish bases that could be used by the airplanes for flights to the east or west as well as over the pole. The loss of the Fokker on the geological trip to the Rockefeller Mountains during the first season of operations necessarily curtailed the work that could be done by airplane. Of all places of interest, both geologically and geographically, the Queen Maud Mountains, especially at their junction with the supposed Carmen Land, had first place. With the loss of the Fokker it was impossible for the geologist to have a plane at his disposal to reach these fields of activity. Consequently it was decided to have the southern sledging trip provide the means for geological and geographical research in this section as well as to lay bases for possible use by the airplanes. The designation of the party was then changed to the Geological Sledging Party under the leadership of the expedition geologist.

To reach the places desired by the geologist it was necessary to plan for a much longer sledge trip than had been originally visioned. These plans were consummated and the long trip was made possible only because of the excellent cooperation of the Supporting Party whose work has been elsewhere described.

A large part of the winter was consumed in making plans and completing preparations for the trip. To understand the reasons for the success of the trip, a knowledge of these preparations is essential. The first thing to occupy our attention was, of course, food; and, with the assistance of Dr. Coman, we worked out the following very generous ration:

Food	Daily rations per man	
Pemmican	8	oz.
Biscuits	10	"
Sugar	4	"
Powdered milk	4	"
Oatmeal	2	"
Soup rolls (Erbswurst)	2	"
Chocolate	2	"
Tea	.5	"
Salt	.25	"

The above items were the essential constituents of our ration, but in addition, more or less as delicacies for occasional use to add variety, we included:

Butter	.59	oz.
Peanut butter	.29	"
Bacon	1.33	"
Cocoa	.14	"
Malted milk	.74	"

The greatest innovation in the above is oatmeal. It was necessary in preparing rations for such a lengthy trip to take food that needed little or no cooking, in view of the fact that our entire fuel supply had to be carried with us. We did some experiments during the winter and found that a vacuum jug made an excellent fireless cooker, and that it was only necessary to bring the oatmeal to a boil and put it into the jug after supper to find it well cooked by morning. Furthermore, after breakfast we filled the jug with hot tea so that we could make our noonday stop and have a hot drink without lighting a fire. This system worked out well, and throughout the summer we had two bowls of hot oatmeal and milk for breakfast with two cups of hot tea and a biscuit: for lunch, two cups of tea, a 4 oz. bar of chocolate and two biscuits: for supper, two or three bowls of rich stew made of pemmican and soup rolls, four biscuits and two cups of tea. The other items in our rations were used from time to time by way of variety.

For a cooker we used an adaptation of the Nansen cooker

designed and built by Victor Czegka, the machinist. For the standard one burner primus, a two burner arrangement was substituted. I dare say no one has ever used a more efficient stove than this one.

Of almost equal importance to our own food, was that of the dogs. It was a rare bit of good fortune that Dr. Malcolm, Professor of Chemistry at Otago University in Dunedin, New Zealand, interested himself in our behalf. He designed a pemmican that represented a correctly balanced diet which the dogs liked and on which they thrived throughout the trip.

Little need be said about our personal equipment, for it did not differ essentially from that used by Admiral Byrd and others who went far afield by air.

The sledges came in for a good deal of alteration. We planned to have five dog teams of nine dogs each with each team hauling two sledges in tandem. When we finally left Little America we used for lead sledges, one single-ended flexible sledge, two double-ended flexible sledges, and two double-ended rigid freight sledges such as had been used so successfully in transporting supplies from the ships to Little America. For the second or trailer sledges we used much lighter types, two single-ended sledges supplied by Amundsen and three sledges with runners made from skis. We found the rigid freight sledges heavy and cumbersome to handle on the trail, and as our loads lightened these were the first sledges we abandoned. In every particular for use on the trail we found the flexible type—that is one bound together by rawhide thongs—superior. All of these flexible sledges which we used were lashed together by Strom and Balchen, and the two double-ended lead sledges were entirely constructed by them. I do not think that any explorers have had better sledges than these two.

In addition to the expected amount of camp gear, ropes and materials for making repairs, we carried a moving picture camera and six thousand feet of film, two still cameras with an abundance of film, a radio receiver and transmitter with hand generator, and flags for marking the trail.

We planned to mark the trail at half mile intervals with small orange flags. Surmounting each depot of dog food, man food and fuel to be laid down at fifty mile intervals from

Little America to the foot of the Queen Maud Mountains, was to be a large flag. Furthermore a line of trail flags, spaced at one-fourth mile intervals, was to be placed to the east and west of the depots for a distance of five miles. The flag sticks thus set out were to be numbered serially beginning with one and proceeding away from the depot on either side. Flags to the east to have a capital E together with the appropriate number, while those to the west were to have a W with appropriate number. Thus a flag stick marked with W-2 would be eight flags or two miles west of the depot. For the first 200 miles of the trip southward, which ended with depot No. 4, this system of marking the trail and laying depots was carried out by the Supporting Party.

As our plans stood completed we planned to sledge directly south from Little America to the foot of the Queen Maud Mountains, where we would establish a base where Admiral Byrd could make a cache of gasoline and oil for refueling on the polar flight. After the polar flight we planned to scale Mt. Nansen, if possible, and then sledge eastward along the foot of the range, at least as far as Carmen Land. We were then to return to our base camp, established when we reached the mountains, and follow our trail back toward Little America as far as depot No. 5 at latitude 82° 35′ south. We then proposed to leave the trail and head northeast to investigate Amundsen's recorded appearances of land, after which we would return to our main trail at depot No. 3, and then back to Little America.

Neither the Supporting Party nor the Geological Party found any evidence of this land on their way south. On his first flight south to lay a cache of gasoline and oil for the polar flight, Admiral Byrd found that there was no land whatever showing toward the east. The Geological Party therefore naturally abandoned its plan to leave the main trail when homeward bound. Otherwise the plans as outlined above were carried out.

By the middle of October both sledging parties were ready to depart. On the morning of October 15, 1929, the Supporting Party took its final departure. We decided to go along with them for a few days, just by way of testing out our own equipment and to have our heavy loads at least a few miles

under way when we took our final departure. In my own un-
enlightened eagerness to be of use, I attempted, with my skis
on, to drive Mike Thorne's team. The results were disastrous.
My skis became entangled with dogs and sledges. I was so
badly bruised as a result that I brought my own party back to
Little America from only 20 miles out. Two days after our
return to Little America the five dog teams departed again on
what we termed the 100 mile trip. I remained in camp to recuperate. They moved our heavy loads out to depot No. 2,
100 miles south of Little America, and then returned to Little
America, arriving on October 28th.

Some seven days were consumed in making desired alterations in our equipment and giving the dogs a good rest. Finally
on November 4th everything was ready for our final departure.
There were six of us—Frederick E. Crockett, dog driver and
radio operator; Edward E. Goodale, dog driver; George A.
Thorne, dog driver and topographer; J. S. O'Brien, dog driver
and surveyor; Norman D. Vaughan, dog driver and in general
charge of all the dogs; and myself in the rôle of navigator,
cook, and of course geologist.

It was a dull gray day with overcast sky—at one P. M.—
that we took our departure.

The first 100 miles, of course, were dead easy, for my companions had previously advanced our heavy sledge load to that
point. From here south it was hard work. Little need be said
about our travel to depot No. 4, established by the Supporting
Party at 81° 43', for they had traversed and marked this part
of our route ahead of us. Their difficulties in crossing the
badly crevassed area between 81° south and depot No. 4 have
been described. The fact that they preceded us and marked
the trail made our crossing relatively easy. Recrossing this
area two months later on our homeward trip was, however, a
different story.

We arrived at depot No. 4, the last outpost of the Supporting Party, on November 17th. From here on our work became heavier, and the dogs had already all the load they should
haul. Yet somehow we had to carry on from here at least 500
pounds of dog food. We loaded it onto our sledges, and on
the morning of November 18th we started southward pioneering our way.

We had long since learned that the dogs keep a straighter course if someone leads the trail ahead. George Thorne, or Mike, as we all called him, was eminently fitted to lead the way. Thus we travelled with Mike ahead, immediately I came driving his team so that I could watch the compass on the sledge and call ahead to him as necessary, "right," "left" or "steady." He had such a good sense of direction that he needed but little steering from me.

This first day with the additional loads was a disheartening one. Everybody was tugging at ropes tied to the sledges trying to help the dogs along, and Mike and Norman even carried heavy packs on their backs. Even so we travelled but 8 miles. The mountains seemed infinitely far away that night. Our sense of slowness in travel was further accentuated that day, for just after noon we suddenly heard behind and above us an unfamiliar and unexpected roar. We looked up to see the Floyd Bennett soaring over us southward bound to lay a cache of gasoline, oil and food for use on the polar flight. A sharper contrast between the old and the new methods of travel could hardly be pictured. Here was Commander Byrd and his party covering in four hours a distance which took us four weeks to cover with our dogs.

November 19th we travelled 12 miles, and the dogs were so utterly tired out that we deemed it best to give them a holiday. Accordingly we let them rest the 20th. This was a good idea. From now on things began to go better. And from here on to the mountains we travelled along without greatly fearing but that we should be able to make our goal.

From the crevassed area to the mountains the Barrier is quite flat and unbroken. The following entries from my log describe typical days over this part of our journey: "Nov. 21. Fairly good surface this morning—few low sastrugi but well coated over. Overcast but with fair visibility this morning. Became steadily worse and at 10 o'clock a light snowfall began. The horizon promptly disappeared, and we are in that sort of milky light when every direction—up, down, left, right—all look alike. One could not even distinguish the snow surface at his feet. One had the curious sensation of being suspended in a world of opaque white. I became fairly dizzy watching the compass and then looking up to see if Mike was on the course. I would level my eyes toward him and then find him up above me 45 degrees, so it seemed."

"November 25. Rough sastrugi which we had to cross diagonally and which made the compass bound about badly and steering, therefore, difficult. As is always the case, these sastrugi trend in an ESE to WNW direction. We were sure at noon that at last we could see the long sought for mountains. Shortly after noon, the southerly haze lifted and there to the southwest, but still very far away, was a grand escarpment of snow covered peaks, nothing dead ahead. By four o'clock we could distinguish a huge mountain mass almost dead ahead of us. This we believe to be Mt. Nansen. It has been a stimulating afternoon after the almost unchanging travel for the past three weeks over the sastrugi surface of the Barrier."

"November 27. Twenty-five to thirty miles of wind this morning with heavy drift, but we would have gone on anyhow but that we were requested to wait until one P. M. for radio schedule with Little America to advise them about the weather, since they were in readiness to take off for the polar flight. Even so we broke camp immediately the schedule was over and were under way by three o'clock.

"The mountains have drawn much nearer today, so much so that it is hard to believe that they are still 50 miles away. Perfect weather this afternoon with only about 5 miles of wind, made the mountains stand out especially clearly. We could see a great gap in the solid wall of rock, which we believe to be Axel Heiberg Glacier, and we have already altered our course to steer directly toward it. (Later we were to learn that it was Liv's Glacier and not Axel Heiberg toward which we were steering.)

"The weather has been perfect since noon. Nothing better could be hoped for for the polar flight, but we learn that it is still cloudy and windy at Little America."

"On the morning of the 28th I sent a message to Commander Byrd to the effect that the sky was cloudless, that the barometer was high, that there was no wind, and that this looked like the day.

"It was the day. We remained in camp or stood by for the flight, listening in by radio ready to start with our dog teams

to the rescue should the plane have a forced landing. We were
not needed, but we did get a real thrill when the Floyd Bennett,
poleward bound, zoomed over us and dropped us a parachuted
load of films, messages and cigarettes.

"November 29. Shortly after 9 o'clock, when we learned
that the Floyd Bennett had landed at Little America, we broke
camp and were under way again.

"The mountains stood out clearly and beautifully, and we
continued to head directly for the great break which we at first
thought was Axel Heiberg glacier, but which we are now convinced is Liv's. The mountains draw perceptibly nearer and it
looks very much as though we would surely reach them tomorrow.

"November 30. The mountains looked so near that we
decided to make them or bust—it came very near being the
latter. We travelled 35 miles over the toughest going we have
ever had, which was complicated by a twenty mile wind from
the SE with heavy drifting snow that stung our faces and
pushed us about where the surface became icy near the mountains. Fifteen miles away from the mountains the Barrier was
pushed up into icy covered ridges by the ice flowing out of the
glaciers, and the whole was cut up by a series of great, almost
parallel crevasses, miles in length, that crossed our course
diagonally. We crossed numberless ones—great huge ones—
little ones—open and closed ones—bridges falling in as we
hurried across.

"Individual dogs always tumbling in, and occasionally part
of a team would fall through and begin to fight amongst themselves, and then again a sledge would break through.

"As we neared the mountains the surface became icy, and
it became increasingly difficult to keep straight on skis and
manage the sledges, but we are camped tonight at the foot of
Liv's Glacier in the very shadow of Mt. Nansen. Very tired
after the long trek, but even if I were not I should need much
more poetic felicity of expression than I can muster to give
any notion of the sublime sight ahead of us—a mighty range
of mountains from ten to fifteen thousand feet high, rising
sheer from the Ross Barrier, which at their feet are less than
300 feet above sea level. We already feel repaid for the long
hard days of travel behind us—up every morning from 5:30 to

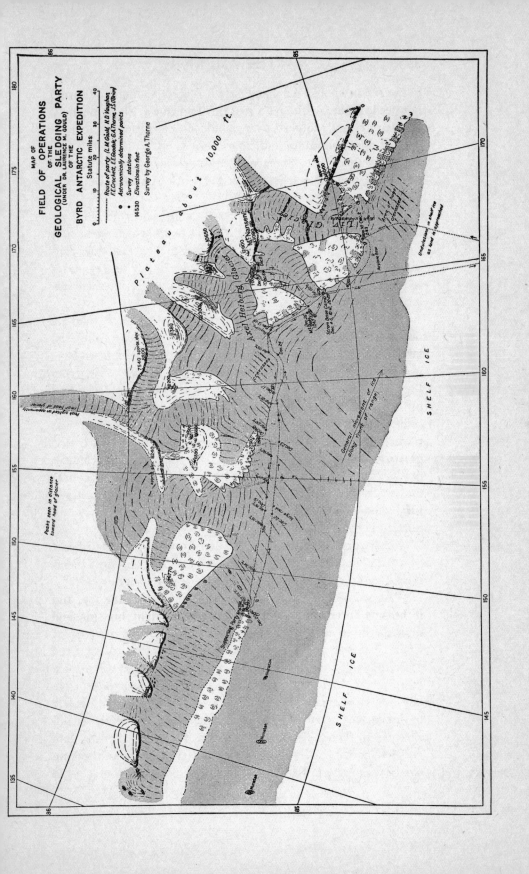

MAP OF
FIELD OF OPERATIONS
OF THE
GEOLOGICAL SLEDGING PARTY
(UNDER DR. LAURENCE M. GOULD)
OF THE
BYRD ANTARCTIC EXPEDITION

Statute miles
10   20   30   40

.... Route of party (L.M.Gould, N.D.Vaughan,
         F.E.Crockett, E.E.Goodale, G.A.Thorne, J.S.O'Brien)
   ⊕   Astronomically determined points
   •   Survey stations
 14530   Elevations in feet

Survey by George A.Thorne

6 o'clock, with temperatures from 5 to 30 degrees below zero, start the primus stove to thaw out our food and melt snow for powdered milk and for tea.   Then the dead quiet (provided the dogs have not begun to stir about) of the Barrier air is disturbed as I howl, 'Breakfast! Norman, Eddie, Freddie, Mike, Obie.'   Then breakfast of oatmeal, steaming hot from the vacuum jug, with plenty of rich milk and sugar, then two cups of tea and a biscuit.   Breakfast over, great haste to get under way as soon as possible.   We stop at noon for a few minutes rest and for two cups of hot tea from the vacuum jug, two biscuits, a bar of chocolate, and a small piece of pemmican. We mush on again until we think the dogs have gone far enough, halt, pitch our tents, picket and feed the dogs. While the others are busy attending to the dogs I am busy getting supper of thick pemmican stew, three biscuits with bacon fat, or, on rare occasions, butter and two cups of tea, and then into our fur sleeping bags.   But now all that is changed, and a month, full of opportunity, lies right before us."

Thus far in our travels we had concentrated entirely on the business of getting to the mountains. Now we were ready to go to work. There were two major tasks ahead of us. We wanted to map or chart as great areas of the Queen Maud Mountains as we could, and here before us lay a veritable paradise for a geologist. Naturally I wanted as much time as possible to devote to my geological and geographical studies. We made a division of labor with George (Mike) Thorne and Jack O'Brien assigned to the task of mapping while I was freed to devote myself to my own particular interests.   I assisted with the mapping to the extent of doing the navigating and making all the astronomical observations.   In the following weeks nothing seemed to please Mike so much as to stand around with his compass on a jacob staff or with the theodolite shooting angles on peaks and glaciers. He was tireless, and it was principally due to his industry that we were able to bring back so complete a map of our travels in and along the front ranges of the Queen Maud Mountains.

We spent three days exploring the lower part of Liv's Glacier and the surrounding mountains. We immediately saw the necessity of getting well into the mountains beyond the foothills if we were to reach the rocks that held the key to the geology. These foothills were composed entirely of the old pre-Cambrian rocks, the very oldest rocks we know, while the higher mountains farther south were seen to have their lower portions of old pre-Cambrian rocks overlain by some kind of flat-lying rocks that appeared to be arranged in layers. If these layers turned out to be sedimentary then we should be able to unravel in part the geological story of this great mountain range.

We had hoped to be able to get at these higher mountains by way of Liv's Glacier, but we found it so steep and so badly crevassed that we were scarcely able to climb it on foot even when shod with crampons. We therefore left this, our first mountain camp, and came along the foot of the range to the southeast and camped on the lower part of what Amundsen indicates on his chart as the western portion of Axel Heiberg Glacier. We established our mountain base here and called it Strom Camp, and immediately set to work making preparations for our projected trips into the mountains and eastward. The most important part of our preparations consisted of taking an accurate inventory of our dog and man food and basing our plans on the amount of food available.

Our first field work necessitated ascending the glacier to get at the rocks that capped Mt. Nansen, which lay at the head of it. We left Strom Camp on December 6th and sledged fourteen miles up the glacier and camped as near as we could to the rocks which I wanted to reach. The flanks of Mt. Nansen were encased in ice which in part pulls away from the rock faces to leave great crevasses which made the ascent to the rocks somewhat uncertain.

The next day Mike Thorne, Ed Goodale, Freddie Crockett, and I started out on skis to climb the steep slope above our camp and thread our way, if possible, among the crevasses to the rocks which were our goal. We dared not attempt to climb about here other than on skis for fear of falling into crevasses, and in my log for December 7th, I find the day described as follows:

"Climbed on skis up saddle between two spurs on southern slope of Mt. Nansen—very steep and difficult with a small ice falls half way up, a series of crevasses transverse to our course from one to eight or eleven feet in width, but usually roofed over. We roped to climb and 'herringboned' and 'sidebilled' our way up on our skis. Had to climb even steeper slope beyond these first crevasses to reach the coveted rocks—a bit hazardous this, for we were climbing along a steep side hill, and some 200 feet below us, paralleling our course, was a great yawning chasm.

"The snow was crusted over, and it was hard to make our skis stick, but we finally reached our rocks, the very rocks that I wanted most to find in the Antarctic. We became so interested in our rock collecting that none of us noted the changing weather. Quite suddenly we were completely engulfed and could see nothing of our surroundings. We hastened to put on our skis, hoping we would be able to retrace our steps. Then it began to snow, and we began to get a bit nervous. We hurriedly roped and began our descent.

"Mike is an expert on skis, but for the rest of us the down going was more difficult than the ascent. We slipped and fell time after time, knowing the big open crevasse was a few feet below us, got up, swallowed our hearts, and skidded on again. Fortunately the snowfall was not sufficient to cover our tracks, and when we had cleared the first steep slope the clouds lifted enough so we could see our way across the worst of the crevasses. Then came the steep, uncrevassed slope with which we began our climb. Here we could take off our awkward ropes. Mike slid grandly down the hill and Freddie Crockett did pretty well following him, but as for Ed Goodale and me, after trying with great difficulty to sidehill our way down, we finally sat down on our skis and disgracefully slid to the bottom."

This was really one of the worst days of the whole summer, and not the least significant of the thrills was the realization that the flat lying rocks that cap Mt. Nansen were a great series of sandstones, containing toward their top seams of impure coaly material. This discovery definitely establishes the fact that we are here dealing with precisely the same mountain structure as those known and studied by British geologists along the western borders of the Ross Sea. In other words the structure of the sandstone demonstrates that Mt. Nansen is part of a great uplifted fault block system of mountains, that takes its rise more than a thousand miles away toward the

west and north. Furthermore the presence of the low grade
coaly material on Mt. Nansen greatly increases the limits of
the coal field that is believed to underlie a large part of the
Antarctic Plateau.

It was also on this first day's climb that Ed Goodale found
lichens on one of the rocks. It was an interesting find for it
was the farthest south at which indigenous life of any sort had
ever been found. We were later to find greater growths of
lichens even farther south than this.

On the 8th of December we moved farther westward to get
at another spur of Mt. Nansen, and Norman Vaughan, Ed
Goodale, Mike and I climbed again to the rocks—up ice faces
where we had to chop our steps and over ragged pinnacled
columns of dolerite—lots of fun and amazingly interesting
rocks.

Another day's work about this side of Mt. Nansen, and
then we headed back down the glacier to make preparations for
our trip eastward along the foot of the range. What a riot it
is driving the dog teams down the steep slopes of the glacier.
The sledges are rough-locked, that is, ropes are put around the
runners to prevent their sliding easily, and then the driver yells
"yake" and tries to keep his team from getting too near another
one and away from any chance crevasses.

Coming down Norm's team and Eddie's got too close together and mixed in one grand fight. I was sliding grandly
along between the sledges. Immediately the fight commenced,
and purely from the standpoint of self preservation, I tried to
stop, but instead I slid right into the middle of the mêlée and
in trying to extricate myself from the jam without getting
bitten I parted the dogs and have not yet confessed to the
drivers that I did not deliberately set out to separate the dogs
for them. I am such an awkward dog driver anyhow, that
when I make a grand splurge like this one I hate to confess
that it was accidental.

Before returning to Strom Camp we climbed what we believed to be Mt. Betty, both to make a search for a cache left
there by Amundsen eighteen years ago, and to get a look up
the eastern part of Axel Heiberg Glacier. We failed to find
the cache and did not get much of a view of Axel Heiberg.
We returned to our base camp to make ready for our proposed

eastern trip.   On the 12th Ed Goodale and I made a successful
search for the cache of food and gasoline laid down by Admiral
Byrd before the polar flight.   We brought the food back to
camp and were glad to have it, for it gave us a great margin
of safety for carrying out our plans without taking too long
chances.

On the morning of the 13th—and it was Friday too—we
started on our eastern trip. To our left the Barrier was heavily
blanketed with clouds, but it was brilliant sunny weather over
the mountains, and what a setting for our start!   Ahead and
disappearing toward the east a great range of mountains unknown and unexplored—fifteen miles away and to our right
was Mt. Nansen in all his Glory.   A great sight is this mountain, dignified and grand as befits anything named for such
a man as Fridtjof Nansen.

We camped part way up Axel Heiberg Glacier with Mt.
Ruth Gade towering above us—a fairy land setting in this
world of white in the brilliant sun.   How different it was the
next morning—sky overcast and snow beginning to fall.   For
three days we were snowbound, with a fall of sixteen inches
of soft wet snow, and so warm that it melted on everything
it touched.   We were wet and, of course, very cold, much
colder than we had been at 25 below when we could keep dry.

Time hung heavy on our hands.   When we left Little
America each man was allowed to bring one book, but of
course these had been left at Strom Camp when we started
eastward.   Someone had brought a pack of cards, so we played
hearts with our daily issue of chocolate for stakes. How different our camp looked when the sun finally came back. The dogs,
as they lay curled in the snow, had melted themselves down
into wells.   They were half buried, and the tents, sagging under
their load, reminded one of evergreens at home with their
branches sagging after a heavy fall of wet snow.

On the 7th when the sun returned, we dug ourselves out
and were under way again—very heavy sledging and skiing.
Directly ahead of us the surface was so badly crevassed that
we had to head out into the Barrier to go eastward. We made
frequent stops for Obie and Mike to do their surveying.   About
two o'clock on the 18th we saw that we were coming to a
great ice field and decided to turn sharply to our right and

go into the mountains and climb up for a look around. We camped at the foot of an interesting looking ridge up which we climbed 2,000 feet after supper. An observation later showed this to be our farthest south, 85° 27', and even here as at Mt. Nansen we found lichens on the rocks, the farthest south that life has yet been found.

The mountains here were composed entirely of the old pre-Cambrian gneisses, schists and granites, the very oldest rocks known. There was no cap rock of sandstone. The great sheets of ice that had at some not very remote geological time covered all these mountains, had long since carried it all away. But any rocks are of interest to the geologist—and all the members of the party had by this time become amateur geologists—so of course they were ever on the outlook for minerals. In general these old rocks were quite barren of interesting minerals. It was about this camp that were found some copper bearing rocks but not in sufficient quantity to suggest any extensive deposits.

We looked out away from the mountains and to the east, and the surface was ice as far as we could see. But we had decided to go eastward, at least as far as Marie Byrd Land which begins at the 150th meridian. In my log for the 19th I find that "We headed out to avoid the ice, but it was no use —soon became so bad that we couldn't stand on our skis but had to take them off and hang onto the sledges. Ice was fairly smooth at first, but after two hours travelling we found ourselves in an area that had been much crevassed. Fortunately most of the crevasses were not of great extent, but they gave us some nasty spills nevertheless. We had to play a sort of game of tag with them. We could see them easily enough, for they were in part bridged with snow, whereas the rest of the ice was swept clean. But seeing the crevasses and avoiding them were two different matters.

"It was almost impossible to guide the sledges or make the dogs go where we wanted them to go. The dogs have gotten pretty smart about crossing crevasses and have learned that their best chance of keeping out is to head straight across them. But once they are across they forget that a change in their course may pull the sledge into the very hole they have been able to avoid. So we often crashed into them with our sledges. Wrecked one of our best sledges and had to abandon it and badly damaged the runners on the others. We had to travel 25 miles before we could find a patch of snow big enough to anchor our tents on."

It was the same thing over again the next day, but most of the time we were going down hill so we made another 25 miles to find ourselves well to the east of the 150th meridian —in Marie Byrd Land—on American soil here in the Antarctic.

Here again we found the same old rocks that form the base of all the mountains and constitute all of the mountains except the great high ones around Axel Heiberg Glacier, where these old rocks are overlain by the sandstone. Here also we found the same fault block structure.

Looking back over the route we have come and the areas we have mapped it is interesting to note that eastward from Mt. Alice W. the mountains are much lower and continue so as far east as we could see. The highest peaks in Marie Byrd Land do not exceed 5000 feet, while Mt. Ruth Gade beside Axel Heiberg Glacier is 15,000 feet. This eastern part of our mountains is also characterized by greater glaciers than Axel Heiberg or Liv's. We charted three great valley or outlet glaciers that should be classed along with the Beardmore which is the largest valley glacier so far known any place in the world.

While Mike was busy finishing his mapping the rest of us climbed the nearest mountain. We called this one Supporting Party Mountain. It was our farthest point from Little America and we had been able to reach it only because of the good work of the Supporting Party. We built a cairn on top of the mountain. In this cairn will be found a page from my notebook with the following note thereon.

"Dec. 21st, 1929
    Camp Francis Dana Coman
        85° 25' 17" S
        147° 55' W
            Marie Byrd Land, Antarctica

"This note the farthest east point reached by the Geological Party of the Byrd Antarctic Expedition. We are beyond or

east of the 150th meridian, and therefore in the name of
Commander Richard Evelyn Byrd claim this land as a part of
Marie Byrd Land, a dependency or possession of the United
States of America. We are not only the first Americans but
the first individuals of any nationality to set foot on American
soil in the Antarctic. This extended sledge journey from
little America has been made possible by the cooperative work
of the Supporting Party composed of Arthur Walden, leader;
Christopher Braathen; Jack Bursey; and Joe de Ganahl. Our
Geological Party is composed of:

> L. M. Gould, leader and geologist
> N. D. Vaughan, dog driver
> G. A. Thorne, topographer
> E. E. Goodale, dog driver
> F. E. Crockett, dog driver and radio operator
> J. S. O'Brien, civil engineer."

When I had collected all the rocks I thought we could carry
and Mike had finished locating his mountains and glaciers
we were ready to start back toward Strom Camp. The essential part of our scientific work was finished. We had mapped
175 miles of the front ranges of the Queen Maud Mountains,
we had demonstrated that this great fault block mountain system is continued almost due eastward from Axel Heiberg
Glacier for more than a hundred miles, we had demonstrated
that there is no such highland as Amundsen thought he saw
and called Carmen Land, and furthermore we had helped to
push the known limits of the Ross Shelf Ice more than one
hundred miles east than they had been known to exist by the
base laying flight made by Commander Byrd.

Westward bound toward Strom Camp we found recrossing
the glacial ice almost as much of a nightmare as it had been
the first time we had crossed. Otherwise the return journey
was devoid of special happenings until we camped Christmas
Day at the foot of Mt. Betty. We had determined to make a
last thorough search of this mountain for the Amundsen cache,
for there was no other place that would fit Amundsen's description of Mt. Betty. As we broke camp, Mike and I skied ahead
down to a ridge where we thought we saw something that
looked like a cairn of rocks. It was.

We signalled the dog teams to come along. What a thrill we did all get on this Christmas Day to stand where Amundsen had once stood and to find, perfectly intact, the cairn he had erected eighteen years before. We couldn't help standing at attention, with hats off, in admiring respect for the memory of this remarkable man before we touched a rock of the cairn. It was one of the most exciting moments of the summer when I pried the lid off the tin can in the cairn and took out a bit of paper which had formerly been a page in Amundsen's note-book, and on which he had briefly recounted his discovery of the South Pole.

Back in Strom Camp again on the 26th. I had wanted to make one more journey into the mountains but the dogs were too tired. We had to give them a few days rest before we began our long trek northward to Little America. We care-fully overhauled our gear and discarded pretty much every-thing except our instruments, our food, and my rock collec-tion. Our good discarded equipment we cached on Mt. Betty not far from Amundsen's cairn. In a tin can within the cairn we left a note giving a brief account of the Expedition and the Geological Party. I left one of my rock hammers on top of the rock cairn we had built around the cache.

On our homeward trip we decided to travel at night, both in order to have the sun behind us and because the sledging and skiing would generally be better than in the day. We had no relish for recrossing the crevasses in front of Liv's Glacier, so we laid our course northeast from Strom Camp hoping to avoid them and to pick up our trail later when we were all out into the solid Barrier again. For several days clouds had hung over the Barrier and mountains, but as if for a good omen they lifted just as we were ready to leave Strom Camp at one o'clock on the morning of the 30th.

Could you who read this have seen the picture that greeted us then, you would know that there had been much beside our geology and cartography to make the summer fascinating. To the south of us lay Mt. Nansen in all his splendor, his cap of shining ice, his blackish shoulders of bare rock loosely wrapped in a ragged old shawl, and the whole made glorious by the touch of the long skeletal fingers of the early morning sun.

This grand old mountain had somehow come to hold the

first place in our affections, and this sight was just what we would all have wished to keep as our last intimate view of the mountains. We finally turned our backs and headed northward toward Little America and home.

Quite as we had planned we did miss the worst part of the crevassed area we had crossed when we had arrived at the mountains, and on the second day of travel we picked up our old trail. How much more easily we travelled along now than when southward bound. We had become much more adept on skis and the dogs were fairly lightly loaded.

Two things furnished the principal variety on the homeward trip until we were again in the crevassed region between latitudes 81 and 82. These were the weather and the character of the Barrier surface as it affected sleding and skiing. For January 3rd I find the following entry in my log:

"Now the morning sun is out and the sky is gorgeous with a great variety of ethereal cirri, and there is a bit of wind from the southeast. It has been overcast and foggy the whole night and most of the morning. In fact late in the morning there was a light fall of fluffy snow as though 'the angels were moulting!' We had to keep close together to keep each other in sight, and even then it frequently happened that we with the front sledge could not see the last sledge behind us. I had to watch the compass fairly closely and call directions to Mike occasionally in order to keep on the course. And I don't believe we missed a single flag that we had previously placed to mark our trail. The thorough marking of the trail on our southbound trip was a good idea, and is already repaying us for the time we spent in doing the work.

"We came by depot no. 6 shortly after noon and stopped only long enough to take on some dog pemmican and some man food."

And on the 4th the following: "Much hardest day we have had since leaving the mountains. Weak crust on the snow broke through under the dogs who plodded and waddled heavily along hauling sledges that went crushing their way through the snow rather than gliding over it easily. The dogs are already quiet. There will be no fighting amongst them tonight for they are very tired. A thin streak of clear sky to the south about midnight gave us one last glimpse of the snow capped mountains which are now far behind and which none of us will likely ever see again."

We didn't need to worry about the weather until we reached the crevassed region. On January 10th the sky was overcast and things were pretty completely hidden from our view by a light fog. And we were nearing the broken area. I carefully watched the sledge meter and at what I thought was the proper time I said, "We'll camp here." We had the usual experience that we had encountered before in areas where there is active deformation of the ice.

There was an almost constant fusilade as of rifle shots about and under us as the ice cracked under its tension. But in the middle of the night after the dogs and camp had been quiet for several hours I woke up and lay awake for a long time without hearing a sound. But when we got up in the morning and began moving about, the noises began all over again. Even though the Barrier is here some hundreds of feet thick, it appears that where we camped it was under such a delicate state of stress that our movements disturbed the equilibrium. When the clouds lifted we found that we had accidentally camped just between two goodly sized crevasses, either one of which we might easily have fallen into without skis.

We had to abandon our former trail through the crevasses on account of the roofs of old ones on the former trail having fallen in and new ones having formed. We travelled three miles and had to stop on account of heavy fog. We waited two days for it to clear but it lightened only partially. Our dog food was getting so low that we could not stay longer without killing some dogs. We didn't want to do that, so Norman, Mike, and I roped and started out on skis in an attempt to find a route we could follow out with safety. This we were able to do and hurriedly retracing our steps we broke camp and headed out. The next day we picked up our old trail just south of depot no. 3 as we had planned to do.

The rest of the homeward journey was uneventful. On the 19th, in the early morning, we saw the tops of the radio towers at Little America. Only then did we have the feeling that we were nearly home—home from a sledge trip on which together with our many side trips we had covered more than

1500 miles. Glad as we were to be back in the comparative luxury of Little America, it was with a feeling akin to the forlorn that we looked back at our sledge tracks disappearing into the limitless white to the south. We had had a good time and had, in some measure, known the joy of achievement.

APPENDIX

C. D. Alexander
Bernt Balchen
George H. Black
Quin A. Blackburn
Christoffer Braathen
Kennard F. Bubier
Jacob Bursey
Richard E. Byrd
Arnold H. Clark
Francis D. Coman
Frederick E. Crockett
Victor H. Czegka
Frank T. Davies
Joe de Ganahl
E. J. Demas
James A. Feury
Edward E. Goodale
Charles F. Gould
Laurence M. Gould
William C. Haines
Malcolm P. Hanson
Henry T. Harrison, Jr.
Harold I. June
Charles E. Lofgren
Howard F. Mason
Ashley C. McKinley
Thomas B. Mulroy
John S. O'Brien
Russell Owen
Alton N. Parker
Carl O. Petersen
Martin Ronne
Benjamin Roth
Joseph T. Rucker
Paul A. Siple
Dean C. Smith
Sverre Strom

George W. Tennant
George A. Thorne, Jr.
Willard Van der Veer
Norman D. Vaughan
Arthur T. Walden

OFFICERS AND CREW *Eleanor Bolling,* VOYAGE BAY OF WHALES
—DUNEDIN, N. Z., FEBRUARY 1929.

Captain Gustav L. Brown, Master
Charles J. McGuinness, 1st Mate
Harry R. King, 2nd Mate
Frank McPherson, Chief Engineer
John Cody, 1st Assistant Engineer
Elbert J. Thawley, 2nd Assistant Engineer
Haldor Barnes, Medical Officer
Lloyd K. Grenlie, Radio Engineer
H. N. Shrimpton, Radio Operator
Leland L. Barter
John Buys
Ben Denson
Carroll B. Foster, Jr.
Frank Fritzson
Charles L. Kessler
John Olsen
A. Walker Perkins
R. Perks
George Sjogren
Lyle Womack

OFFICERS AND CREW, *City of New York,* VOYAGE BAY OF
WHALES—DUNEDIN, N. Z., FEBRUARY 22, 1929.

Captain Frederick C. Melville, Master
Bendik Johansen, Ice Pilot (also 2d mate)
*Harry Adams, 1st Mate
S. D. I. Erickson, 3d Mate
Ralph F. Shropshire, Hydrographer
Esmonde M. O'Brien, Chief Engineer
John J. Bayer, 1st Assistant Engineer
John L. Sutton, 2d Assistant Engineer
Lloyd V. Berkner, Radio Engineer
Arthur Berlin
Max E. Boehning

* Relieved Sverre Strom as 1st Mate, who stayed at Little America as
a member of the Winter Party.

Arthur B. Creagh
William Gavronski
Sydney Greason
John Jacobson
Richard W. Konter
Louis Reichart
S. Edward Roos
Vaclav Vojtech
Percy J. Wallis

OFFICERS AND CREW *Eleanor Bolling* ON LAST VOYAGE, DUNEDIN,
N. Z.—NORTHERN EDGE OF ICE PACK, FEBRUARY 1930.

Captain Gustav L. Brown, Master
Charles J. McGuinness, 1st Mate
Harry Adams, 2d Mate
Frank McPherson, Chief Engineer
Elbert J. Thawley, 1st Assistant Engineer
Leland L. Barter, 2d Assistant Engineer
*Haldor Barnes, Medical Officer
Lloyd K. Grenlie, Radio Engineer
G. Samson, Radio Operator
H. Austin
D. Blair
John Buys
M. W. Dobson
Carroll B. Foster, Jr.
William Gavronski
W. Harvey
J. Jones
Charles L. Kessler
N. Newbold
Frank Paape
A. Walker Perkins
R. Perks
Louis Reichart

OFFICERS AND CREW, *City of New York*, VOYAGE DUNEDIN,
N. Z.—BAY OF WHALES, ARRIVING FEBRUARY 18, 1930, TO
EMBARK WINTER PARTY.

Captain Frederick C. Melville, Master
Bendik Johansen, Ice Pilot and 1st Mate
S. D. I. Erickson, 2d Mate

* Services of medical officer loaned to S. S. *Kosmos,* as doctor had
been lost in an airplane used by that vessel in connection with whaling
operations. Dr. Barnes joined the *Kosmos* via the *City of New York.*

A. B. Robinson, 3d Mate
Esmonde M. O'Brien, Chief Engineer
John J. Bayer, 1st Assistant Engineer
John L. Sutton, 2d Assistant Engineer
Hilton L. Willcox, Medical Officer
Ralph F. Shropshire, Hydrographer
Lloyd V. Berkner, Radio Engineer
J. R. Orbell, Radio Operator
W. J. Armstrong
Arthur Berlin
John R. Bird
A. C. Brustad
Arthur B. Creagh
R. Eva
W. Gribben
Richard W. Konter
Walter Leuthner
F. Lockwood
J. Robinson
S. Edward Roos
Alan Innes Taylor
Vaclav Vojtech
Percy Wallis
M. C. Woolhouse
R. Young

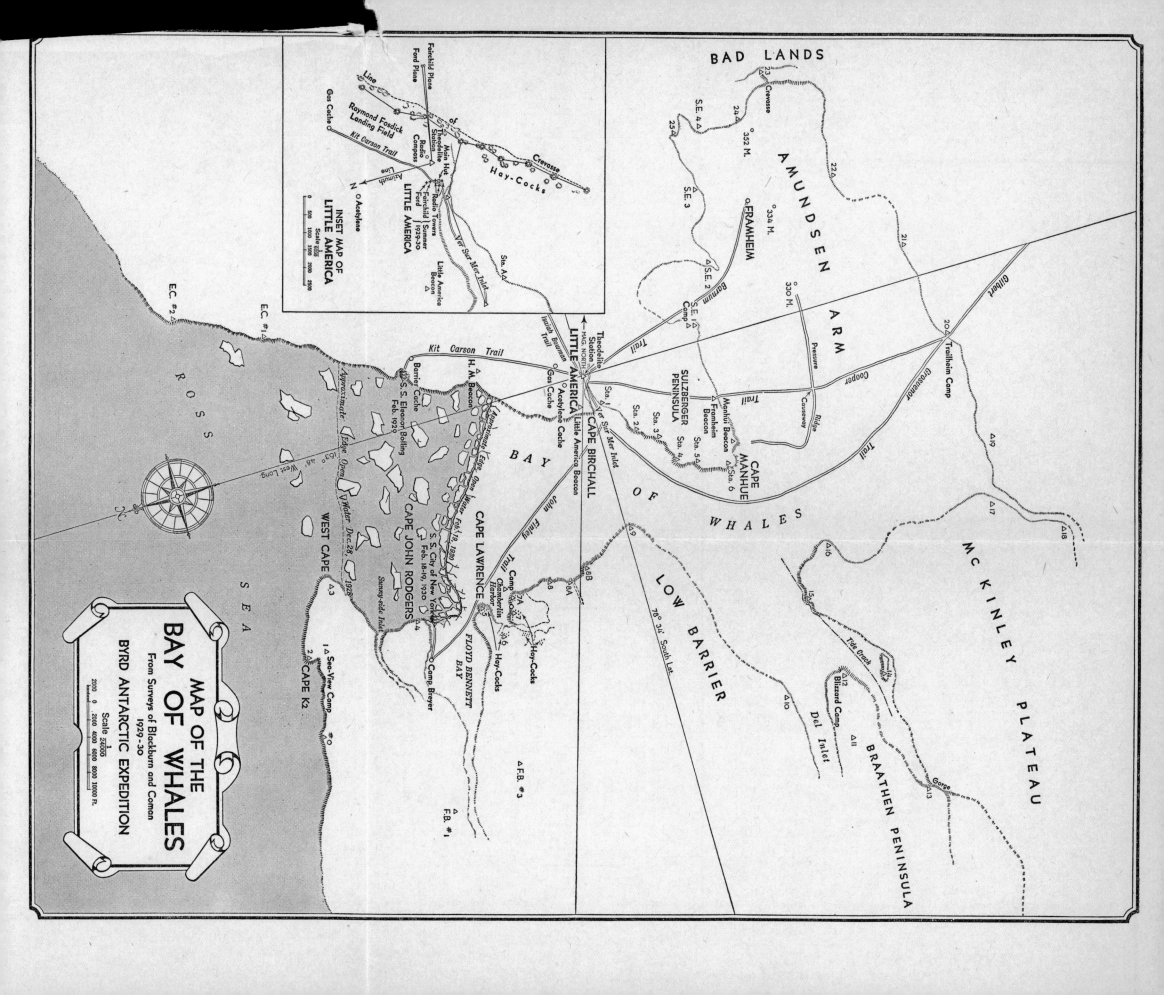

BAD LANDS

INSET MAP OF LITTLE AMERICA

Ford Plane
Fairchild Plane
Line
of
Gas Cache
Raymond Fosdick Landing Field
Radio Compass
Theodolite Station
Main Hut
Kit Carson Trail
Azimuth Line
Radio Towers
Fairchild Summer
Ford
N
Acetylene
Little America Beacon
LITTLE AMERICA 1929-30
Ver Sur Mer Inlet
Sta. A.
Hay-Cocks
Crevasse
Scale 6000
0 500 1000 1500 2000 2500

AMUNDSEN ARM

Crevasse
S.E. 4
S.E. 3
352 M.
334 M.
FRAMHEIM
330 M.
S.E. 2
Barrum
S.E. 1 Camp
Pressure
Cooper
Trail
Ridge
Causeway
Trailheim Camp
Grossvater
Gilbert
Trail

E.C. #2
E.C. #1

ROSS
SEA

Approximate Edge Open Water Dec.28
S.S. Eleanor Bolling Feb.1929
Barrier Cache
Kit Carson Trail
Isaiah Bowman Trail
Gas Cache
Acetylene Cache
LITTLE AMERICA
MAG. NORTH
Theodolite Station
Ver Sur Mer Inlet
Little America Beacon
CAPE BIRCHALL
Sta. 1
Sta. 2
Sta. 3
Sta. 4
Sta. 5
Sta. 6
SULZBERGER PENINSULA
Framheim Beacon
Manhui Beacon
CAPE MANHUE
Trail

H. M. Beacon
Approximate Edge Open Water Feb.19, 1930
S.S. City of New York Feb.18-19, 1930
CAPE JOHN RODGERS
Swmg-side Inlet
CAPE LAWRENCE
John Friday Trail
BAY OF WHALES
LOW BARRIER

WEST CAPE
1928
△3
Sea-View Camp △1
△2 CAPE K2
#0
Camp Breyer
FLOYD BENNETT BAY
Camp Chamberlin
Chamberlin Harbor
Hoy-Cocks
Hoy-Cocks
△8B
△8A
△9
76° 34' South Lat.
△F.B. #3
F.B. #1
△10
△17
△18
△19
△16
△15
Tide Creek
△14
Blizzard Camp
△12
Del Inlet
△11
Gorge
△13
BRAATHEN PENINSULA
McKINLEY PLATEAU

163° 48' West Long.

MAP OF THE BAY OF WHALES
From Surveys of Blackburn and Coman
1929-30
BYRD ANTARCTIC EXPEDITION
Scale 1/24000
2000 0 2000 4000 6000 8000 10000 Ft.

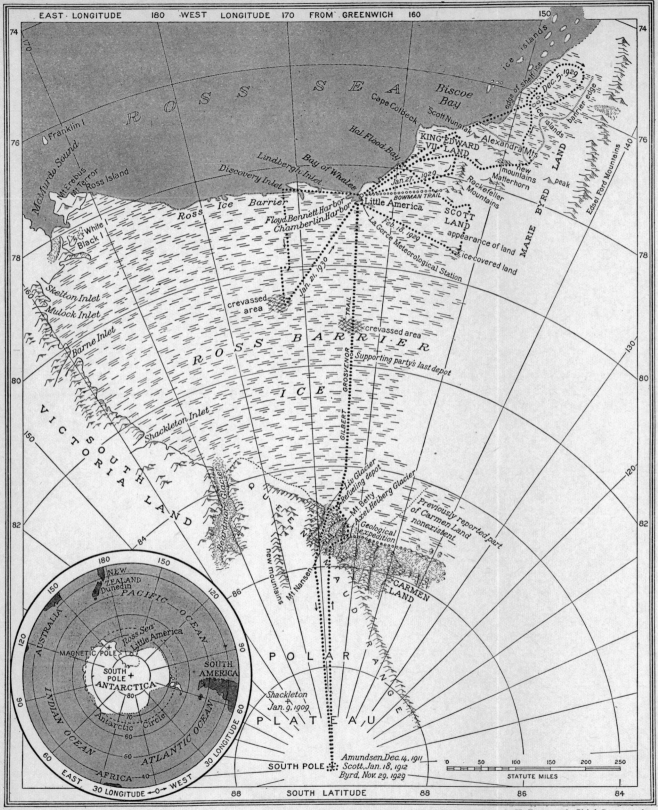

EAST·LONGITUDE   180   WEST·LONGITUDE 170 FROM·GREENWICH 160   150

Prepared by The National Geographic Society, A. H. Bumstead, Chief Cartographer.

THE POSITIONS OF THE MOUNTAINS AND THE NEWLY DISCOVERED LAND ARE ONLY APPROXIMATE. A COMPLETE SCIENTIFIC MAP
IS NOW BEING MADE AND WILL BE PUBLISHED AS SOON AS IT IS COMPLETED.

INDEX

Adams, Lieut. Harry, 72

Adare, Cape, 44

Adelie Land, wind velocities in, 13; minerals in, 39; discovery of, 42

Admiralty mountain range, 43-4

Aerial surveying, types of, 204-5

Aircraft, problem of use of, in the Antarctic, 13 ff.

Airplane exploration, cost of, 8; first flight over the Barrier, 102 ff.; to King Edward VII Land, 117 ff.; discovery of the Rockefeller mountains, 124-5; second flight to the east and discovery of new land, named for Captain Scott, 139 ff.; photographic mapping survey of coast line, 143-4; Prof. Gould's expedition for geological survey of Rockefeller mountains, 167, 168, 170, 173, 174 ff.; base-laying flight preliminary to polar flight, 305 ff.; the flight to the South Pole, 326 ff.; flight of the Ford to the eastward of Little America, 346 ff.

Airplanes, the expedition's three, 32-3

Alexandra Mountains, 47 n., 106, 121, 124, 350

Alice W., Mount, 407

America, trans-Atlantic flight of, 14 n.

Amundsen, Roald, 14, 22, 24, 26, 35, 47, 164, 166, 186n., 291, 311 ff., 331, 332, 340, 341, 344; passage of southern ice pack, 18; tent left at South Pole by, found by Scott, 22; first to reach South Pole, 24 n.; advice on project to reach South Pole by airplane, 24-5; on the Great Barrier as a base and his theory of the formation of Bay of Whales, 86; effort to locate his camp in Bay of Whales, 194-6; uses dogs for his dash for the South Pole, 240-1; mountains seen by, 249 and n.; finding of cairn left by, by Geological Party, 360, 408-9

Amundsen-Ellsworth aerial expeditions in the Arctic, 14 n.

Andresen, Captain, 69, 361, 370

Antarctic, cost of expeditions to, 8; season of possible passage to the continent through the ice pack, 12 n.; problem of using aircraft in, 13 ff.; wind velocities in, 13-14; visibility conditions in, 15, 80; importance of coal in problem of basing in, 16; difficulties of reaching the continent through the ice pack, 17-18; economic resources of, and a brief sketch of its exploration and our knowledge of, 38 ff.; ancient beliefs regarding, 40-1; estimates of coastal limits of continent, 45; a continent still in the ice age, 46-7; deglacierization of, 46 n.; winter temperatures, 191, 197, 230 ff., 273; effect of the winter on personnel, 197-9; the Antarctic night, 228, 229; study of radio conditions in, 268-9; center of the Antarctic ice sheet, 337; theory that Antarctic is not a continent but a series of islands, 346-7

Arctic Expedition, the MacMillan, of 1925, 10; Amundsen-Ellsworth aerial expeditions in, 14 n.

Aurora australis, 197, 224 n., 228-9

Axel Heiberg Glacier, 243 n., 314, 315, 316, 319, 330, 331, 332, 342, 343, 347, 393, 402, 405

Balchen, Bernt, senior in charge of aviation unit, 14 and n., 33, 79, 81, 88, 92, 102, 118, 123, 124, 139, 167, 329 ff.

Balleny Islands, 18, 361

Barnes, Dr. Haldor, assistant medical officer, 31, 361, 391

Barratt, Edgar, 155, 156

Barratt, Roswell, 155, 156

Base-laying flight in preparation for flight to South Pole, 305 ff.

Bay of Whales, wind conditions make it a place of comparative safety for aircraft, 14; reasons for selection as base of expedition, 47; Murray's description of, 84-5; Shackleton at, 84-5, 86; Amundsen's theory of formation of, 86;